INTERNATIONAL SERIES OF MONOGRAPHS ON
SEMICONDUCTORS

EDITOR: HEINZ K. HENISCH
University of Reading

VOLUME 4

THERMAL CONDUCTION
IN SEMICONDUCTORS

OTHER TITLES IN THE SERIES ON SEMICONDUCTORS

THERMAL CONDUCTION IN SEMICONDUCTORS

by

J. R. DRABBLE

Ph.D., F.Inst.P.

Department of Physics
University of Exeter

and

H. J. GOLDSMID

Ph.D., F.Inst.P.

The General Electric Company Ltd.
Hirst Research Centre

PERGAMON PRESS

OXFORD · LONDON · NEW YORK · PARIS

1961

PERGAMON PRESS LTD.
Headington Hill Hall, Oxford
4 and 5 Fitzroy Square, London, W.1

PERGAMON PRESS INC.
122 East 55th Street, New York 22, N.Y.
1404 New York Avenue N.W., Washington 5, D.C.

PERGAMON PRESS S.A.R.L.
24 Rue des Ecoles, Paris V

PERGAMON PRESS G.m.b.H.
Kaiserstrasse 75, Frankfurt am Main

Library of Congress Card Number 61-14037

Set in Baskerville 11/12 pt. and
Printed in Great Britain by J. W. Arrowsmith Ltd., Bristol

CONTENTS

PREFACE

DURING the last few years the thermal conductivity of semiconductors has become a subject of increasing technological importance. For this reason, and to avoid prohibitive length, the present treatment makes no explicit attempt to deal with solids as a whole but is restricted mainly to semiconducting materials. It is hoped that this limitation will make the book particularly useful to those whose interests in the semiconductor field are essentially practical. It is not assumed that the reader's knowledge of general semiconductor theory lies beyond the level expected for an honours degree in physics.

We might add that the range of processes which govern the thermal conductivity in semiconductors is so wide that the extreme manifestations which occur in metals and insulators may, at least in outline, be considered under the same heading. Indeed, the work carried out on semiconductors has played an important part in promoting our understanding of thermal conduction in solids and there is every reason to suppose that this trend will continue. Until recently, the relationship between the theoretical and experimental aspects of the subject was in a very unsatisfactory state. On the experimental side, there were very few measurements carried out under conditions which allowed an unambiguous interpretation of the results. On the theoretical side many of the available formulae were rather imprecise because of mathematical difficulties and lack of information about the fundamental parameters of the solid. The study of semiconductors has provided detailed information on structure and composition and the general position is, therefore, improving rapidly at the present time.

In this book the theory of irreversible thermodynamics is shown as a framework into which all the transport properties can be fitted and considered in their proper relation to each other. The concept of entropy production, and the associated principle that this is a maximum under given conditions, provides a common basis for all quantitative calculations. In this complex and rapidly expanding subject such a unified viewpoint should be of considerable value.

Wembley

J. R. DRABBLE
H. J. GOLDSMID

Chapter 1

INTRODUCTION
THERMAL CONDUCTIVITY OF SOLIDS

THE conduction of heat in solids has until recently been a comparatively neglected subject. There are, of course, several reasons why this
situation should have developed. A major factor is the great difficulty
in making really accurate measurements of thermal conductivity
particularly at very high or very low temperatures where many of
the more interesting effects are observed. Again, in electrical conductors the phenomena associated with the transport of charge have
attracted much more attention than those relating to energy transfer.
Another factor is the major theoretical difficulty in dealing with the
transport of heat by lattice vibrations; even now, theories of these
processes are only in the earliest stages of development.

There are two important reasons why the study of semiconductors
is helping to improve this situation. In the first place, the fabrication
of transistors has introduced the requirement of unparalleled standards
of purity and crystal perfection. The processes of heat conduction in
transistor materials have therefore been less complex than those in
solids of only normal chemical purity. Secondly, the possibility of
using semiconductors in thermoelectric applications has concentrated
attention on the selection of crystalline materials with a low lattice
thermal conductivity. Attempts to predict good thermoelectric materials
have encouraged the efforts to understand the heat transfer processes.
Moreover, in certain semiconductors, heat conduction phenomena
not encountered in metals or insulators have been observed.

It is intended that this chapter should introduce the reader to the
various mechanisms involved in the conduction of heat. These mechanisms will, of course, be dealt with in detail later in the book. In
Section 1.1 we shall consider the effects in dielectric solids; in this case,
heat is transported by the lattice vibrations. Such heat transport is

1

relatively unimportant in metals, which will be dealt with in Section 1.2. Then, in Section 1.3, these ideas will be extended to semiconductors and the processes arising from the existence of a finite energy gap between the conduction and valence band will be mentioned.

1.1 DIELECTRICS

The first important observation relating to heat conduction in electrical insulators was made by Eucken (1911:1). From an analysis of experimental data he showed that the thermal conductivity of a dielectric crystal is inversely proportional to the absolute temperature. This rule has since been substantiated for a large number of crystalline solids and holds, at least approximately, at high temperatures. In this context, high temperatures are those which are greater than the Debye characteristic temperature. In fact, Eucken's experimental law (often briefly referred to as the $1/T$ law) sometimes holds down to relatively low temperatures, perhaps an order of magnitude lower than the Debye temperature. Thus, the first requirement of any theory of heat conduction in dielectrics is that it should explain the $1/T$ law.

It has, of course, for long been realized that the effect of raising the temperature of a solid is to increase the amplitude of vibration of the atoms of which it is composed. Suppose that heat is supplied to one face of a solid body to increase the intensity of atomic vibrations near this face. There is then a tendency, due to the interatomic forces which hold the solid together, for the more strongly vibrating atoms to pass on some of their motion to their neighbours. In this way a body in thermal isolation from its surroundings, and with no internal source of heat, is gradually brought to a uniform temperature. Alternatively, if the body is held between a source of heat and a sink, heat is conducted towards the latter.

Since the atoms in a solid are bound together by forces, the motion of each atom in the solid affects the motion of all the other atoms. Thus, the correct way of thinking about the atomic motion is not in terms of the vibration of *individual* atoms but rather in terms of *collective* vibrations of the whole system of atoms. For a crystalline solid, in which the atoms have a spatially regular arrangement and in which the interatomic forces can be assumed to be truly elastic, these collective vibrations take the form of displacement waves, acting throughout the volume of the solid, which produce a systematically coupled simple harmonic motion of the individual atoms. From this point of view, the thermal energy of the solid is described in terms of the energies of the separate collective vibrations and the thermal conductivity in terms of the propagation of energy through the crystal by the displacement waves.

In 1914, Debye, who had already formulated his remarkably accurate theory of the specific heat of solids (1914:1), attempted to derive a theory of thermal conductivity. Debye treated the crystal as a continuum rather than a discontinuous atomic array. However, in neither case can a finite thermal conductivity be explained if it is supposed that the binding forces are completely elastic so that Hooke's law is obeyed. If this situation existed the thermal conductivity would be infinite, assuming the crystal to be boundless and free from defects. In order to explain the behaviour of real crystals it is necessary to suppose that the atoms do not undergo harmonic motion; that is, the vibrations must be *anharmonic*.

Throughout the discussion on heat conduction by the lattice vibrations it will be found useful to bear in mind the following facts. The propagation of displacement waves through a medium is governed by its density and its elastic moduli. The former determines the displaced mass while the latter relate the restoring force to the displacement. If the medium is perfectly elastic, the moduli of elasticity are constants and the restoring force is strictly proportional to the displacement. On the other hand, for so-called anharmonic behaviour, this is no longer the case and the elastic moduli are functions of the displacement.

As long as the density and moduli of elasticity are homogeneous, a displacement wave can propagate itself through a medium without loss of energy. In order for the thermal conductivity to be finite, some mechanism for scattering the lattice waves must exist. *Any* such mechanism involves the presence of local regions in the medium where either the density, or the elastic moduli, or both, are different from their bulk values. In particular, in a structurally perfect crystal, a displacement wave will create such regions only if the elastic moduli vary with displacement, that is if there is anharmonic behaviour. Other waves, encountering such regions, will then experience elastic moduli which differ from their bulk values and will be scattered.

In a crystal, the scattering of the lattice waves is the more marked, the greater the maximum displacement of the atoms from their mean positions in the lattice. This is the reason for the reduction of thermal conductivity as the temperature is raised. It also accounts for the observation that the thermal conductivity of hard solids, like diamond, composed of light atoms is higher than that of solids composed of heavy atoms which are loosely bound together. At a given temperature, the maximum effective displacement of atoms from their mean positions is much greater in the latter case.

A considerable advance on Debye's simple theory of thermal conductivity was made by Peierls (1929:**1**). As Debye showed in his specific heat theory, there is a finite number of collective modes of vibration of a crystal with finite boundaries. Each of these modes (the "normal" modes) is associated with a lattice displacement wave of a particular wavelength, wave number, etc. In Peierls' theory these normal modes are quantized; the energy in each normal mode cannot have any arbitrary value but must be made up of an integral number of quanta. These quanta are called *phonons* by analogy with the photons of electromagnetic radiation. The conduction of heat in a dielectric solid is, then, to be described in terms of phonons. More correctly, since the normal mode which is quantized is a collective vibration extending throughout the whole solid and, thus, a single phonon is associated with the whole volume of the solid, it is necessary, in discussing the transfer of energy from one part of the solid to another, to introduce the concept of *phonon wave packets*. These are formed by the interference between normal modes of slightly different frequencies and wavelengths. The energy of such phonon wave packets can be localized in one part of the solid.

In a perfect crystal with elastic forces between the atoms, these wave packets (which are implicit in any further use of the term "phonons") propagate through the crystal without interfering with each other but in actual crystals they are scattered by various mechanisms. It is customary to associate a mean free path length l with the wave packets, l representing the average distance which they travel before being scattered. The thermal conductivity κ_L is then given by

$$\kappa_L = \tfrac{1}{3} C_v \bar{v} l, \tag{1.1.1}$$

where C_v is the thermal capacity per unit volume and $\bar{v}$ the velocity of sound.

At high temperatures, phonons are scattered predominantly by other phonons. Peierls showed that the most important processes involve the exchange of energy between three normal modes. Either one phonon is annihilated to yield two others or two phonons disappear to form a third. These three-phonon processes can be separated into two classes. First, there are the *normal* processes (N-processes) in which momentum† is conserved; these processes do not contribute directly to the thermal resistance but they must be taken into account since they change the distribution of phonons between the various modes. Secondly, there are *umklapp* processes (U-processes) in which momentum is not conserved. Peierls showed that it is the umklapp processes which limit the thermal conductivity.

According to Peierls' theory the thermal conductivity above the Debye temperature should be inversely proportional to the absolute temperature. However, for a perfect crystal, as the temperature is lowered below the Debye temperature, the thermal conductivity should rise exponentially. Thus, Peierls directed attention towards the behaviour of the thermal conductivity at low temperatures and much of the most important experimental work has since been carried out in this region. De Haas and Biermasz (1935:**1**) made measurements on quartz; the general behaviour which they observed has been reproduced for other materials examined later.

In some crystals, in accordance with Peierls' theory, the thermal conductivity starts to rise, as the temperature falls below the Debye temperature, more rapidly than expected from the $1/T$ law. For other crystals there is a negligible departure from the $1/T$ law in this range. In either case, as the temperature is lowered, the thermal conductivity reaches a maximum at a temperature about one-twentieth of the Debye temperature, and, at still lower temperatures, it falls rapidly to become zero at $0°K$. Casimir (1938:**1**) provided in quantitative form a simple explanation of this behaviour. As the temperature falls the phonon free path length becomes increasingly large until it reaches the order of magnitude of the dimensions of a real crystal. Since the boundaries of the crystal are never good reflectors of phonons, the free path length cannot exceed this order of magnitude. It so happens that boundary scattering is usually important at temperatures for which the specific heat is not constant but proportional (according to Debye's theory) to T^3. Thus, at the lowest temperatures, we expect the thermal conductivity to vary as T^3. It should be noted that the phonon free path length is limited by scattering at the sample boundaries only in a single crystal; for polycrystalline material the maximum free path length is, of course, smaller.

† The term "momentum" is used here in a non-classical sense since phonon motion does not involve the transfer of mass. For a fuller discussion, see Section 3.4.

Although it is difficult to support the idea of phonons in amorphous solids (e.g. glass), the behaviour of such material does agree with the above theory. In amorphous solids there is no long-range order. Thus, if we consider any solid body as being composed of one or more crystals, in an amorphous solid these "crystals" would have to be regarded as extending only over about an atomic volume. We therefore expect "boundary" scattering to dominate at all temperatures and the "phonon" free path length to be temperature independent. The thermal conductivity should then be proportional to the specific heat, i.e. to T^3 at low temperatures and independent of temperature at high temperatures. Qualitatively these ideas fit the experimental facts quite well although at low temperatures the apparent free path length rises (Kittel, 1949:**1**). Klemens (1951:**1**) showed that the thermal conductivity of an amorphous solid at low temperatures should be proportional to T rather than T^3.

The processes mentioned so far provide a qualitative explanation of the behaviour of most real crystals but they do not explain exactly either the observed temperature variation or magnitude of the thermal conductivity. In particular, the maximum value of the thermal conductivity is usually much less than the value predicted for a combination of boundary scattering with umklapp scattering. One or more of a number of other phonon scattering processes may be responsible. For example, any impurity atoms will scatter phonons as will any departures from perfection in the crystal lattice such as lattice vacancies, interstitial atoms or dislocations. In recent years it has been possible to prepare crystals in which these departures from the ideal situation have been negligible and yet the maximum thermal conductivity has still fallen short of the expected value. It has been shown that this is due to the fact that a naturally occurring element consists, not of atoms of a single atomic weight, but, in general, of a number of isotopes. The fluctuations in density resulting from the presence of atoms of different weight lead to the scattering of phonons. In cases where it has been possible to enrich a major isotope at the expense of other isotopes (e.g. in germanium, 1958:**1**) the thermal conductivity has risen.

To return briefly to the high temperature region, it should be mentioned that the $1/T$ law depends on the predominance of the three-phonon scattering processes. Pomeranchuk (1941:**1**) has shown that four-phonon processes might occur at high temperatures and would lead to a more rapid variation of the thermal conductivity with temperature. Little experimental evidence for four-phonon processes has been found but this may be due to the difficulties of carrying out accurate experiments at high temperatures. The effects of external heat losses, mostly by radiation, rapidly become more important in this range. Moreover, if the sample is at all transparent to infrared radiation, photons as well as phonons may contribute to the internal transfer of heat.

1.2 METALS

The specific heat of a metal at ordinary temperatures is almost wholly due to the vibrations of atoms about their mean positions in a crystal lattice. Thus, as in an electrical insulator, conduction of heat by the lattice vibrations does take place and for some metals at some temperatures it may be predominant. However, it is usually found that another heat conduction process is far more important. This is the conduction of heat by the charge carriers—the quasi-free electrons. In the general case, we express the total thermal conductivity κ as the sum of a lattice component κ_L and an electronic component κ_e,

$$\kappa = \kappa_L + \kappa_e. \tag{1.2.1}$$

Then, in most metals κ_e is much greater than κ_L.

It has long been recognized that free electrons should carry thermal energy as well as electrical charge. Even the primitive theory, which could explain neither the temperature variation nor the magnitude of the electrical conductivity, gave a reasonably accurate relation between the thermal and electrical conductivities. This relationship was formulated from experimental data by Wiedemann and Franz who stated that the ratio of the thermal conductivity to the electrical conductivity is the same for all metals at a given temperature. Lorenz extended this law by showing that the ratio is proportional to the absolute temperature.

We consider first the high temperature region where the electrical resistivity of a metal is proportional to the absolute temperature. The existence of the Wiedemann–Franz law shows, of course, that heat conduction in metals must be primarily an electronic process. In the earliest treatments, the kinetic theory of gases (in which heat conduction is attributed to the exchange of energy in atomic collisions) was extended to cover the free electron gas. The precise relationship between the thermal and electrical conductivities must depend to some extent on the details of the process by which the electrons are scattered. In the simplest case, the free path length of electrons (as of atoms in a gas) is supposed to be independent of their velocity and the relation takes the form

$$\kappa_e = 2\left(\frac{k}{e}\right)^2 \sigma T, \tag{1.2.2}$$

where k is Boltzmann's constant, e the electronic charge and σ the electrical conductivity. This equation contains both the Wiedemann–Franz and Lorenz laws.

It is, of course, now known that comparatively few of the free electrons of the classical model can contribute to the flow of electric current in a metal. The rigorous quantum-mechanical treatment takes into account the possible transitions between energy states of *all* the quasi-free electrons, but, in applying the quantum-mechanical principles to the classical model, it appears that only the electrons of highest energy (within one or two kT of the Fermi level) can contribute to current. The success of the classical theory in explaining the Wiedemann–Franz law was due to the fact that it is also only these electrons of highest energy which are responsible for the flow of heat. In other words, the classical theory makes almost the same error in predicting both the electrical and thermal conductivities. Only a comparatively small change in expression (1.2.2) arises from the use of the correct Fermi–Dirac statistics of the quantum theory. For a completely degenerate metal

$$\kappa_e = \frac{\pi^2}{3}\left(\frac{k}{e}\right)^2 \sigma T. \tag{1.2.2a}$$

At low temperatures ($T \ll \theta_D$, where θ_D is the Debye temperature) the electrical conductivity of a metal no longer varies as $1/T$. It starts to rise much more rapidly as the temperature is lowered. The associated free path length for electrons does not go on increasing to an infinite value; it is ultimately limited by scattering at the crystal boundaries or by defects or impurities. Thus, at the very lowest temperatures, the electrical conductivity becomes temperature independent, its value usually depending on the impurity content of the specimen.

The electrical resistivity $1/\sigma$ at low temperatures can be split into two parts,

$$\frac{1}{\sigma} = \frac{1}{\sigma_I} + \frac{1}{\sigma_0}, \tag{1.2.3}$$

where $1/\sigma_I$ is the resistivity due to impurities and $1/\sigma_0$ is that due to the scattering of electrons by the atomic vibrations. In this temperature range the thermal resistivity can also be separated into two parts (this is Matthiessen's rule). Thus,

$$\frac{1}{\kappa_e} = \frac{1}{(\kappa_e)_I} + \frac{1}{(\kappa_e)_0}. \tag{1.2.4}$$

It is important to note that thermal resistivity due to impurity scattering $1/(\kappa_e)_I$ is related to $1\sigma_I$ through equation (1.2.2a) which applies above the Debye temperature. Thus, the Lorenz number L, defined as $\kappa_e/\sigma T$, has the same value at the lowest temperatures, for which impurity scattering is predominant, as it has at high temperatures.

The expression for the ideal thermal conductivity $(\kappa_e)_0$ is much more complicated and the interested reader should refer to a specialist treatment (1953:1). In general it may be stated that the Lorenz number falls below the value $\pi^2(k/e)^2/3$ in the temperature range below θ_D. The minimum value for L may be an order of magnitude less than the high temperature value $\pi^2(k/e)^2/3$ for a very pure sample; for an impure sample the fall in the Lorenz number is less marked.

It should be realized that the electronic thermal conductivity in most metals is at least an order of magnitude greater than the thermal conductivity in most insulators. Furthermore, phonons can be scattered by charge carriers and such scattering in a metal is effective in reducing the lattice thermal conductivity below its value in a comparable insulator. It is clear, then, that the electronic component of the thermal conductivity of a metal should be very much greater than the lattice component. At ordinary temperatures it is rarely necessary to take any account at all of lattice conduction in metals. It is only for such metals as antimony and bismuth (which have low carrier concentrations and are so unlike most metals that we have thought fit to consider them in Chapter 5 of this book) that the lattice thermal conductivity becomes important.

1.3 SEMICONDUCTORS

The semiconductors with which we shall be concerned may be divided into two distinct classes. First, there are those having a high electrical resistivity, that is high enough for the electronic component of the thermal conductivity to be neglected. In these materials it is their high purity, and the crystalline perfection which one associates with the preparation of semiconductors for use in transistors, that makes them of interest, particularly at low temperatures. Secondly, we shall be interested in semiconductors having an electrical resistivity which is sufficiently low for the electronic thermal conductivity to be appreciable. Here it is useful to study the behaviour of the thermal conductivity in the ranges of partial degeneracy or non-degeneracy (including the region of intrinsic conduction). This study is impossible for metals, which are always degenerate.

For the first class of semiconductor, e.g. silicon and germanium at low and moderate temperatures, there is no need to elaborate at this stage on the heat-conduction processes, which have already been described for electrical insulators. Lattice heat conduction in the second class of material, e.g. the tellurides of lead and bismuth, may likewise be dismissed from this section. It should, however, be noted that it is the magnitude of the lattice thermal conductivity in the latter materials which is primarily important in determining their usefulness in thermo-electric devices.

A precise determination of the electronic thermal conductivity in the non-degenerate region for an extrinsic semiconductor (that is, one in which conduction takes place through a single type of carrier, either electrons or positive holes) would be of use in enabling the scattering law for the charge carriers to be determined. It has already been stated that, when the free path length of the carriers is velocity (or energy) independent, the Lorenz number is $2(k/e)^2$. For ionized-impurity scattering, the free path length increases with the energy of the carriers; the mean energy transported by the charge carriers therefore rises and the Lorenz number also rises, according to the simplest theory (1950:1), to $4(k/e)^2$.

In practice, the exact determination of the total thermal conductivity κ and of the lattice component κ_L is so difficult as to rule out, in general, the possibility of predicting the scattering law from the magnitude of the electronic component κ_e. However, it is at least possible to calculate the electronic component using data obtained from electrical measurement and then to see if the measured thermal conductivity is consistent with this calculation. Thus, suppose that the free path length for electrons is thought to be independent of energy. Then, for very low carrier concentrations we expect the thermal conductivity to approach the value κ_L corresponding to lattice conduction only. We predict that the thermal conductivity should rise with carrier concentration so that

$$\frac{d\kappa}{d\sigma} = 2\left(\frac{k}{e}\right)^2 T.$$

Then, as the material is made degenerate by further increase of the

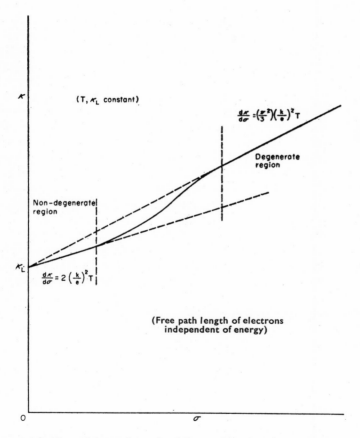

FIG. 1.3.1. Plot of thermal conductivity against electrical conductivity for a simple extrinsic semiconductor.

carrier concentration, it is expected that the rate of increase $d\kappa/d\sigma$ should become greater until for complete degeneracy

$$\frac{d\kappa}{d\sigma} = \frac{\pi^2}{3}\left(\frac{k}{e}\right)^2 T,$$

as in a metal. This behaviour is illustrated qualitatively in Fig. 1.3.1.

In fact, such a curve is seldom observed in its entirety because of a number of complicating features. For example, in order to achieve high electrical conductivities it is necessary to dope the semiconductor heavily with impurities. These doping agents are likely to reduce the lattice thermal conductivity κ_L (which has been assumed constant in Fig. 1.3.1.) and lower the value of $d\kappa/d\sigma$. Equally important, the lowest values of the electrical conductivity are reached for intrinsic or near-intrinsic material in which electrons and holes simultaneously play an appreciable part in the conduction processes. Now, when there are only *either* electrons *or* holes present there can be no continuous flow of charge carriers from one temperature region to another. However, if carriers of both signs are present, a flow of electrons can be balanced by a flow of positive holes so as to prevent the building-up of electrical charge. Thus, bipolar diffusion is possible and leads to the transport of *ionization* energy as well as *kinetic* energy. The Lorenz number associated with the bipolar thermodiffusion process can be an order of magnitude greater than that which relates to the flow of carriers of but one sign.

Various workers have claimed to have observed behaviour in certain semiconductors which cannot be explained in terms of the heat-conduction effects which we have mentioned so far. For example, it is possible for heat to be transported by excitons (electron–hole pairs which remain associated so that they can carry energy but not charge). However, the experimental evidence is conflicting and more conclusive results are needed before it can be stated with certainty that such mechanisms must be taken into account.

Chapter 2

MEASUREMENT OF THERMAL CONDUCTIVITY

2.1 INTRODUCTION

MOST of the methods adopted for the measurement of the thermal conductivity of semiconductors do not differ, in principle, from those used for any other materials in the solid state. An exception is to be found in the case of those semiconductors which are suitable for thermoelectric applications; as will be shown in Section 2.5, a special method, which cannot be employed generally, may be used with these materials, but, even so, their thermal conductivities are usually obtained by more conventional means. It seems worthwhile to summarize the various methods of measurement and then to describe, by way of example, some of the apparatus which has been used for semiconducting materials.

The first choice lies between the static and the dynamic methods. In the former it is only after equilibrium has been reached that measurements are made. This condition assists in the achievement of a high degree of accuracy but, particularly for poor thermal conductors, the attainment of equilibrium may be a lengthy process. Thus, the total time involved in measurements on a sample at several different temperatures may be very great. In contrast, by using a dynamic method in which the thermal gradients are observed as a function of time, a wide range of temperature may be covered much more rapidly and in rather more detail than is possible with a static method. However, dynamic measurements have their own disadvantages and it is difficult to obtain a very high order of accuracy with them. A method with certain attractive features is that devised by Ångström in which the periodic changes of temperature associated with thermal waves are observed.

A distinction must be drawn between the absolute and the comparative measurements. In an absolute method, the heat which passes

13

through the sample is measured directly, usually as the electrical energy supplied to one end. On the other hand, in a comparison method, the same quantity of heat passes through the specimen under test and a sample of known thermal conductance which is placed in series with it. The flow of heat is calculated from the temperature gradient over the standard sample. The thermal conductivities of the standard and test materials should be of the same order. Absolute methods are usually employed below room temperature but, because of the small size of most semiconductor specimens, a comparison method is often preferable at higher temperatures. The transfer of heat to the surroundings by radiation is then not so important.

The size and shape of the sample which is to be measured depend largely on the order of magnitude of its thermal conductivity. In choosing the most suitable dimensions it is essential to bear in mind the various sources of error which may arise in a heat-conduction measurement. In determining the *electrical* conductivity of a semiconductor one can usually assume that the electric current passes only through the specimen; the surrounding space is, for practical purposes, a perfect electrical insulator. However, in a *thermal* conductivity measurement there is always the possibility of heat transfer through the surrounding medium. If this medium is air, heat may be passed both by conduction and convection; even if the sample is held in a high vacuum, heat may still be transferred by radiation. In order to make the lateral heat losses relatively small, it is best to use a short sample with a large cross-section area. A difficulty then arises in the accurate determination of the temperature gradient. If thermometers are attached to the sample itself they disturb the temperature distribution and it is not always easy to measure the distance between them. Alternatively, one might determine the difference between the temperatures of blocks attached to the opposite faces of the sample but, in this case, any temperature gradients across the contacts become important; from this point of view, long samples are preferable. It is necessary, therefore, to compromise between the two mutually contradictory sets of requirements. In practice, it is usual to employ a long bar of the material if it is a good thermal conductor (1865:**1**, 1908:**1**) and a short disk or plate if it is a poor conductor of heat (1898:**1**).

2.2 ABSOLUTE MEASUREMENTS

A number of semiconductors have thermal conductivities of the same order as most metals. Other semiconductors, which are only moderate conductors of heat at room temperature, become quite good conductors at low temperatures. It is important, therefore, that a description should be given of an absolute measurement suitable for materials of high thermal conductivity. On the other hand, those

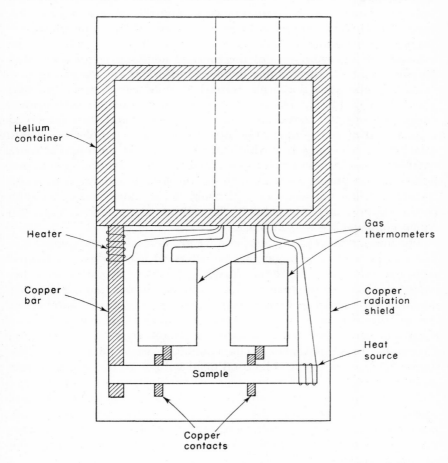

FIG. 2.2.1. Rosenberg's apparatus for the measurement of thermal conductivity at low temperatures (1954:**1**).

semiconductors which are used in thermoelectric devices all have a low thermal conductivity so an absolute method which has been employed with such materials will also be described.

2.2.1 ROSENBERG'S MEASUREMENTS AT LOW TEMPERATURES

Rosenberg (1955:1) has measured the thermal conductivity of a number of metals at low temperatures using the apparatus shown in Fig. 2.2.1. He has also used it for measurements on the semiconductors silicon and germanium (1954:1). His work illustrates not only the principles of determination of the thermal conductivity of good conductors but also the techniques involved in work at low temperatures.

Each sample took the form of a rod of some 5 cm length and from 1 to 3 mm diameter. The source of heat was a length of 47-gauge eureka wire of 100 Ω resistance, wound around, and then cemented to, one end of the sample. The other end of the sample was firmly attached to a copper bar which projected below the high pressure chamber of a Simon expansion liquefier; this chamber contained liquid helium during measurements at the lowest temperatures. With certain metallic samples, one end could be threaded and screwed in to the copper bar; alternatively the sample was soldered to a stub which could be screwed in place.

The measurement of the temperature gradient along the sample was carried out using helium gas thermometers. Other workers have often used carbon resistance thermometers (1955:2); thermocouples become insensitive in the region of helium temperatures. Annular copper contacts were soldered to the sample and to the copper chambers of the gas thermometers, which were each of about 3 ml volume. These chambers were connected by stainless steel capillaries to a glass U-tube containing butyl phthalate. The capillaries were anchored to the liquid helium container. The total dead volume of the thermometers was about 1 ml.

The chamber was evacuated and a copper radiation shield surrounded the specimen so that, at the low temperatures employed, lateral losses from the sample were negligible. The vacuum also prevented heat from entering the helium container and, thus, reduced the rate of consumption of liquid helium.

The temperature range between 1·4 and 4·2°K was covered by allowing the liquid helium to boil at a reduced pressure. In the range

4·2 to 10°K high pressure helium was expanded through a needle valve. Above 10°K liquid hydrogen was employed; at 55°K liquid oxygen was boiled at reduced pressure. Use was also made of the heater wound on the copper bar for the maintenance of intermediate temperatures.

2.2.2 An Apparatus for Poor Thermal Conductors

Besides being important for thermoelectric applications, semi-conductors which are poor conductors of heat are valuable in studies of the electronic contribution to the thermal conductivity, particularly when the charge carriers are in a state of low degeneracy. Above room temperature, radiation losses tend to limit the degree of accuracy which may be obtained. Thus, the range below room temperature is often studied. The apparatus which will be described enables measurements to be made between about 130 and 330°K (1956:**1**). It is illustrated in Fig. 2.2.2 and has found application for materials having conductivities ranging from below 0·01 W cm^{-1} °C^{-1} to greater than 0·1 W cm^{-1} °C^{-1}.

The source of heat consisted of an insulated nichrome coil embedded in a copper block, the power supplied being calculated from current and voltage measurements. The specimens were of about 1 cm square cross-section and were ground flat and parallel, electroplated, and soldered in position with Wood's metal to ensure good thermal contact. The sink consisted of a copper cylinder which slid over a copper block soldered to the top of the specimen. The temperatures of the heat source and sink were measured using copper–constantan thermocouples. All the electrical leads, which were made from 40-gauge wire, passed through a clamp at the same temperature as the sink and the enclosure was evacuated. The loss of heat from the source, other than through the specimen, was thus small and definite; its value, measured over the full range of temperature, without a specimen in place, was found to be close to the figure predicted from the dimensions of the apparatus and consequently a reliable correction could be applied. The small thermal resistance of the end-contacts was determined by comparing the results obtained with samples of different length.

Control of the temperature of the sink was obtained by varying the degree of vacuum in the space which separated it from an outer cylinder immersed in liquid air, and by adjusting the current flowing in a nichrome heating coil. For samples with thermal conductivities of about 0·02 W cm⁻¹ °C⁻¹, it was estimated that the total error did not exceed 3 per cent over the whole temperature range. The errors in the measurement of the Seebeck coefficient, which could be carried out simultaneously, were thought to be rather smaller.

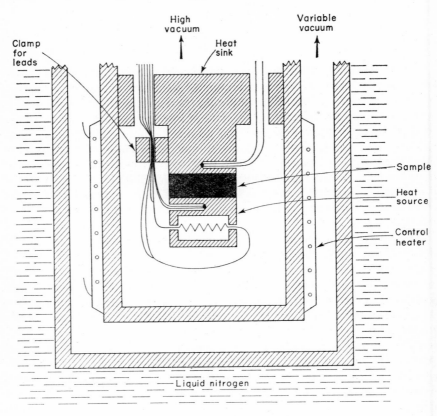

Fig. 2.2.2. Apparatus for the absolute determination of the thermal conductivity of poor conductors (1956:**1**).

2.3 COMPARISON OF THERMAL CONDUCTIVITIES

When the thermal conductivity of a solid at elevated temperatures s to be determined by an absolute method it is desirable that a sample of large cross-section area should be available. Radiation losses, particularly from the heat source, become of rapidly increasing importance as the temperature is raised. The relative importance of these losses cannot be reduced indefinitely by decreasing the length of the sample since this makes any contact resistances of greater significance. However, by increasing the cross-section area, without increasing the length of the specimen, radiation can be made less important. Unfortunately the cross-section area of semiconducting samples is usually limited to perhaps a square centimetre. In this case it is preferable to employ a comparison method for the measurement of thermal conductivity above room temperature.

2.3.1 STUCKES AND CHASMAR'S APPARATUS

The method employed by Stuckes and Chasmar (1956:2) had the advantage of simplicity and was, moreover, accurate to within 10 per cent. It could be used up to more than 400°C.

The apparatus is shown in Fig. 2.3.1. The specimen of semiconductor and two samples of a material of known thermal conductivity were sandwiched between four silver blocks, below a heat source, by means of a load applied through a ball bearing. The heat source consisted of a nichrome coil wound on to a stainless steel cylinder. The column rested on a heavy copper base which, with the enclosing copper walls, acted as a heat sink at a uniform temperature. The required level of temperature was maintained by insertion of the apparatus in a vacuum furnace.

The temperatures near the faces of the silver blocks were measured with six nickel–chromium, nickel–aluminium thermocouples made from wires of 0·005 in. diameter. The thermocouple junctions were enclosed in insulating sheathing and inserted in cylindrical holes in the blocks; the depth of insertion had to be at least eight times the diameter of the sheathing if no errors in the temperature measurement were to arise. The fine thermocouple wires were connected to thicker wires of the same materials before leaving the apparatus.

Ideally, the same quantity of heat should have passed through the two standards and the sample under test but, in practice, some heat was inevitably lost from the sides of the specimens and the silver blocks. By polishing the components of the apparatus, the radiation losses were reduced. Some check on their magnitude was given by a comparison of the thermal gradients in the two standards. An allowance was made for any losses from the sides of the column by taking the mean value for the flow of heat through these two specimens.

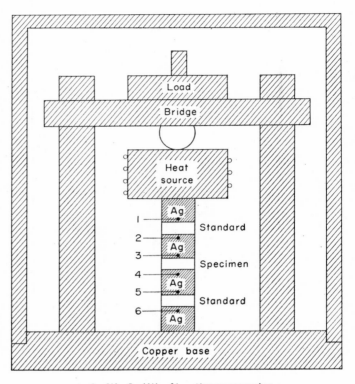

I-6 Ni-Cr/Ni-Al   thermocouples

FIG. 2.3.1. The method used by Stuckes and Chasmar for comparison of thermal conductivities (1956:2).

The samples, of course, had to make good contact with the silver blocks. It was not sufficient merely to grind the faces, so that they were flat, or to polish them. However, thermal contacts of sufficient quality could be obtained by use of indium amalgam.

The thermal conductivity of the standard materials had to be close to that of the material under test. Stuckes and Chasmar used blocks of stainless steel in their original work but they recommended the use of quartz with semiconductors of low thermal conductivity.

2.3.2 THE METHOD OF BOWERS *et al.*

A comparison method was also used by Bowers *et al.* (1959:**1**) in their measurements on indium arsenide and indium antimonide extending up to over 800°C. The apparatus, which was based on that of Francl and Kingery (1954:**2**) is shown in Fig. 2.3.2.

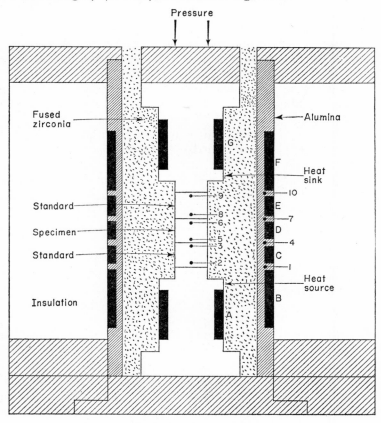

1–10 Pt–Pt/10% Rh thermocouples
A–G Heaters

FIG. 2.3.2. The apparatus for comparison of thermal conductivities used by Bowers *et al.* (1959:**1**).

A flow of heat through the column was maintained using the heaters *A* and *G*. The remaining heaters, *B*, *C*, *D*, *E* and *F*, were used in producing a distribution of temperature in the cylindrical alumina shield similar to that in the central column. The platinum–platinum rhodium thermocouples (1)–(10) were inserted in the positions shown. Those placed in the standard blocks and in the specimen occupied $\frac{1}{32}$ in. holes which had been cut with an ultrasonic drill. Alumina tubing was used to prevent contamination of the thermocouples at high temperatures. A flow of helium through the apparatus prevented oxidation of the components.

The faces of the blocks were ground smooth and flat to improve the thermal contact between them. In fact, the errors due to thermal resistances at the contacts were minimized by connecting the thermocouples directly to the samples which were being compared. This was demonstrated by an additional experiment in which colloidal graphite was applied to the surfaces; the results were not affected by this treatment.

Dense alumina was employed as a standard material; its thermal conductivity had been determined by comparison with that of Armco iron.

Bowers and his colleagues found that the results obtained with their apparatus at room temperature lay within 2 per cent of those given by an absolute determination on the same materials.

2.4 DYNAMIC AND PERIODIC METHODS

2.4.1 IOFFE AND IOFFE'S DYNAMIC METHOD

Ioffe and Ioffe (1952:**1**) realized that one can obtain more accurate thermal conductivity measurements using an equilibrium, rather than a non-equilibrium, method but they decided to adopt the latter because it led to a reduction in the time necessary to complete a given number of observations. They set out to eliminate or reduce the usual sources of error and claimed that the results obtained from their apparatus were correct to within 3 or 5 per cent. Their method was suitable for poor, rather than good, conductors of heat.

The apparatus is illustrated in Fig. 2.4.1. The sample under test took the form of a block with plane parallel faces and was clamped between two copper blocks by means of a vertical screw. The bridge which carried this screw was insulated from the lower copper block by methyl methacrylate plates which also acted as the walls of the apparatus. Copper–constantan thermocouples were inserted into the

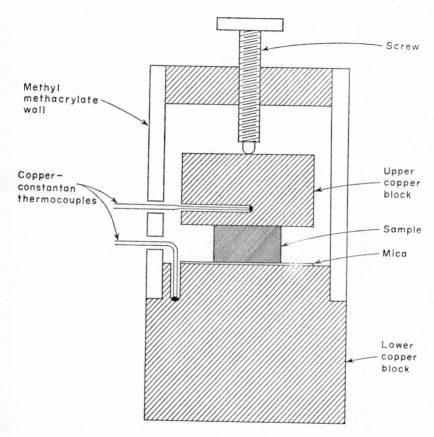

Screw

Methyl
methacrylate
wall

Copper–
constantan
thermocouples

Upper
copper
block

Sample

Mica

Lower
copper
block

Fig. 2.4.1. Ioffe's dynamic method for the determination of thermal conductivity (1952:**1**).

copper blocks in the vicinity of the sample. A thin sheet of mica was interposed between the specimen and the lower block for electrical insulation; the thermocouples could then be connected differentially for determination of the temperature difference.

3

Initially the whole apparatus was brought to the same temperature. Then the lower block was immersed in a cooling bath and the temperature difference between the blocks and the absolute temperature of one of them were continually recorded. The rate at which heat was removed from the upper block of thermal capacity C_2 and temperature T_2 was $C_2\,\mathrm{d}T_2/\mathrm{d}t$ where t represents time. Ideally this quantity should have been equal to $\kappa(T_2 - T_1)A/l$ for a specimen of thermal conductivity κ, cross-section area A and length l, T_1 being the temperature of the lower block. Thus, in principle, κ could be calculated.

However, some of the heat entering the lower block came from the sample itself rather than from the upper block. A correction for this factor was made by adding a fraction of the thermal capacity C_s of the sample to C_2. This meant that the specific heat of the semiconductor had to be known but, since in practice C_2 was very much larger than C_s, it was not necessary to determine the latter very accurately.

A correction also had to be applied for heat transfer between the upper block and the surrounding walls. Since the apparatus was not evacuated there was the possibility of condensation of water vapour from the air but this effect proved to be almost negligible. The other lateral heat transfer processes involved a correction of a few per cent which was determined by measuring the temperature difference between the blocks when equilibrium was reached. The heat conducted through the sample was then equal to that which was transferred from the walls to the upper block. Lateral heat transfer could have been reduced by evacuation of the apparatus and by maintaining the enclosure at a temperature which did not differ too much from that of the cold bath.

Transport of heat between the two copper blocks by convection was reduced by making the volume of the intervening air as small as possible. Convection was, in any case, of minor importance since the lower block was the cooler. The heat passing through the air which surrounded the specimen was determined by replacing the latter with a paper block of very low, known thermal conductivity.

It was important to ensure that the temperature difference between the thermocouples really corresponded to that over the sample. In other words, the thermal resistances at the contacts had to be negligible. It was claimed that such good contacts were achieved if the gaps between the surfaces were filled with gallium, an amalgam, glycerine or oil. A small correction for the thermal resistance of the sheet of mica insulation had to be applied. Care was taken that there were no appreciable thermal gradients between the faces of the copper blocks and the thermocouples under the experimental conditions.

Ioffe and Ioffe's apparatus was later refined for the more accurate determination of the thermal conductivity of semiconductors at room temperature (1958:2). In the newer apparatus, the enclosure consisted of a copper cylinder which was maintained at the same temperature as the upper block. By this means the lateral heat transfer to this block was eliminated.

The detailed theory of Ioffe and Ioffe's method has been given by Kaganov (1958:3) and Swann (1959:2). One consequence of this theory is that the time interval, over which one can make measurements leading to accurate results, is limited. The rate of change of temperature with time should not be measured too soon after the lower block is placed in its cooling bath. The measurements should not be continued when the temperatures of the two blocks have become nearly equal. Kaganov has dealt with this problem in particular.

The full equation, which can be used over the restricted time interval, is

$$\frac{\mathrm{d}T_2}{\mathrm{d}t} = \frac{(T_2 - T_1)\kappa}{(C_2 + C_s/3)}(1 + a' - a''),\tag{2.4.1}$$

where a' and a'' are small corrections which depend on the thermal conductances of the surrounding air and the thermal resistance of the contacts respectively.

2.4.2 ÅNGSTRÖM'S METHOD

Ångström (1861:1) developed a method in which the application of a periodic source of heat to one end of a sample leads to the determination of its thermal diffusivity k_d. k_d is defined as $\kappa/\rho C$ where ρ is the density and C the specific heat. Thus, the thermal conductivity may be obtained by measuring the diffusivity, if the density and specific heat are known (See also 1959:3).

Let us suppose that the temperature at one end of a very long bar is made to vary sinusoidally with a periodic time $2\pi/\omega$. The resulting temperature wave is attenuated as it moves along the bar. It will be supposed that the ratio of the amplitudes of the wave at two positions separated by a distance l is α ($\alpha > 1$). Since the wave travels with only a finite velocity there will be a phase difference β between the two positions ($\beta > 0$). If there are no lateral losses of heat from the bar, the thermal diffusivity may be determined from the magnitude of α or β:

$$k_d = \frac{\omega l^2}{2 \ln^2 \alpha} = \frac{\omega l^2}{2\beta^2}.$$

However, in the more general case, where, for example, radiation from the surface occurs, k_d may not be expressed simply in terms of either α or β alone, but it may be shown that

$$k_d = \frac{\omega l^2}{2\beta \ln \alpha}.$$

Thus, by measuring both α and β it is possible to determine the thermal diffusivity even if there is appreciable lateral heat transfer. This suggests that the method should be particularly useful above room temperature where the effect of radiation becomes more important. The method has an advantage in that the thermal contact between the source of heat and the sample need not be perfect.

In practice it is difficult to produce a sinusoidal variation of temperature at the source. However, even if the initial wave is of square form, a Fourier analysis of the temperature variation at a point may be carried out and attention can then be confined to the fundamental frequency. In any case, the higher harmonics are very rapidly attenuated.

Nii (1958:**4**, 1959:**4**) has measured the thermal diffusivity of lead telluride and bismuth telluride using the apparatus shown in Fig. 2.4.2. The lower end of the sample was soldered to a copper rod around which was wound a heating coil. The current through the heater was alternately switched on and off with equal periods in each state. The temperature was recorded continuously at the points (1) and (2). The sample was sufficiently long so that the end which was remote from the heat source remained effectively at a constant temperature.

Green and Cowles (1960:**1**) found it convenient to utilize the Peltier effect rather than the Joule effect at the heat source. In their apparatus the current in a thermocouple of large cross-section area (consisting of p-type and n-type bismuth telluride) was periodically reversed so that the junction, which was in contact with one end of the sample, was alternately heated and cooled. The Joule effect was not completely negligible, but by employing a slightly higher current during the cooling part of the cycle it was possible to bring the time-average of the heat input to the specimen to zero; there was then no tendency for the mean temperature to drift. Another advantage of

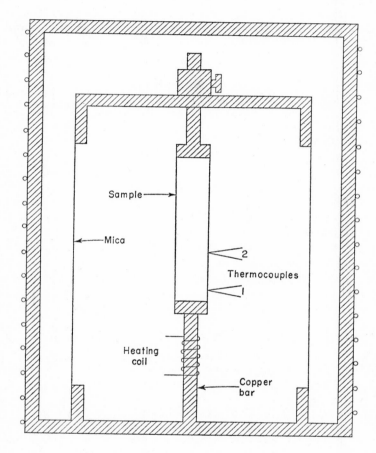

Fig. 2.4.2. Measurement of thermal diffusivity by Ångström's method. Nii's apparatus (1958:4).

using the Peltier effect to generate the temperature waves is that the input wave form becomes almost symmetrical. Thus, the even harmonics, and in particular the second harmonic, become negligible;

this assists in obtaining a sensibly sinusoidal temperature wave at a short distance from the source.

The principles of Green and Cowles' apparatus are shown in Fig. 2.4.3. A novel feature was the use of the Seebeck effect of the sample itself in measuring the relative temperature. Probes, consisting of 0·05 mm diameter chromel wires, were welded to the sample at positions (1) and (2), and at the top which remained at a constant

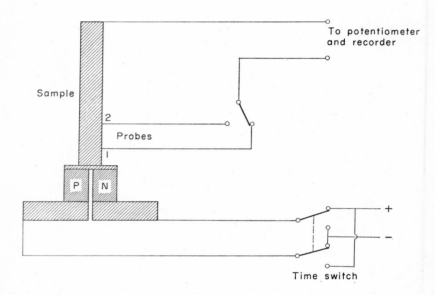

FIG. 2.4.3. The thermal diffusivity apparatus of Green and Cowles (1960:1).

temperature. The thermoelectric voltage between either of the lower probes and the top of the sample was a measure of the relative temperature difference. Since the sample was a semiconductor, its Seebeck coefficient was considerably higher than that of any metallic thermocouple material. Thus, the use of the sample as its own thermometer increased the sensitivity of the method.

Green and Cowles made their measurements on bismuth telluride, which has a thermal diffusivity of about 0·014 cm²/sec at room temperature. They used a 30 sec periodic time and found that the temperature wave was sensibly sinusoidal at about 5 mm from the heat source even though the latter generated a saw-tooth wave. A separation between probes (1) and (2) of 8 mm was found to give an amplitude ratio of about 9 : 1 and a phase difference of just over 2 rad.

2.5 SPECIAL METHODS FOR ELECTRICAL CONDUCTORS

2.5.1 KOHLRAUSCH'S METHOD

Most of the heat loss in an absolute thermal conductivity measurement originates directly from the heater. Thus, Kohlrausch (1900:**1**) devised a method, which may be applied to electrical conductors, in which the source of heat is an electric current passing through the sample. This method, which was improved by Jaeger and Diesselhorst (1900:**2**), has recently been applied to semiconductors by Birkholz (1958:**5**).

The ends of the sample, through which the current passes, are kept at a fixed temperature. The middle portion of the specimen then rises in temperature until the rate of electrical heating is balanced by the rate at which heat is conducted towards the ends. The amount by which the temperature rises for a given potential gradient along the sample depends on its electrical and thermal conductivities. The higher the electrical conductivity, the greater the electric current and, thus, the larger is the increase of temperature. On the other hand, a high thermal conductivity tends to make the rise of temperature small. The temperatures T_1 and T_2 at any two points in the bar are related to the potential difference $(V_2 - V_1)$ by the equation

$$\int_{T_1}^{T_2} \frac{\kappa}{\sigma} \, dT + \tfrac{1}{2}(V_2 - V_1)^2 + A(V_2 - V_1) + B = 0, \qquad (2.5.1)$$

where σ is the electrical conductivity and A and B are two constants of integration. There are three unknowns so that it is necessary to make measurements at three different points. In the usual arrangement one of these points is situated at the centre of the bar and the other two are equally spaced on either side. In view of the symmetry of the system the temperatures T_1 and T_3 at the latter two points should be equal. It may then be shown that

$$\int_{T_1}^{T_2} \frac{\kappa}{\sigma} \, dT = \tfrac{1}{8}(V_3 - V_1)^2. \qquad (2.5.2)$$

Birkholz found that the situation for the semiconductor bismuth telluride was complicated by an internal Peltier effect, which arose because the material was not completely homogeneous, as well as by radiation losses. Thermoelectric effects were eliminated by reversing the direction of the current or by using an alternating current. In order to determine the radiation loss, the ends of the sample were heated while the enclosure was maintained at room temperature. The centre of the sample reached a lower temperature than that at the ends because of radiation from the surfaces; the emissivity of the material could be calculated from the temperature distribution in this case.

2.5.2 Measurements on Thermoelectric Materials

Much of the present interest in the measurement of thermal conductivity arises from the need to determine this quantity for those semiconductors which are employed in thermoelectric refrigeration or generation (1957:**1**, 1960:**2**). For these materials, a particularly convenient experimental arrangement has been adopted by Harman (1958:**6**). He showed that, not only the thermal conductivity, but also the Seebeck coefficient (otherwise known as the thermoelectric power or thermal e.m.f. coefficient) and the electrical resistivity, could be measured in a single apparatus.

In Harman's method a temperature gradient along the sample is established by means of the Peltier effect. When an electric current is passed through the sample, held between metallic contacts, there is heating at one end and cooling at the other. If the current is small enough, the Joule heating effect may be neglected; the Peltier heating and cooling depend on the first power of the current, while the Joule heating depends on its square. In order that a reasonable temperature difference between the ends may be established, it is necessary that the materials should have a reasonably high figure of merit.†

In a practical apparatus, copper current leads and chromel–alumel thermocouples were soldered to the ends of a rectangular block of

† The figure of merit z is usually defined as $Q^2\sigma/\kappa$ where Q is the Seebeck coefficient and σ the electrical conductivity (see Appendix 1).

material as shown in Fig. 2.5.1. A pair of alumel probes were also attached (e.g. by spot-welding) to the surface of the sample.

First, a known alternating current was passed through the sample and the potential differences, between the alumel probes and the alumel thermocouple wires, respectively, were measured. These measurements allowed the electrical resistivity and the electrical resistance between the contacts (including any contact resistances) to be determined. The use of an alternating current prevented the formation of a temperature gradient by the Peltier effect.

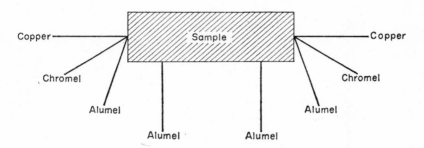

FIG. 2.5.1. Harman's method for obtaining the thermal conductivity of thermoelectric materials (1958:6).

Next, a direct current was passed through the specimen and the temperature difference between its ends was found after equilibrium had been reached. The Peltier effect transferred heat at the rate πI, π being the Peltier coefficient and I the current. This was balanced by heat conduction at the rate $\kappa(\Delta T)A/l$, ΔT being the temperature difference between the ends, A the cross-section area and l the length. According to Kelvin's first law of thermoelectricity π is equal to QT where Q is the Seebeck coefficient, so

$$IQT = \frac{\kappa\Delta T A}{l}. \qquad (2.5.3)$$

The Seebeck coefficient was determined by measuring the potential difference between the ends after the temperature difference ΔT had become established. After the potential difference due to the electrical resistance of the sample had been subtracted, the remainder corresponded to the thermoelectric voltage $Q\Delta T$. It should be noted that this gave the differential Seebeck coefficient with respect to alumel; the Seebeck coefficient of the latter with respect to copper had to be added to obtain the value of Q for insertion in equation (2.5.3).

The values of the thermal conductivity obtained by this method agreed with those obtained by other means if adequate precautions were taken. The sample had to be maintained in an evacuated enclosure to prevent heat transfer by convection or conduction through air. Also, the lead wires had to be fine enough to prevent appreciable heat conduction over their length; Harman recommended the use of 40-gauge wires. A current of from 20 to 40 mA was found to be suitable for use with a block of bismuth telluride of 2 cm length and with a cross-section area of from 0·1 to 0·2 cm².

Harman *et al.* (1959:5) have more recently published the detailed theory of the method taking into account the transfer of heat by radiation from the surface of the sample and from the end contacts. Equation (2.5.3) must then be modified to include a number of extra terms; these extra terms introduce two additional unknown quantities, the thermal conductance of the leads and the radiating power of the surfaces. The quantities may be determined in practice by using samples of different length and cross-section area.

Chapter 3

THEORY OF THE FLOW OF ENERGY AND CHARGE IN SOLIDS

OUR main concern in this book is the flow of heat in semiconductors in the presence of a temperature gradient. However, before proceeding to the detailed calculations appropriate to this problem, we shall outline some of the main features of the theory of the transport processes of solids in general. There are two main reasons for this approach. In the first place, much of the basic theory is applicable to solids other than semiconductors. Thus, a description of this theory can act as a basis for comparing the properties of semiconductors with highly conducting metallic solids on the one hand and with insulating dielectric solids on the other. Secondly, the generalization of the theory to include transport processes other than thermal conduction is essential to give an adequate discussion of the latter. The reason for this is that the flow of energy in a conducting solid, governing its thermal conductivity, is intimately related to the flow of electronic charge governing other transport properties. By considering these two flows together, the relations between the various properties can be obtained in a very simple way.

In this chapter, therefore, we shall first establish the theoretical description of a solid which, to a good approximation, can be thought of as composed of two systems—an electron system (Section 3.3) and a lattice, or phonon, system (Section 3.4). Sections 3.3 and 3.4 provide the basis for a general description of the flow of energy and charge in solids (Sections 3.5 to 3.8).

3.1 PHYSICAL DESCRIPTION OF A SOLID

A solid body is composed of a very large number of individual atoms which are held together by mutual forces. The origin of these forces is that the atoms in the solid do not in general possess the same electronic structure as would isolated atoms of the same chemical species. Such isolated atoms consist of a central nucleus carrying a positive charge (equal, in units of the electron charge, to the atomic number of the chemical species) around which are grouped a number of electrons so that the whole atom is neutral.

The description of such isolated atoms on the basis of quantum mechanics leads to the result that the electrons are grouped into "shells" around the nucleus. To a close approximation, its particular shell defines the energy by which an electron is bound to the nucleus, this energy being closely related to the mean distance of the electron from the nucleus. Each shell is capable of accommodating only a certain fixed number of electrons and, in any particular atom, the shells are filled up in the order of increasing energy. Thus (except for the rare gases) in any particular isolated atom, there is an incompletely filled shell which accommodates those electrons which are least tightly bound to the nucleus. This shell is called the *valence shell* because its properties determine the interaction of the atom with other atoms in chemical reactions. The remaining part of the atom, i.e. the nucleus and the inner shells, is called the *core*. When such an atom is brought into sufficiently close proximity with another atom, interaction may take place between them in such a way that the energy of the final system is lower than the sum of the individual energies of the two separate atoms. In this case, a stable complex is formed and, by a continuation of the process, a solid body is built up. The interaction leading to a binding force between the atoms arises, almost exclusively, through a modification of the electronic structure of the valence shells of the individual atoms. The cores of these atoms remain unaffected in the process of reaction. The various modifications that can take place in the valence shells depend on the particular atoms concerned and can vary widely, giving rise to different types of chemical binding. Two extreme cases can be distinguished corresponding to the so-called *ionic* bond and to the *metallic* bond. In the first of these, one or more electrons may be transferred from the valence shell of one atom A to the valence shell of a second atom B, to give an ionic complex A^+B^-. The extra energy required to give such a stable complex comes from the Coulomb interaction between A^+ and B^-. The electrons responsible for the binding in this case are localized in the valence shells of the individual atoms. They are, therefore, more tightly bound to these atoms than is the case for other types of chemical binding. In the second extreme case, electrons become completely detached from the valence shells of the parent atoms and form a "gas" of negatively charged centres in the solid, in which are embedded the cores which carry a positive charge. The binding energy in this case arises from the interaction between these two types of centre. The electrons responsible for the binding are free to move easily through the crystal; they are not bound tightly to any one position. This is the origin of the high electrical conductivity of metals, since the electrons can be induced to flow readily through the solid by means of an electric field. In contrast, in an ionic solid, since the electrons are all comparatively tightly bound, an electric field does not produce a flow of current.

In between these two extreme cases there is a whole range of possibilities, all of which are characterized by the fact that the electrons which are responsible for the binding are more or less localized in the region of the parent atoms. However, they are not so completely localized as in the extreme ionic case. The typical example of such an intermediate case is the *covalent* bond which may arise between two similar atoms. Each atom loses an electron from its valence shell and these electrons remain predominantly in the region between the atoms, and provide binding between them. These binding electrons, however, are not so tightly bound to the parent atoms as in a completely ionic compound and a comparatively small amount of extra energy may be sufficient to detach them from their stable position. If this happens the electrons become free to move through the crystal. In particular, the thermal energy of the solid at a moderate temperature may be sufficient for this to occur so that a number of "free" electrons may be present in the solid at this temperature. This number will increase with increasing temperature and may be sufficient to give an appreciable electrical conductivity in a solid which is an insulator at lower temperatures. This is the process associated with *intrinsic* semiconducting behaviour. A similar situation can arise when the two atoms are not of the same type, the main difference from the above being that the distribution of the binding electrons is not then symmetrically disposed with respect to the two atoms.

The above discussion has been mainly concerned with the origin of the interatomic forces between two atoms. In considering the structure of the solid as a whole, the effect of the formation of one bond by an atom on its ability to form other bonds has to be considered in obtaining the overall structure of minimum energy. Various considerations (e.g. 1955:3) indicate that this structure should be based on a so-called *space lattice*. This is characterized by the repetition in space of a unit parallelepiped, which contains a certain arrangement of atoms. This *unit cell* is defined by three non-coplanar vectors $\mathbf{a}_1$, $\mathbf{a}_2$ and $\mathbf{a}_3$ and the solid is built up by a stacking together of unit cells to fill the space occupied by the solid. The mathematical description of this situation expresses the property of translational symmetry and states that the physical properties of the solid are invariant with respect to lattice translations of the forms

$$\mathbf{R}_L = l_1\mathbf{a}_1 + l_2\mathbf{a}_2 + l_3\mathbf{a}_3 \qquad (3.1.1)$$

where l_1, l_2 and l_3 are any integers (positive, negative or zero). Thus, if $V(\mathbf{r})$ is some function describing the variation of a physical property V throughout the solid, then

$$V(\mathbf{r}+\mathbf{R}_L) = V(\mathbf{r}) \qquad (3.1.2)$$

for any lattice vector $\mathbf{R}_L$ and any position vector $\mathbf{r}$. In any actual solid, of course, there must be the restriction that $\mathbf{r}$ and $\mathbf{r}+\mathbf{R}_L$ lie within the region enclosed by the solid. However, since all finite solids contain a very large number of unit cells, it is usual to remove this restriction and to discuss an infinite solid which is built up from the finite solid in such a way that the above condition (together with a second one which will be discussed later) applies throughout the whole of space.

The lattice structure of actual solids is, of course, well established by X-ray diffraction although the complete regularity of the ideal case discussed above is found to be modified, in practice, by a number of factors. Nevertheless, an ideal solid based on a space lattice forms a useful basis for a discussion of actual solids. This is because the modifications in most cases of interest result in a comparatively small perturbation of the ideal structure which can then be handled by the perturbation methods of quantum mechanics.

3.2 QUANTUM-MECHANICAL DESCRIPTION OF A SOLID

The quantitative treatment of the physical model of a solid discussed in the last section has to be based on the methods of quantum mechanics (1955:4). In this section, we shall confine ourselves to a summary of those aspects of quantum mechanics which are needed for the subsequent discussion.

If we were treating the system of electrons and nuclei forming the solid by classical mechanics, it would be necessary to write down the equations of motion for each of the constituent particles. Since the particles interact with each other, we would find that the equation of motion of one particle depends on the position of all the other particles and we would end up with a system of mutually dependent equations which have to be solved simultaneously. In practice, this procedure becomes impossible for other than the simplest systems because of its complexity. Certain general results, however, can be obtained. For example, if the system is isolated from external influences the dynamical property that we call the total energy of the system remains constant with time.

Other dynamical quantities that have the same property are the components of the total linear momentum of the system and the components of the total angular momentum. In classical mechanics it is possible, in principle, to influence the system (before isolation) in such a way that these dynamical quantities can take on any desired values; after removal of the influence they will retain these values.

In quantum mechanics, however, as its name implies, this last statement is no longer true. In particular, there are limitations, imposed by the very nature of the particles (electrons and atomic nuclei) constituting the system, which restrict the possible values of the total energy of the system. A similar statement applies to other dynamical properties of the system but we shall from now on restrict ourselves to the energy in view of its fundamental importance. The starting point of most problems in quantum mechanics is the determination of the possible energy levels for a system imposed by its structure and composition.

The way in which this is done is to set up the so-called *Schrödinger equation* for the system. This is a linear second-order differential equation involving the derivatives of the so-called *wave function* of the system. This wave function, which will be denoted by the symbol ψ, is a function of the co-ordinates of all the particles composing the system, and also depends on time.

The form of the Schrödinger equation is obtained after deriving the classical expression for the total energy of the system in what is called the *Hamiltonian* form. It will be sufficient for our purposes to restrict the discussion of this form to the case where the positions of the particles of the system are given in Cartesian co-ordinates. Although this restriction is not necessary and the whole formulation can be much more general, the special case of Cartesian co-ordinates is followed more easily.

When the co-ordinates of the jth particle are specified by the three parameters x_α^j ($\alpha = 1$, 2 or 3) we define the associated momentum of the particle by its components

$$p_\alpha^j = m^j \frac{dx_\alpha^j}{dt} \qquad (3.2.1)$$

where m^j is the mass of the jth particle. The kinetic energy E_{kin}^j of the jth particle can be expressed in terms of these momentum co-ordinates as

$$E_{kin}^j = \frac{1}{2m^j}[(p_1^j)^2 + (p_2^j)^2 + (p_3^j)^2]. \qquad (3.2.2)$$

The total kinetic energy of the whole system is

$$E_{kin} = \sum_j E_{kin}^j \qquad (3.2.3)$$

where the summation is taken over all the particles of the system.

In addition to its kinetic energy, the system in a given configuration possesses a certain amount of potential energy due to the forces acting between the various particles of the system. This is described, in the systems of interest to us, by a function V which depends on the configuration of the system, or in other words V is a function of all the co-ordinates x_α^j (j takes the values 1 to N, where N is the total number of particles of the system).

The classical Hamiltonian H of the system is an expression for the total energy in terms of the co-ordinates and associated momentum components of the particles. Thus, in the above formulation

$$H = V + \sum_j \frac{1}{2m^j}[(p_1^j)^2 + (p_2^j)^2 + (p_3^j)^2]. \qquad (3.2.4)$$

In classical mechanics, the equations of motion of the system can be obtained directly from the Hamiltonian. Quantum mechanics, as mentioned above, proceeds differently. The classical Hamiltonian H is replaced by the Hamiltonian operator $\mathscr{H}$, which is a differential operator derived from H by making the substitutions $-i\hbar(\partial/\partial x_\alpha^j)$ in place of p_α^j ($\alpha = 1$, 2, 3. $j = 1$ to N). Here $\hbar$ is Planck's constant h

divided by 2π, and i is the square root of -1. Thus, the Hamiltonian operator for the type of system considered above is

$$\mathcal{H} = \sum_{j=1}^{N} -\frac{\hbar^2}{2m^j} \nabla_j^2 + V \qquad (3.2.5)$$

where ∇_j^2 is the Laplacian differential operator for the jth particle.

$$\nabla_j^2 = \frac{\partial^2}{\partial(x_1{}^j)^2} + \frac{\partial^2}{\partial(x_2{}^j)^2} + \frac{\partial^2}{\partial(x_3{}^j)^2}. \qquad (3.2.6)$$

Having set up the Hamiltonian operator for the system, the Schrödinger equation can be written as

$$\mathcal{H}\psi = i\hbar\frac{\partial\psi}{\partial t} \qquad (3.2.7)$$

where, as stated, previously, ψ is a function of the co-ordinates of the particles and of time. This equation is a linear partial differential equation which has to be solved for the function ψ.

The physical content of what so far is purely a mathematical argument is contained in the wave function ψ. As indicated in the above discussion, the various dynamical properties of the system are represented in quantum mechanics by operators (usually in the form of differential operators). One of the foundations of quantum mechanics is the realization that there is a fundamental limitation to the accuracy with which it is possible to measure the dynamical properties. Thus, the predictions of quantum mechanics are confined to statements about the probable values of such quantities. In the formulation that we have discussed above, the product $\psi^*\psi$, where ψ^* is the complex conjugate function to ψ, is a function of the co-ordinates of the system. For a given set of values of these co-ordinates this product represents the relative probability that the system is in the configuration corresponding to this particular set. More precisely, the product

$$\psi^*(x_1{}^1, x_2{}^1 \ldots x_3{}^N)\psi(x_\alpha{}^j)\, \mathrm{d}x_1{}^1\, \mathrm{d}x_2{}^1 \ldots \mathrm{d}x_3{}^N$$

gives the relative probability that the system is in a configuration in which the co-ordinates $x_\alpha{}^j$ lie in the range $x_\alpha{}^j$ to $x_\alpha{}^j + \mathrm{d}x_\alpha{}^j$ ($j = 1$ to N, $\alpha = 1$ to 3). In view of this interpretation, it is customary to go through the process of normalizing the wave function, i.e. to multiply it by a constant value such that

$$\int \psi^* \psi \, d\tau = 1$$

where $d\tau$ stands for the element of configuration space $dx_1^1 \, dx_2^1 \ldots dx_3^N$.

The expressions for the physical properties of the system in terms of the wave function require that the form of this function possesses certain mathematical properties which are called boundary conditions. The most direct of these requirements are that the wave function is bounded (i.e. has finite value) at all points of configuration space (i.e. for all possible configurations of the system) and that its first-order derivatives are finite and continuous at all parts of configuration space.

In general (with certain exceptions) the solutions of the Schrödinger equation (3.2.7) do not possess these properties. Let us consider this equation in more detail. Following the standard method of dealing with such equations we attempt to find a solution of the equation which can be expressed as the product of two functions $\psi(\mathbf{r}^j)$ and $\psi(t)$. The first of these is a function only of the positions of the particles specified by the vectors $\mathbf{r}^j$ and the second is a function only of the time t. Since the Hamiltonian operator only acts upon the co-ordinates, we can write

$$\psi(t)\mathscr{H}\psi(\mathbf{r}^j) = i\hbar\psi(\mathbf{r}^j)\frac{d\psi(t)}{dt}. \tag{3.2.8}$$

Rearranging this we obtain

$$\frac{1}{\psi(\mathbf{r}^j)}\mathscr{H}\psi(\mathbf{r}^j) = \frac{i\hbar}{\psi(t)}\frac{d\psi(t)}{dt}. \tag{3.2.9}$$

In this form, the left-hand side of the equation is purely a function of the co-ordinates $\mathbf{r}^j$ and the right-hand side is a function only of time. This is clearly impossible in general unless both sides of the equation are equal to a constant which is independent of both types of variable. Let us denote this constant by E. Then, instead of a single equation, we now have to consider the two equations

$$\mathscr{H}\psi(\mathbf{r}^j) = E\psi(\mathbf{r}^j), \tag{3.2.10}$$

$$\frac{d\psi(t)}{dt} = -\frac{iE\psi(t)}{\hbar}. \tag{3.2.11}$$

The second of these equations can be solved immediately to give

$$\psi(t) = \exp\left(\frac{-iEt}{\hbar}\right). \tag{3.2.12}$$

Equation (3.2.10) can be solved in principle for any value of E, but generally the solutions will be of such a form that they do not satisfy the auxiliary conditions discussed above, which allow us to give a physical interpretation of the properties of the system. Solutions satisfying these conditions arise only for certain values of E. These are called *eigenvalues* of the Hamiltonian operator $\mathscr{H}$ and the solution corresponding to a particular eigenvalue is called the *eigenfunction* associated with that eigenvalue. Quantum mechanics asserts that a particular system can only have values of its total energy corresponding to the eigenvalues of the Hamiltonian operator for the system. These eigenvalues are obtained by solving equation (3.2.10) with the Hamiltonian operator appropriate to the system. This equation is called the *time-independent Schrödinger equation*. When the eigenvalues of this equation have been determined, together with the associated functions $\psi(\mathbf{r}^j)$, the complete eigenfunctions of the time-dependent equation (3.2.7) are obtained by combining these functions with the corresponding $\psi(t)$ given by equation (3.2.12).

The system in which we are interested, namely a solid, consists of an assembly of very large numbers of two types of particle, viz. the electrons and nuclei of the constituent atoms. It is clear, right from the start, that a completely accurate description of such a system is impossible, in view of the large number of variables involved. Resort must be made to various approximations in order to solve the associated Schrödinger equation. The first stage of these approximations is the so-called *adiabatic approximation* which allows the Schrödinger equation for the whole system of electrons plus nuclei to be split into two equations, one for the electrons and one for the nuclei. The physical basis of this is that the nuclei can be assumed to be moving very slowly compared with the electrons because of their very much larger mass. If they were, in fact, at rest in a given configuration (assumed to be known), the problem would be one of finding the eigenfunctions and eigenvalues of the electrons distributed throughout this configuration of nuclei. The corresponding Hamiltonian would then contain the momenta of the electrons (not of the nuclei). The fixed co-ordinates of the nuclei would appear in the problem as parameters leading to different electron wave functions for different configurations of the nuclei.

It is known from X-ray diffraction and other methods that the nuclei in a solid are not completely at rest but vibrate about mean positions, the amplitude of vibration increasing with increasing temperature. This amplitude is always small compared with the average distance between atoms even near the melting point of the solid. The mean positions conform to some type of space lattice possessing the property of translational symmetry discussed in the last section. Hence, as a first step in the process of solving the general Schrödinger equation, a Schrödinger equation for the electrons of the system is considered for which all the nuclei are at rest in their mean positions. A second equation exists for the (small) motion of the nuclei and the solution of this when obtained can be used to modify (slightly) by perturbation theory the results obtained for the electrons.

Thus, we arrive at the point where it is reasonable to suppose that the main features of the electron system can be obtained from a wave function which corresponds to all nuclei being at rest in their mean positions. Modifications to some of these features will be necessary to allow for the fact that this does not correspond completely to the actual situation in a solid but there exist well established techniques for calculating such modifications.

In the next section, we shall concentrate on the properties of the electrons and in the subsequent section on those of the nuclei.

3.3 THE ELECTRONS IN A SOLID

3.3.1 THE ONE-ELECTRON APPROXIMATION

The discussion of the last section leads to the conclusion that the main features of the electrons in a solid will be described by a wave function which is obtained as the solution of a Schrödinger equation corresponding to all the nuclei being at rest in their mean positions. This wave function will be a function of all the co-ordinates of all the electrons.

Although alternative methods are available for dealing with such many-body wave functions, the usual method is by means of the so-called *one-electron approximation*. The mathematical basis of this approximation has been discussed thoroughly elsewhere [see, in particular, the article by Reitz (1955:**5**)]. Physically, it corresponds to thinking of each electron in the solid as moving in the same potential field, this field being determined by the forces between the electron and the nuclei and between the electron and all the other electrons in the solid. In view of the very large number of electrons, this last factor is very nearly the same for all electrons.

This one-electron view of the solid is extremely useful since it corresponds to the classical way of thinking about the electrons in a solid as a collection of individual particles forming an electron gas. It allows us to define one-electron quantum states which we can interpret as the allowed quantum states for individual electrons in the solid. These allowed quantum states are specified by wave functions which are functions of the co-ordinates of one electron. These wave functions satisfy a Schrödinger equation of the form

$$\left[-\frac{\hbar^2}{2m}\nabla^2 + V(\mathbf{r})\right]\psi = i\hbar\frac{\partial\psi}{\partial t}. \tag{3.3.1}$$

In this equation, the expression in square brackets on the left-hand side is a Hamiltonian operator for one electron only. Thus, m is the mass of one electron and $V(\mathbf{r})$ is the potential energy of a single electron in the crystal; as discussed above, this is an average which is the same for all electrons. In view of the previous discussion, we are concerned with obtaining the eigenfunctions and eigenvalues of this equation which correspond to all the nuclei being at rest in their mean positions. This condition implies that the function $V(\mathbf{r})$ satisfies the basic periodicity condition expressed by equation (3.1.2), i.e.

$$V(\mathbf{r}+\mathbf{R}_L) = V(\mathbf{r}). \tag{3.3.2}$$

The one-electron operator acts upon a function $\psi(\mathbf{r}, t)$ which is a function of the co-ordinates of one electron only and of the time.

Following the discussion of the preceding section, this function can be expressed as

$$\psi(\mathbf{r}, t) = \psi(\mathbf{r})\psi(t) \tag{3.3.3}$$

where

$$\psi(t) = \exp\left(\frac{-iEt}{\hbar}\right) \tag{3.3.4}$$

and $\psi(\mathbf{r})$ satisfies the time-independent equation

$$\left[-\frac{\hbar^2}{2m}\nabla^2 + V(\mathbf{r})\right]\psi(\mathbf{r}) = E\psi(\mathbf{r}). \tag{3.3.5}$$

This last equation determines the eigenvalues of the energy from the boundary conditions on the function $\psi(\mathbf{r})$. In general the number of such eigenvalues is unlimited. Since (3.3.1) is a linear equation, any linear combination of the eigenfunctions $\psi_j(\mathbf{r}, t)$ associated with the eigenvalues E_j is also a solution of the equation. Thus, we can write a general solution of equation (3.3.1) as

$$\psi(\mathbf{r}, t) = \sum_j A_j \psi_j(\mathbf{r}, t) \tag{3.3.6}$$

in which the A_j are arbitrary constants and the summation is taken over all eigenfunctions. The parameters A_j can be adjusted to give a solution of equation (3.3.1) satisfying particular conditions over and above those common to all eigenfunctions. We shall come across an example of this later in Section 3.3.3.

We shall not discuss here the rather complicated question of the relationship of these one-electron wave functions to the correct wave function for the crystal as a whole. It is sufficient to state that the eigenvalues E_j and the associated eigenfunctions $\psi_j(\mathbf{r}, t)$ are regarded as giving the possible energy levels for electrons in the solid. Also, for reasons of simplicity, we have omitted any reference to the quantum-mechanical aspects of the spin of the electron. Again we resort to a statement that the only effect of this on the overall picture of the energy levels of a solid is that each eigenvalue is associated with two quantum-states when this spin is taken into account. The difference in properties between these two states need only be taken into account when the fine details of the eigenvalue distribution are required or when effects associated with strong magnetic fields are considered.

3.3.2 ELECTRON ENERGY BANDS IN CRYSTALS

On the basis of the preceding discussion, the quantum-mechanical treatment of the electrons in a solid reduces in the first place to the problem of obtaining the eigenvalues and associated eigenfunctions of equation (3.3.5), in which the potential function $V(\mathbf{r})$ possesses three-dimensional periodicity. This problem has been discussed so many times already that there is no point in giving a further derivation here. As we put in different values of E varying from $-\infty$ to $+\infty$ in the equation we find that eigenfunctions (well behaved solutions) arise only for certain ranges of E, the so-called *energy bands* and that these intervals are separated from each other by intervals in which no eigenfunctions are possible. Within each allowed energy interval, the independent eigenfunctions can be specified by the value of a three-dimensional vector $\mathbf{k}$ which is called the *wave vector* of the eigenfunction. Thus, a particular eigenfunction and its associated eigenvalue is defined by an index n denoting the energy band and a wave vector $\mathbf{k}$. The time-independent eigenfunction associated with $n, \mathbf{k}$ has the form

$$\psi_{n,\mathbf{k}}(\mathbf{r}) = u_{n,\mathbf{k}}(\mathbf{r}) \exp(i\mathbf{k} \cdot \mathbf{r}) \tag{3.3.7}$$

where $u_{n,\mathbf{k}}(\mathbf{r})$ is a function which has the same periodic behaviour as the potential function $V(\mathbf{r})$, i.e.

$$u_{n,\mathbf{k}}(\mathbf{r}) = u_{n,\mathbf{k}}(\mathbf{r} + \mathbf{R}_L) \tag{3.3.8}$$

for any $\mathbf{r}$ and any lattice vector $\mathbf{R}_L$. Substitution of this last equation into the preceding one shows that

$$\psi_{n,\mathbf{k}}(\mathbf{r} + \mathbf{R}_L) = \psi_{n,\mathbf{k}}(\mathbf{r}) \exp(i\mathbf{k} \cdot \mathbf{R}_L). \tag{3.3.9}$$

In the derivation of these results, this last equation is the basic property from which the others follow. It also leads to the result that all the independent eigenfunctions and energy eigenvalues for a particular band can be obtained by restricting the wave vector $\mathbf{k}$ to lie within a certain enclosed zone called the *first Brillouin zone* in $\mathbf{k}$ space, since all values of $\mathbf{k}$ outside this zone can be shown to possess the same basic defining property given by equation (3.3.9) as some $\mathbf{k}$ value within the zone. Alternatively one can say that the eigenfunctions and energy eigenvalues are periodic functions in $\mathbf{k}$ space.

Within the first Brillouin zone, only certain allowed values of $\mathbf{k}$ give rise to eigenfunctions. These allowed values can be determined by imposing extra boundary conditions on the functions given by equation (3.3.7). The number of allowed $\mathbf{k}$ values within the first Brillouin zone turns out to be equal to the number of unit cells in the crystal and these values are distributed uniformly throughout the zone. The volume of the Brillouin zone in $\mathbf{k}$ space is the reciprocal of ($8\pi^3$ times the volume in ordinary space of a unit cell). Since the number of allowed $\mathbf{k}$ values is very large, it is possible for most purposes to treat $\mathbf{k}$ as a continuous variable, subject to the condition that the number of allowed $\mathbf{k}$ values in a small volume element $d\mathbf{k}$ of $\mathbf{k}$ space is given by

$$\frac{V}{8\pi^3} d\mathbf{k} \tag{3.3.10}$$

where V is the total volume of the crystal. Thus, within each band of energy $E_n(\mathbf{k})$ can be regarded as a continuous function of $\mathbf{k}$ which is periodic in $\mathbf{k}$ and has maximum and minimum values either within, or on the boundary of, the first zone. The term "energy band" will henceforth be used to denote such a set of quantum states obtained by allowing $\mathbf{k}$ to vary throughout all its allowed values in the first zone. The various energy bands in actual crystals may overlap in energy with other bands or may be separated from all other bands by energy intervals in which there are no eigenfunctions of equation (3.3.5). Which of these various possibilities arise is determined by the form of the potential function $V(\mathbf{r})$.

The calculations of the form of the energy bands in actual solids are extremely involved and it is useful to be able to discuss them in terms of empirical parameters whose values are to be obtained from experimental measurements. One way in which this can be done is of particular interest in semiconductors where, for most purposes, the quantum states of interest are those lying near the minimum or maximum energies of a band. In these cases, the dependence of the energy on $\mathbf{k}$ can be expressed in the form of a three-dimensional Taylor series expanded about the state of extreme energy. In the most general case this series has the form

$$E(\mathbf{k} - \mathbf{k}_0) = E_0 + \frac{1}{2}\left(\frac{\partial^2 E}{\partial k_x^2}\right)_0 (k_x - k_{0x})^2 + (y \text{ and } z \text{ terms}) +$$

$$+ \frac{1}{2}\left(\frac{\partial^2 E}{\partial k_x \partial k_y}\right)_0 (k_x - k_{0x})(k_y - k_{0y}) + (yz \text{ and } zx \text{ terms}) + \qquad (3.3.11)$$

$$+ \text{higher powers.}$$

The terms in the first derivatives, which normally appear, are zero since an expansion is made about an extreme point for which these derivatives are zero. The various second derivatives can be regarded as empirical parameters, describing the quantum states of interest. Together, they form the components of a second-order tensor. The simplest form of this tensor occurs when it reduces to a scalar which would be the case, for example, in a crystal of cubic symmetry when the extreme point is at $\mathbf{k}_0 = 0$, i.e. the centre of the first zone. In other cases, symmetry considerations may reduce the number of independent parameters to something greater than one but less than the most general possibility (six).

3.3.3 ELECTRON WAVE PACKETS IN PERFECT CRYSTALS

Following the discussion of Section 3.2, the time-dependent one-electron eigenfunctions which satisfy equation (3.3.1) are obtained by combining the time-independent eigenfunctions with a time function of the form of equation (3.3.4). Thus the resulting functions have the form

$$\psi_{n,\mathbf{k}}(\mathbf{r},\ t) = u_{n,\mathbf{k}}(\mathbf{r}) \exp\left\{i\left[\mathbf{k}\cdot\mathbf{r} - \frac{E_n(\mathbf{k})t}{\hbar}\right]\right\}. \qquad (3.3.12)$$

The physical properties associated with an electron which is described by such a wave function are obtained as follows. The product of this with its complex conjugate gives the probability distribution for finding the electron at the point $\mathbf{r}$. This is

$$\psi^*\psi = u^*u, \qquad (3.3.13)$$

and, hence, the probability is the same for all unit cells in the crystal since $u(\mathbf{r})$ repeats from one unit cell to another (see equation (3.3.8)).

The mean value of the momentum of an electron described by a wave function ψ is given by the expression

$$\int \psi^*(-i\hbar\ \mathbf{grad}\ \psi)\ \mathrm{d}\mathbf{r}, \qquad (3.3.14)$$

where the integral is taken over the whole of the volume occupied by the electron. For the wave functions (3.3.12), this turns out to be equal to $\hbar\mathbf{k}$. Thus, the wave function (3.3.12) describes an electron whose energy is $E_n(\mathbf{k})$, momentum $\hbar\mathbf{k}$ and which is equally likely to be found in any one of the unit cells of the crystal. Such functions, while of interest in some cases, do not correspond to the situations that we wish to discuss, viz. the motion of an electron where we require to define its position, its velocity and its acceleration under the influence of external forces. Wave functions for dealing with such problems must satisfy the general equation (3.3.1) and hence, as already discussed, can be built up by a linear combination of functions like (3.3.12). Such combinations should have a large probability amplitude in some small interval $\delta\mathbf{r}$ and fall off to zero outside this interval in order to be able to define the position of the electron. These combinations are called *wave packets*. In accordance with the quantum-mechanical uncertainty principle, the closer one attempts to localize a wave packet in $\mathbf{r}$ space by making the amplitude at some point large, the more wave functions of the type (3.3.12) with different **k** have to be used and so the less precise is the specification of the momentum of the wave packet.

Thus, the electrons in a solid are represented by wave packets which have a certain mean position **r** and a certain mean momentum $\hbar\mathbf{k}$ both of which can, in general, vary with time. The velocity of the wave packet is given by

$$v_n(\mathbf{k}) = \frac{1}{\hbar}\frac{\mathrm{d}}{\mathrm{d}\mathbf{k}}E_n(\mathbf{k}), \qquad (3.3.15)$$

corresponding to the group velocity of a wave system. The rate of change of the mean momentum has the same form as for a classical particle, viz.

$$\frac{\mathrm{d}}{\mathrm{d}t}(\hbar\mathbf{k}) = \mathbf{F} \qquad (3.3.16)$$

where **F** is the force acting on the electron, which in the general case is given by

$$\mathbf{F} = -e(-\mathbf{grad}\,\phi + \mathbf{v} \wedge \mathbf{B}), \qquad (3.3.17)$$

where ϕ is the electrostatic potential and **B** is the magnetic induction. A combination of equations (3.3.15) and (3.3.16) leads to the expression for the acceleration of the wave packet

$$\frac{\mathrm{d}}{\mathrm{d}t}\mathbf{v} = \frac{1}{\hbar}\frac{\mathrm{d}}{\mathrm{d}t}\mathbf{grad}_k E,$$

$$= \frac{1}{\hbar}\mathbf{grad}_k \cdot \mathbf{grad}_k E \times \frac{\mathrm{d}\mathbf{k}}{\mathrm{d}t},$$

$$= \frac{1}{\hbar^2}\mathbf{grad}_k \cdot \mathbf{grad}_k E \cdot \mathbf{F},$$

$$= (m^*)^{-1} \cdot \mathbf{F}, \qquad (3.3.18)$$

where $(m^*)^{-1}$ is in general a second-order tensor whose components are given by

$$[(m^*)^{-1}]_{ij} = \frac{1}{\hbar^2}\frac{\partial^2 E}{\partial k_i \partial k_j}. \qquad (3.3.19)$$

These components will of course in general vary with both n and **k,** i.e. between and within bands. Equation (3.3.18) is an extension of the equation of motion for a classical particle and, by analogy with this latter case, m^* is called the *effective mass* tensor of the wave packet.

The above results summarize the basic properties of electrons as deduced by quantum mechanics for the case of an "ideal" solid in which the potential field is perfectly periodic. In particular, from equation (3.3.16) we see that, in the absence of any external field, the mean momentum of an electron and, hence, also its energy, does not change with time, in such an ideal solid.

3.3.4 ELECTRONS IN REAL CRYSTALS

In any real solid, there must be departures from the ideal situation discussed above. We have already stated that the nuclei of the atoms in the solid are never completely at rest in positions corresponding to an ideal space lattice, but vibrate with small amplitudes about such positions. These vibrations give rise to a "blurring" of the potential inside the solid and, hence, to departures from perfect periodicity. This will happen in all the unit cells throughout the crystal. In addition to this effect, which must happen in all solids, there may be localized imperfections, such as foreign atoms and crystalline defects of various kinds which cause localized departures of the potential from ideal periodicity.

The presence of such imperfections gives rise to two main modifications of the results obtained for the ideal lattice. First, the distribution of quantum states is affected by the presence of, in particular, localized imperfections. In most cases of interest, the number of such imperfections is small compared with the number of unit cells in the crystal and the main features of the quantum state distribution for an ideal crystal are retained giving rise to the well defined energy bands. In addition to these, however, other states are introduced which cannot be described in terms of a wave vector $\mathbf{k}$. The wave functions of these states are highly localized in the region of the corresponding imperfection and it is not possible to build up wave packets from such functions representing electrons moving through the crystal. Electrons occupying such quantum states are bound in the region of the imperfection and do not contribute directly to transport processes. Such states, however, may have a profound effect on the density of electrons occupying states in the band levels and can thus indirectly affect the transport properties which depend on the density and behaviour of electrons in the band levels.

The second feature associated with departures from perfect periodicity is that, even in the absence of external forces, an electron will not stay in the same quantum state indefinitely. In the language of quantum mechanics, the wave functions (3.3.12) are not stationary states. The usual method of dealing with this situation is by use of perturbation theory which relies on the fact that the actual potential function departs by only a relatively small amount from ideal periodicity. Perturbation theory then leads to the conclusion that an electron makes transitions between the quantum states of the unperturbed problem, i.e. in our case between states of different n and $\mathbf{k}$ values. The theory gives expressions for the transition probability $W(n, \mathbf{k}; n', \mathbf{k}')$ which represents the probability per unit time that an electron in the state n, $\mathbf{k}$ will change to the state n', $\mathbf{k}'$. The expression for W involves the difference between the actual potential and the potential which would be present in the absence of the imperfection and, of course, is different for different types of imperfections.

The physical description of this situation is that, in the absence of imperfections, an electron can move freely throughout the crystal without change of momentum or energy, but that, when imperfections are present, every so often the electron makes a collision with an imperfection (crystalline defect or displaced nucleus) and suffers a change in momentum and energy. These collisions thus provide a mechanism by which an electron can exchange energy and momentum with other parts of the system, i.e. with the nuclei and the other electrons.

3.3.5 STATISTICS OF ELECTRONS IN CRYSTALS

From the discussion of the previous sub-sections, it follows that, if we consider a particular quantum state in an actual crystal, the number of electrons occupying this state will vary with time. If external forces are acting, electrons will be entering and leaving this state because of the change in their $\mathbf{k}$ values with time expressed by equation (3.3.16). In addition, electrons will enter and leave the state as a result of collisions.

Although these processes are going on all the time, the resultant fluctuations in the electron population of a particular state occur at intervals of time which are so short that the effects of the fluctuations are not accessible to physical observation except in special circumstances. The only observable effects are those obtained by averaging the population over a length of time which is still small by macroscopic standards but yet is very long compared with the average time between fluctuations. For example, the average time between collisions of electrons in a solid is typically of the order of 10^{-14} sec, so that if we take an average over a million collisions, the time involved is still only 10^{-8} sec.

Thus, in ordinary physical processes we expect to observe only the effects obtained by averaging the electron population of quantum states over a large number of collisions. This time-average for a particular state may be interpreted as the probability that the state is occupied by electrons under the particular conditions to which the crystal as a whole is subjected. The probability of occupation will in general vary from one state to another and, for the crystal as a whole, this variation is described by a probability distribution function. The calculation of this function under prescribed conditions is of basic importance in the theory of solids, and is carried out by the methods of statistical mechanics. In general, a knowledge of the detailed aspects of the collision processes is required but, for the specially important case of a system in thermal equilibrium, the distribution function can be obtained without such knowledge. The only factors required in this case are those specifying the overall equilibrium state of the system, in particular the total number of electrons and the total internal energy.

For the case of electrons, it is necessary to take into account the *Pauli exclusion principle*, which states that no quantum state can be occupied by more than one electron at a given time. In statistical mechanics, the probability distribution function is obtained by setting up first a basic expression for the thermodynamic quantity called the *entropy* of the system. This entropy is a measure of the number of possible distributions of the available electrons over all the available quantum states which can give rise to the specified thermodynamic state of the whole system. For electrons, where the exclusion principle has to be taken into account, the expression for the entropy has the form

$$S = k \sum_j \{G_j \ln G_j - N_j \ln N_j - (G_j - N_j) \ln (G_j - N_j)\}. \quad (3.3.20)$$

In deriving this expression, the quantum states are divided up into groups such that the states within a particular group j all have the same energy (or very nearly so). The number of states within the group j is G_j and the number of electrons occupying quantum states within this group is N_j. The quantity k (not to be confused with the wave vector) is a constant, called Boltzmann's constant. The ratio N_j/G_j is clearly the mean occupation probability for group j which has associated energy E_j. Denoting this by f_j we find

$$S = -k \sum_j G_j\{f_j \ln f_j + (1-f_j)\ln(1-f_j)\}. \tag{3.3.21}$$

To specify that f_j refers to a particular overall state of the system, we have the subsidiary conditions

$$E = \sum_j G_j E_j f_j, \tag{3.3.22}$$

$$N = \sum_j G_j f_j. \tag{3.3.23}$$

If small changes in the overall thermodynamic properties of the system take place, we shall get a new distribution function differing from f_j by δf_j. This will lead to values of the total entropy, total energy and total number of particles which differ from the above expressions by

$$\delta S = -k \sum_j G_j \ln[f_j/(1-f_j)]\delta f_j, \tag{3.3.24}$$

$$\delta E = \sum_j G_j E_j \delta f_j, \tag{3.3.25}$$

$$\delta N = \sum_j G_j \delta f_j, \tag{3.3.26}$$

since we are still concerned with the same distribution of quantum states.

In thermodynamics, there is a relation between these last three quantities which holds for all small reversible changes about the state of thermodynamic equilibrium. This relation is

$$T\delta S = \delta E - \mu \delta N \tag{3.3.27}$$

provided that the volume of the system remains constant, as it does for the electrons in a solid. In this equation T is the absolute temperature and μ is called the *chemical potential* of the system. It is a measure of the amount of energy necessary to remove an electron from the system at constant volume and temperature.

If we use this relation with the values (3.3.24) to (3.3.26) which must then refer to the thermodynamic equilibrium values, we have the relation

$$\sum_j G_j\{E_j - \mu + kT \ln[f_j/(1 - f_j)]\}\delta f_j = 0, \qquad (3.3.28)$$

which must hold for all small changes δf_j about the equilibrium position. This can only be true if the term in parentheses vanishes identically for the equilibrium state and so we obtain the equilibrium distribution function f_{0j} as

$$f_{0j} = \frac{1}{1 + \exp[(E_j - \mu)/kT]}, \qquad (3.3.29)$$

or, dropping the subscript j, we have the result that the time-average of the population of a quantum state having an energy E is given, for thermal equilibrium, by

$$f_0(E) = \left[1 + \exp\left(\frac{E - \mu}{kT}\right)\right]^{-1}, \qquad (3.3.30)$$

where μ and T are the same for all the electrons. The further conditions are that, the total energy is given by

$$\sum G_j E_j f_{0j}, \qquad (3.3.31)$$

and the total number of electrons by

$$\mathcal{N} = \sum G_j f_{0j}. \qquad (3.3.32)$$

The equilibrium distribution function given by equation (3.3.30) is called the *Fermi-Dirac distribution function*.

For the quantum states in solids, we have seen that within an energy band the energy varies continuously. For such cases, the summations in the last two expressions are replaced by integrals. A *density of states distribution function* $g(E)$ is defined such that $g(E)\delta E$ is the number of states in the energy interval δE. Then, the contributions to the total energy and the total number of electrons from an energy interval E_1 to E_2 over which the energy varies continuously are, respectively,

$$\int_{E_1}^{E_2} g(E)Ef_0(E)\ \mathrm{d}E \quad \text{and} \quad \int_{E_1}^{E_2} g(E)f_0(E)\ \mathrm{d}E. \qquad (3.3.33)$$

The thermodynamic parameter μ defined by equation (3.3.27) depends on the constitution of the system and also, in the case of charged particles, it depends on the electrostatic potential to which the system may be subjected. For systems of charged particles it is called the *electrochemical potential* and may be expressed as the sum of two terms, one, called the chemical potential, which depends on the composition and temperature of the system, and a second, electrostatic part $q\phi$ where q is the charge per particle and ϕ is the electrostatic potential. In the usual notation the electrochemical potential is denoted by $\bar{\mu}$ and is written

$$\bar{\mu} = \mu + q\phi. \qquad (3.3.34)$$

($q = -e$ when the system consists of electrons.) The preceding discussion then applies with $\bar{\mu}$ replacing μ in equation (3.3.27) and the equilibrium distribution function is

$$f_0(E) = \left[1 + \exp\left(\frac{E - \bar{\mu}}{kT}\right)\right]^{-1}. \qquad (3.3.35)$$

When appearing in this equation, $\bar{\mu}$ is called the *Fermi Level* for the system of electrons.

A basic thermodynamic property of the Fermi level is that, like the temperature, its value is constant throughout all parts of a thermodynamic system between which exchange of electrons can take place and which are in thermodynamic equilibrium with each other. This can be seen most readily in the case of two bodies, each containing electrons, which are brought into electrical and thermal contact with each other. In the final equilibrium situation, the temperature of the two bodies is the same and, further, the entropy of the combined system must be a maximum with respect to small interchanges of electrons between the two parts. Thus, if $\delta\mathcal{N}_1$ electrons are transferred from system 2 to system 1, we have

$$T\delta S_1 = \delta E_1 - \bar{\mu}_1 \delta \mathcal{N}_1,$$

and

$$T\delta S_2 = \delta E_2 - \bar{\mu}_2(-\delta\mathcal{N}_1).$$

Further, $\delta E_1 + \delta E_2 = 0$ and $\delta S = \delta S_1 + \delta S_2 = 0$ so that

$$\bar{\mu}_1 = \bar{\mu}_2. \qquad (3.3.36)$$

The argument can easily be extended to the different parts of a single system and, thus, in thermal equilibrium, the Fermi level of the electrons is everywhere the same. Since the Fermi level is composed of two parts as given by equation (3.3.34), it follows that, in a non-homogeneous body, there will in general exist a variation in the electrostatic potential of the electrons in thermal equilibrium, satisfying the condition

$$\mathbf{grad}\ \bar{\mu} = \mathbf{grad}\ \mu - e\ \mathbf{grad}\ \phi_0 = 0, \tag{3.3.37}$$

where the local value of the chemical potential μ is determined by the local composition and temperature.

The variation of the electrostatic potential in such cases means that the position of the Fermi level with respect to the distribution of quantum states in the solid may vary with position. Let us consider two regions of a body which are small in the macroscopic sense, so that the electrostatic potential may be considered as constant throughout the region, but which are nevertheless large enough to contain a large number of atoms. Then, on applying the discussion at the beginning of this section to each of the regions in turn, we would have Schrödinger equations corresponding to (3.3.5) for the two regions containing potential functions $V_1(\mathbf{r})$ and $V_2(\mathbf{r})$ for which we may write

$$
\begin{aligned}
V_1(\mathbf{r}) &= V_c(\mathbf{r}) - e\phi_1, \\
V_2(\mathbf{r}) &= V_c(\mathbf{r}) - e\phi_2,
\end{aligned} \tag{3.3.38}
$$

where $V_c(\mathbf{r})$ is the periodic potential function of the crystal and ϕ_1, ϕ_2 are the corresponding electrostatic potentials, assumed constant for the small regions. All potentials are, of course, referred to the same zero level. It is easily seen that the eigenvalues E_1 and E_2 of these equations are related to the eigenvalue E_c in the absence of an electrostatic potential ϕ by

$$
\begin{aligned}
E_1 &= E_c - e\phi_1, \\
E_2 &= E_c - e\phi_2,
\end{aligned} \tag{3.3.39}
$$

since the substitution of these expressions in equation (3.3.5) with the appropriate V leaves the solution of the equation unaffected. Thus, the band energy level scheme of the solid is shifted with respect to the common zero by an amount $-e\phi$. The Fermi level, however, must have a constant value with respect to the zero level of energy and, thus, the positions of the energy bands are shifted relative to the Fermi level in the presence of a varying electrostatic potential by the same amount.

5

The above discussion, which applies to non-homogeneous bodies in thermal equilibrium, has been included because it forms a useful introduction to the thermodynamic discussion for non-equilibrium situations. This discussion will be postponed to Section 3.5, after we have considered the description of the lattice of the solid.

3.3.6 STATISTICS OF ELECTRONS IN SEMICONDUCTORS

We shall close this section by considering some aspects of the electron system in solids which are of particular relevance to the theory of semiconductors. The position of the Fermi level with respect to the band scheme of the solid is of basic importance in determining the transport properties since, as we have already noted, it is only the electrons in band levels which are free to move through the crystal; the number of such electrons is determined by the position of the Fermi level. It is simplest to discuss this situation at the absolute zero of temperature since the distribution function f_0 (equation 3.3.35) then has the property that its value is 1 if $E < \bar{\mu}$ and 0 if $E > \bar{\mu}$. Under these conditions, a certain number of bands, from $n = 1$ upwards, will be completely filled with electrons. The number of independent $\mathbf{k}$ values defining the quantum states within a band can be shown to be equal to the number of unit cells in the crystal. When the quantum considerations governing the so-called spin of the electron are taken into account, it is found that each value corresponds to two quantum states having the same spatial properties but corresponding to different spin states. Thus, the total number of electrons that can be accommodated in a band is twice the number of unit cells in the crystal. Depending on the total number of electrons that are available in the solid, the Fermi level near the absolute zero may be either within a continuous range of quantum states or in a region between energy bands in which there are no quantum states. In this latter case there may be localized quantum states, which originate from the presence of imperfections, in the immediate vicinity of the Fermi level.

Whichever of these cases occurs, the distribution does not change very greatly as the temperature is raised and the major modifications occur only for those quantum states which lie within a few times kT of the position of the Fermi level. In practice this means that, at all ordinary temperatures, most of the bands which are filled at absolute zero will still remain completely filled and most of those which are unoccupied will still remain unoccupied. The only exceptions are those bands whose energy ranges either overlap the position of the Fermi level at the absolute zero and, in the second case mentioned above, the bands of highest energy which are filled at absolute zero and the bands of lowest energy which are unoccupied at this temperature.

The bands which remain filled with electrons at all temperatures do not make any contribution to the transport processes in the solid. The reason for this can be made apparent in several ways, one of which is to consider the expression for the entropy, equation (3.3.21). This expression is valid for non-equilibrium states of the system and, as already discussed, takes its maximum value (through the form of the distribution function) for the thermal equilibrium condition. Thus the state of a system associated with a non-equilibrium transport process has a lower entropy than the thermal equilibrium state. However, a band which is completely filled with electrons does not, by virtue of the exclusion principle, allow a change in the distribution function, which must always be unity for all states in the band. Thus, the contribution to the entropy is the same as for thermal equilibrium and, hence, such a band cannot contribute to the transport processes. In fact, inspection of equation (3.3.21) shows that a full band ($f = 1$ for all states) gives zero contribution to the entropy, just as does a completely empty band.

Thus, the theory of transport processes associated with the electrons in a solid is concerned only with those energy bands which are so placed in energy that they are either not completely filled or not completely empty of electrons under the particular conditions considered. Even within these bands, the distribution function is not usually altered very much from its thermal equilibrium value and either f_0 or $(1 - f_0)$ is small for energies more than a few kT from the equilibrium Fermi level. The contribution to the transport processes from such states falls off rapidly with increasing energy departure from the Fermi level.

In the case of metals, where the Fermi level at absolute zero falls in the middle of the band, the number of states in the vicinity of the Fermi level is very large, being of the same order as the number of atoms in the solid. This number, therefore, cannot be appreciably altered by extra quantum states arising from the presence of imperfections. At temperatures above the absolute zero, the change in the form of the distribution function does not lead to any major re-adjustment and the major contribution to the transport processes comes from those states in the immediate vicinity (i.e. within a few times kT) of the Fermi level.

For semiconductors, however, the density of quantum states at the Fermi level at the absolute zero vanishes. Consequently, at higher temperatures, the redistribution of electrons over the band states closest to the zero temperature value of the Fermi level can be profoundly affected by the presence of temperature and by the presence of quantum states associated with imperfections. The important band states are situated either near the minimum energy of a band which is completely empty at the absolute zero or near the maximum energy of a band which is completely filled at the absolute zero. The former type of band is called a *conduction* band and the latter a *valence* band. For the quantum states of interest in such bands, we may, under certain conditions, make use of the approximation represented by equation (3.3.11). We can then express the relation between the energy and wave vector in terms of empirical parameters, which are related theoretically to the curvature of the band at its extreme value, but whose values are to be determined by experiment. In the simplest possible case, where the second-order derivative tensor reduces to a scalar, the relation between E and $\mathbf{k}$ for the states in the conduction band has the form

$$E(\mathbf{k}) = E_c + \frac{\hbar^2 k^2}{2m_c}, \tag{3.3.40}$$

where E_c is the minimum energy of the band, k is the absolute value of the wave vector and m_c is a positive parameter whose value is the effective mass for the bottom of the band, as given by equation (3.3.19). The density of states distribution function in this case is obtained by combining equations (3.3.10) and (3.3.40) to give the number of $\mathbf{k}$ values in a shell of radius k and allowing for the fact that each $\mathbf{k}$ value corresponds to two quantum states. This gives the distribution function for the quantum states near the minimum energy of the conduction band as

$$g(E) = \frac{V}{2\pi^2} \left(\frac{2m_c}{\hbar^2}\right)^{3/2} (E - E_c)^{1/2}, \tag{3.3.41}$$

where V is the volume of the crystal.

An analogous situation holds for the states near the maximum energy E_v of the valence band. If this occurs at $\mathbf{k} = 0$ in a crystal of cubic symmetry, the expression corresponding to (3.3.40) is

$$E(\mathbf{k}) = E_v - \frac{\hbar^2 k^2}{2m_v}. \tag{3.3.42}$$

The negative sign occurs because E is a maximum at $\mathbf{k} = 0$. The associated density of states function is

$$g(E) = \frac{V}{2\pi^2}\left(\frac{2m_v}{\hbar^2}\right)^{3/2}(E_v - E)^{1/2}. \tag{3.3.43}$$

For the reasons given previously, the vast majority of the states in the valence band remain occupied under all conditions of interest and make no effective contribution to the transport processes. In dealing with the transport properties of such a band, it is preferable to focus attention on the comparatively few unoccupied states for which $(1-f)$ is not zero. This can always be done since there is complete symmetry of the basic expression for the entropy with respect to f and $(1-f)$. For the states near the top of a band, it is well known (1950:2) that the transport properties can be described in terms of positively charged quasi-particles called *holes*, one such hole being associated with each unoccupied quantum state. For the simple case represented by equation (3.3.42) and (3.3.43), the holes have an effective mass m_v.

3.4 THE LATTICE OF A SOLID

3.4.1 CLASSICAL DESCRIPTION OF THE NORMAL MODES OF A LATTICE

The remaining part of a solid, other than the valence electrons, consists of the cores of the atoms which constitute the solid. We have seen that to a good approximation these cores will have the same electronic structure as for the case where the atoms are isolated. However, in the solid, they are, of course, subject to the mutually interacting forces which hold the solid together. Thus, there is a contribution to the total energy of the solid arising from such forces and similarly energy can be propagated through the solid by the interactions between the cores.

In the ideal solid, which was used as a basis for the treatment of the electrons, it was assumed that the cores were distributed on a regular three-dimensional space lattice. In practice, of course, although the forces binding the cores to such positions are strong, they are not infinitely strong; thus, the cores will have some tendency to escape from their mean positions. This tendency obviously increases with increasing temperature finally reaching its limit when the solid melts. In between the absolute zero and the melting point the energy of the cores will increase and there will be an increasing tendency for the core to be displaced from its mean position. The increasing energy of the cores appears as an increased amplitude of vibration about their mean positions. This amplitude of vibration is always small compared with the average distance between the cores even at temperatures approaching the melting point.

The problems to be solved are rather similar to those occurring for the valence electrons. First, we have to set up a description of the vibrations of the cores which will allow us to express the energy of the system; this can be done generally for the case of an ideal solid. Next, we have to consider the effect of external forces on the solid and investigate the means by which energy can be propagated through the solid via the interactions between the cores. At some stage it will also be necessary to consider how the situation in actual solids differs from the ideal.

The problem of describing the behaviour of a system of mutually interacting particles whose positions at any time differ by only a small value from their equilibrium values is a standard one in classical mechanics and can be treated readily by quantum mechanics. The problem is solved by assuming that the potential energy of the system can be expressed as a quadratic function of the displacements of the particles from their equilibrium positions. There are no terms linear in these displacements since the potential energy is a minimum for an equilibrium situation and, hence, the first derivatives with respect to the displacements vanish. Provided that the quadratic terms are the only ones that matter, the motion of each particle about the mean position can be expressed as the superposition of a number of simple harmonic vibrations, each having its own characteristic frequency. The same basic set of simple harmonic vibrations can be used to describe the motion of all the particles in the system although the amplitude and phase of the contribution of any one of them, in general, varies from one particle to another. The various simple harmonic vibrations, which enter for a particular system, are called the *normal modes* of the system and the characteristic frequencies can be determined, in principle, from the mutual forces acting between the particles of the system.

In the case of a space lattice, the regular form of the equilibrium configuration is reflected in the particular form of the normal modes. Each such normal mode gives rise to a simple harmonic motion which is also periodic in space, so that its effect is the same, apart from a phase factor, for atoms in corresponding positions in different unit cells in the crystal. This is the characteristic property of a wave and the normal modes can be represented by a set of displacement waves travelling through the crystal. Each such wave produces a simple harmonic displacement at the atoms of the lattice and is characterized by three parameters. The first of these is its wave vector $\mathbf{q}$ whose magnitude defines the wavelength λ of the wave by the relation $\lambda = 2\pi/|\mathbf{q}|$ and whose direction specifies the direction of propagation of the wave. Secondly, there is the angular frequency ω which defines the frequency of vibration and, thirdly, there is the direction in which atoms are displaced by the wave, the so-called *polarization* specified by a unit vector $\boldsymbol{\epsilon}$.

The set of $\mathbf{q}$ values which are used to specify the normal modes bear a one-to-one correspondence with the set of $\mathbf{k}$ values used to define the quantum states for electrons (see Section 3.3). The reason is that in both cases the same basic translational symmetry arises in expressing the fact that the properties are the same for corresponding points in different unit cells. Thus, the set of $\mathbf{q}$ values is equal in number to the number of unit cells in the crystal and is distributed uniformly throughout the first Brillouin zone.

To each value of the wave vector $\mathbf{q}$ there corresponds a number of normal modes, in general having different frequencies ω. Thus, the complete set of normal modes is specified by $\omega_j(\mathbf{q})$. The subscript j takes on integral values from 1 to $3S$ where S is the number of atoms per unit cell for the particular solid considered. This makes the total number of normal modes conform to the number of degrees of freedom of the whole system, which is three times the number of atoms in the system. The characteristic frequencies $\omega_j(\mathbf{q})$ can, in principle, be calculated from a knowledge of the mutual forces acting between the cores.

For a given value of j, as $\mathbf{q}$ varies, the frequency $\omega_j(\mathbf{q})$ varies continually with $\mathbf{q}$ throughout the Brillouin zone and defines a branch of the so-called *vibrational spectrum*. The three branches of lowest frequency are called the *acoustic branches* since they determine the acoustic properties of the solid. The highest frequency branch of the acoustic branches is generally called the *longitudinal* acoustic branch since, in simple structures, the displacement produced by modes associated with this branch is parallel to the direction of propagation. The remaining two branches are termed *transverse* acoustic. The relation between the polarization and the direction of propagation is less direct in most crystal structures.

In crystals with only one atom per unit cell, the acoustic branches are the only ones present but in other crystals there are branches of higher frequency, known as the *optical branches* because the corresponding frequencies lie in the infrared part of the spectrum.

The complete calculation of the vibration spectrum of a particular solid is a very complicated problem. Apart from the purely mathematical complexity, a detailed knowledge of the binding forces is required. So far, these are not known very accurately although a number of attempts have been made to derive the spectrum for simple semiconductors. There is a close analogy between this problem and the calculation of band structures, where the difficulty lies in knowing the correct form of the crystal potential. In the latter case, such calculations have in recent years been subordinated, where possible, to experimental methods which yield directly the relevant information about the band structure, using the techniques of cyclotron resonance. In the absence of such direct information, the procedure has been to take the simplest type of assumption and to assume that the relevant part of the band structure can be defined by a single parameter, the so-called effective mass m^*, it being assumed that the relation between E and $\mathbf{k}$ is given by

$$E = E_0 + \frac{\hbar^2 \mathbf{k}^2}{2m^*}.$$

Various experiments can then be used to determine m^* but there is no good reason (unless the assumption about the band structure is true) why these should give a common value of m^*. The value of such a simplified approach lies largely in its qualitative rather than quantitative predictions.

A parallel situation occurs in the discussion of the vibration spectrum. It now appears that the methods of neutron diffraction can be used to determine experimentally at least the major part of the vibrational spectrum. Other methods can be used to obtain more limited information. In the absence of such experimental information, considerable use is made of a simple theory of the vibrational spectrum. This is based on the idea of replacing the actual solid by a continuous solid; the relation between the frequency and the wavelength can be obtained rather simply in this case. This is the so-called *Debye approximation*. It applies only to the acoustic modes and leads to a linear relation between the frequency and the modulus of the wave vector for a particular acoustic branch. The number of normal modes for a continuous solid would be infinite, whereas for a real crystal lattice this numb r is finite. Consequently, the vibration spectrum for a lattice is arbitrarily cut off at a characteristic frequency to give the correct number of degrees of freedom. This characteristic frequency ω_D defines the Debye temperature θ_D of the solid through the relation $\hbar\omega_D = k\theta_D$, and many of the properties of the solid can be expressed in terms of θ_D. It must be stressed that the value of this approximation lies largely in its amenability to mathematical computation and there is conclusive evidence that it is widely violated in actual solids. Nevertheless, it does provide a qualitative estimate of effects associated with the lattice vibrations.

In the case where optical modes are also present, the customary approximation is to assume that the frequency of the modes in a particular branch is constant. There are good reasons for supposing this to be a good approximation both on theoretical and experimental grounds. The corresponding frequencies give rise to well defined optical absorption bands in the infrared part of the spectrum and can, thus, in principle, be determined experimentally.

3.4.2 QUANTUM-MECHANICAL DESCRIPTION OF THE NORMAL MODES

The above discussion of the normal modes of an ideal crystal lattice has been based on classical mechanics. The modifications introduced when quantum mechanics are used are simple to deal with. On the classical picture, each normal mode, specified by its wave vector $\mathbf{q}$ and branch j can be represented by a travelling wave form

$$\mathbf{u}(\mathbf{r}) = \epsilon_j(\omega)b_j(\mathbf{q})\cos(\mathbf{q}\cdot\mathbf{r} - \omega_j(\mathbf{q})t), \qquad (3.4.1)$$

which gives the displacement $\mathbf{u}(\mathbf{r})$ of the atom at position $\mathbf{r}$ in the lattice. Thus, the expression is really defined only at the lattice points. $\epsilon_j(\omega)$ is a unit vector, specifying the direction of displacement. The quantity $b_j(\mathbf{q})$ gives the amplitude of the simple harmonic vibration, which is the same for all atoms, for a particular mode. Whereas in the classical case this amplitude can take on any value and the corresponding energy of vibration of the atom is not restricted, it is well known that the quantum-mechanical treatment of a simple harmonic oscillator leads to a quantized set of values of the energy given by

$$E_N = \hbar\omega(\mathcal{N}+\tfrac{1}{2})$$

where ω is the angular frequency of vibration and $\mathcal{N}$ is a positive integer or zero.

The corresponding treatment of a normal mode leads to the result that the energy of a normal mode, by which we mean the energy of vibration of the atoms induced by the mode, is quantized according to a similar rule. The energy of a normal mode in branch j of wave vector $\mathbf{q}$ and angular frequency $\omega_j(\mathbf{q})$ is thus restricted to one of the values

$$E_j(\mathbf{q}) = \hbar\omega_j(\mathbf{q})[\mathcal{N}+\tfrac{1}{2}]. \qquad (3.4.2)$$

Which one of these values actually exists in a given situation depends on the total energy contained in the whole lattice and the way in which this total energy is distributed among the normal modes.

Instead of saying that a particular normal mode is in the $\mathcal{N}$th excited state it is customary to say that the normal mode contains $\mathcal{N}$ phonons. The phonons represent the quanta of energy $\hbar\omega_j(\mathbf{q})$ in multiples of which a normal mode $(j, \mathbf{q})$ can change its energy.

How do such changes of energy come about? The answer is that, in the ideal situation postulated so far, no such changes occur and a particular normal mode, once containing a given number of phonons, will retain this number indefinitely. The normal modes discussed above represent stationary states of the idealized situation that we have been discussing, in which it will be recalled that the two basic assumptions are those of perfect regularity of the lattice and the restriction to terms in the potential energy of the system which are quadratic in the displacements.

Departures from this idealized situation will always be present in any actual solid. Even if it were possible to get a really perfect lattice, there would always be some perturbation present since it is never strictly correct to ignore the higher-order terms in the potential energy. When the displacements are small, as at low temperatures, this perturbation is very small but it becomes more important as the temperature rises. In any actual solids, of course, perturbations from the ideal situation will arise through the presence of crystal imperfections of various kinds.

As in the case of electrons discussed previously, the effect of such perturbations, as treated by perturbation theory, is that energy is exchanged between the stationary states of the unperturbed system so that the number of phonons in a particular normal mode changes with time. In an overall steady state, such as that when the lattice is in thermal equilibrium, it is possible to define a time-averaged number of phonons $\bar{N}_j(\mathbf{q})$ representing the average number of phonons in a particular normal mode $(j, \mathbf{q})$ over a time interval sufficiently long in comparison with the time interval associated with the discrete changes of the phonon content. For the case of thermal equilibrium this average number can be calculated by statistical mechanics, independently of the perturbation processes and has the value

$$\bar{N}_0 = \left[\exp\left(\frac{\hbar\omega}{kT}\right) - 1\right]^{-1}. \tag{3.4.3}$$

3.4.3 PHONON WAVE PACKETS IN CRYSTALS

The above discussion which applies specifically to the state of thermal equilibrium, can be extended along similar lines to those used in discussing the electrons, to cover the case of transfer of energy through the lattice. The energy of the normal modes discussed above is distributed uniformly throughout the atoms of the lattice and is non-localized in space. Thus, the normal modes cannot be used to discuss the transfer of energy through the crystal. For this purpose, we have to construct wave packets by combining the displacement waves within a small interval $d\mathbf{q}$ of the wave vector. The resultant wave packet then represents a local concentration of energy travelling through the crystal. The velocity of propagation of a wave packet of mean wave vector $\mathbf{q}$ is

$$\mathbf{v}(j, \mathbf{q}) = \frac{d}{d\mathbf{q}}\omega_j(\mathbf{q}). \tag{3.4.4}$$

On this approach, the phonons are represented by wave packets travelling through the lattice. The properties of such wave packets bear a close resemblance to the concept of a classical particle in that a certain mean momentum can be ascribed to them together with an energy and a velocity. The relation between these quantities is

$$\mathbf{v} = \frac{\mathrm{d}}{\mathrm{d}\mathbf{p}}E$$

which is analogous to the above equation with $E = \hbar\omega$ and $\mathbf{p} = \hbar\mathbf{q}$.

In the absence of external forces, in a perfect crystal, a phonon wave packet moves freely through the crystal and its mean "momentum" $\hbar\mathbf{q}$ stays constant with time. When the situation is not ideal such wave packets make "collisions", either with other wave packets or with the localized imperfections. The analogy with classical particles is, however, not in general retained in such collision processes. The reason is that, in contrast to a classical particle and, also, to an electron wave packet, a phonon wave packet can exist only in a form in which it has a certain precise energy. In collisions of classical particles or of electrons, the requirements of conservation of momentum can be met by a continuous adjustment of the energy and momentum of the particles involved. This cannot be done where collisions of phonon wave packets are involved. What happens instead is that phonon wave packets are destroyed or created in their entirety in collision processes in such a way that total energy is conserved. There is a complication in the momentum requirements, caused by the fact that the momentum of a wave packet is not uniquely defined by its wave vector $\mathbf{q}$ since values of $\mathbf{q}$ outside the first Brillouin zone are equivalent to values inside. Subject to this extra factor, however, the total momentum of the phonon wave packets involved is conserved in collision processes.

The average distance that a wave packet travels before making a collision is called its *mean free path*, and the corresponding time is the mean free time. Thus, in a steady state situation we visualize the following picture. Phonons (wave packets) are being created and destroyed over periods of time comparable with the mean free time. Over a time interval sufficiently long compared with this there will be, on the average, a certain number of phonon wave packets associated with a particular value of the wave vector $\mathbf{q}$ in the jth branch. This number is given by equation (3.4.3) for thermal equilibrium. In future, when we talk about phonons it will be understood that we are talking about wave packets possessing a certain energy, velocity and momentum.

3.5 TRANSPORT PROCESSES IN SOLIDS— PHENOMENOLOGICAL THEORY

The transport processes in solids involve a flow of either charge, or energy, or both, arising from certain external processes acting on the solid. These external processes are described in terms of electric fields, temperature gradients and magnetic fields. The relations between the flows and the forces which produce them, define the transport coefficients, e.g. the electrical and thermal conductivity, the various thermoelectric coefficients and the galvanomagnetic coefficients.

Our ultimate object in the theory is to be able to calculate these relations in terms of the detailed properties of the electron and phonon systems of the solid. Before doing this, however, it is desirable to consider these relations in a general way, corresponding to the application of ordinary thermodynamics to systems which are in equilibrium. The extension of statistical mechanics and thermodynamics to non-equilibrium situations forms a branch of theoretical physics which is called *irreversible thermodynamics*. In this section, we shall consider those aspects of irreversible thermodynamics which are relevant for a discussion of the transport processes. The justification for doing this is that it gives a precise framework for defining the transport coefficients and leads to certain general relations between them.

3.5.1 THE GENERAL PHENOMENOLOGICAL EXPRESSIONS FOR THE FLOW OF ELECTRONS AND ENERGY

In discussing the electron and phonon systems of a solid, we have stated that, in a state of thermodynamic equilibrium, the electrochemical potential and temperature of the electron system and the temperature of the phonon system are constant throughout the volume of the solid. In making these statements, it was implied that some meaning could be attached, for example, to the phrase "temperature at a particular point". In fact such a statement is not strictly correct. The concepts of temperature and electrochemical potential are essentially statistical in nature, having a meaning only for systems which contain a large number of particles. Thus, these parameters cannot be defined strictly at a point. However, they can be defined for regions around a point which, although small in extent compared with macroscopic dimensions, still contain a sufficiently large number of particles to allow the statistical definitions to apply. It is in this sense of local values that we can speak of temperature and other statistical parameters as possessing certain values at a point and it is in the same sense that the constancy of these parameters is defined for the state of thermodynamic equilibrium of the solid. For certain physical situations, the concepts break down [see the article by Herring and Nichols (1949:2)] but for the problems with which we are concerned in this book, the above procedure raises no difficulties.

For non-equilibrium situations, we assume that it is still possible to define local values of the statistical parameters in the above sense. The justification of this procedure is that, if we consider a small volume of the solid which still contains a large number of particles, then the interactions between the particles within this volume are very much stronger than the interactions with other parts of the solid. Thus, a state of local equilibrium exists for the small volume and the temperature and electrochemical potential can again be defined on a local basis. In contrast to the overall equilibrium state, however, the values of these parameters will vary throughout the solid.

The result of such variations is to set up processes which, in accordance with general principles, attempt to restore an overall thermodynamic equilibrium situation. These processes are a flow of electrons and a flow of energy. Part of this latter flow is associated with the electrons and part with the phonons.

An important aspect of this situation is that it is not possible in general to associate any one particular flow uniquely with any one particular "force", defining this last expression in terms of the spatial variations of the temperature and of the electrochemical potential, although we may distinguish between *direct* effects and so-called *cross* effects. For example, if the temperature is constant but the electrochemical potential $\bar{\mu}(\mathbf{r})$ of the electrons varies, the primary effect will be to produce a flow of electrons in an attempt to restore uniformity of $\bar{\mu}$. The electrons, however, have energy associated with them and, thus, a flow of electrons implies a flow of energy. This must be regarded as a "cross" effect produced by the variation in $\bar{\mu}$ since we normally expect energy flow to be produced primarily by a temperature difference. A second "cross" effect results from the interaction between the electrons and phonons which leads to the possibility of exchange of energy between them. The energy flow in the electron system can, as a result of such interactions, give rise to an energy flow in the phonon system and this is a second "cross" effect, produced by a variation of $\bar{\mu}$.

The flows of energy and electrons in the solid are defined by vectors **w** and **j** which are functions of position. Thus, for example, the expression **w** · **n**δA gives the rate at which energy is flowing across a small surface element of area δA situated at a point **r** in the solid, where **n** is the unit vector normal to the surface element. The flows vanish in the equilibrium state where $\bar{\mu}$ and T are constant. We therefore assume that, if the spatial variations of these parameters in a non-equilibrium state are sufficiently small, then we can express the flows as linear functions of these variations which are specified by the vector gradients of $\bar{\mu}$ and T.

So far, the procedure is fairly obvious on physical grounds. However, the theory of irreversible thermodynamics leads to some further general results, which take the form of relations existing between certain of the coefficients appearing in these linear expressions. The main features of the theory are given in Appendix 2. We write the expressions for the components of the flow of electrons **j** and of the energy **w** in the form

$$-j_i = \sum_k L_{ik}^{(1)} \frac{\partial}{\partial x_k}\left(\frac{\bar{\mu}}{T}\right) + \sum_k L_{ik}^{(2)} \frac{\partial}{\partial x_k}\left(\frac{1}{T}\right),$$

$$w_i = \sum_k L_{ik}^{(3)} \frac{\partial}{\partial x_k}\left(\frac{\bar{\mu}}{T}\right) + \sum_k L_{ik}^{(4)} \frac{\partial}{\partial x_k}\left(\frac{1}{T}\right), \qquad (3.5.1)$$

where the various coefficients $L_{ik}^{(n)}$ are functions of the local conditions and are, in addition, functions of the magnetic field **B** acting on the solid. Then, in addition to any other relations which may exist between these coefficients on symmetry grounds (see later), the following relations are also satisfied

$$\left.\begin{aligned}
L_{ik}^{(1)}(\mathbf{B}) &= L_{ki}^{(1)}(-\mathbf{B}), \\
L_{ik}^{(4)}(\mathbf{B}) &= L_{ki}^{(4)}(-\mathbf{B}), \\
L_{ik}^{(2)}(\mathbf{B}) &= L_{ki}^{(3)}(-\mathbf{B}).
\end{aligned}\right\} \qquad (3.5.2)$$

These relations are called the *Onsager relations*. Their ultimate basis is the principle of microscopic reversibility which states that for any solution of the equation of motion of a particle under specified conditions, there is another equally valid solution in which the time is reversed, provided that the magnetic field is reversed in direction.

Equations (3.5.1) and (3.5.2) may be written much more compactly in tensor notation as follows

$$-\mathbf{j} = L^{(1)} \cdot \mathbf{grad}\left(\frac{\bar{\mu}}{T}\right) + L^{(2)} \cdot \mathbf{grad}\left(\frac{1}{T}\right),$$

$$\mathbf{w} = L^{(3)} \cdot \mathbf{grad}\left(\frac{\bar{\mu}}{T}\right) + L^{(4)} \cdot \mathbf{grad}\left(\frac{1}{T}\right), \qquad (3.5.3)$$

and

$$L^{(1)}(\mathbf{B}) = \tilde{L}^{(1)}(-\mathbf{B}); \quad L^{(4)}(\mathbf{B}) = \tilde{L}^{(4)}(-\mathbf{B}); \quad L^{(2)}(\mathbf{B}) = \tilde{L}^{(3)}(-\mathbf{B}) \quad (3.5.4)$$

It is important to note that the Onsager relations are valid only when all interacting parts of the system are considered. In particular, we may split the total energy flow into a flow of energy $\mathbf{w}_e$ in the electron system and a flow $\mathbf{w}_p$ in the phonon system, and write

$$\mathbf{w}_e = {}^{(e)}L^{(3)} \cdot \mathbf{grad}\left(\frac{\bar{\mu}}{T}\right) + {}^{(e)}L^{(4)} \cdot \mathbf{grad}\left(\frac{1}{T}\right),$$

$$\mathbf{w}_p = {}^{(p)}L^{(3)} \cdot \mathbf{grad}\left(\frac{\bar{\mu}}{T}\right) + {}^{(p)}L^{(4)} \cdot \mathbf{grad}\left(\frac{1}{T}\right), \qquad (3.5.5)$$

so that

$$L^{(3)} = {}^{(e)}L^{(3)} + {}^{(p)}L^{(3)}. \qquad (3.5.6)$$

There are in general no cross relations, existing directly between ${}^{(e)}L^{(3)}$ and $L^{(2)}$, i.e. between the energy and particle flow in the electron system. However, we saw previously, that ${}^{(p)}L^{(3)}$, whose components define the energy flow in the phonon system as a result of the spatial variation of the electrochemical potential $\bar{\mu}$ of the electron system, is determined by the strength of the interactions between the electrons and the phonons. In many cases of interest, this term is very small compared with the corresponding term in the expression for $\mathbf{w}_e$ and can be ignored. Its presence gives rise to physical effects which are classified as *phonon-drag* effects.

A situation, similar in principle to the above, is of special interest in semiconductors in which case we frequently wish to split up the flows of electrons and energy in the electron system into two or more parts each of which is associated with a particular energy band. In such cases, we can write down expressions analogous to (3.5.3) for each band and obtain the total flows by adding these expressions for the various bands. The last of the Onsager relations (3.5.4) cannot be applied to each band separately but only to the flows as a whole. Under certain conditions, however, where the different energy bands do not interact appreciably with each other, each band can be treated as a separate thermodynamic system to which the Onsager relations apply. This is usually the case when the semiconductor is in the so-called *extrinsic* range where the value of the electrochemical potential (Fermi level) is such that it lies much closer to one band than to any others.

For the sake of completeness, it should be mentioned that the division of a solid into sub-systems for the purposes of detailed calculation of energy and electron flows, raises certain difficulties which are associated with the definitions of temperature and electrochemical potentials for the various sub-systems. In particular, the questions arise as to whether a common temperature can be assigned (on a local basis) to all the various sub-systems and whether a common electrochemical potential applies locally to all the electrons for a steady, non-equilibrium state of the solid as a whole. It is well known that, in fact, there are situations in which such an assumption is inadequate. For example, it is possible to maintain a steady non-equilibrium state of a semiconductor in which the conduction band is not locally in equilibrium with the valence band and, in this case, different electrochemical potentials (called quasi-Fermi levels) are used for the two bands. Similarly there are situations in which different temperatures must be assigned to the electrons and phonons. Although such situations are of considerable importance in practice (for example, the first case covers the theory of transistor operation), they are not usually of interest in the theory of thermal conductivity, being associated with rather special conditions, and will not be considered in this book. It will be assumed henceforth that the local temperature is the same for all the electrons and the phonons and that the local electrochemical potential is the same for all the electrons. It is on this basis that we have written equations (3.5.1).

3.5.2 THE EFFECT OF CRYSTAL SYMMETRY ON THE PHENOMENOLOGICAL COEFFICIENTS

The set of phenomenological coefficients appearing in equation (3.5.1) provides a complete description of the transport properties of

6

the solid. The number of independent coefficients is limited only by the Onsager relations for a general solid.

In most of the cases occurring in practice, this number is usually very much further reduced by taking into account the overall symmetry properties of the solid. The minimum set to which they can reduce, in practice, occurs in solids possessing cubic symmetry. In this case, in the absence of a magnetic field, the components of each tensor, with a suitable choice of reference axes, satisfy the relations

$$L_{11} = L_{22} = L_{33}; \quad \text{all other } L_{ij} = 0. \tag{3.5.7}$$

These relations are required by the symmetry of the solid and, since the Onsager relations lead to $L_{11}{}^{(2)} = L_{11}{}^{(3)}$, there are only three independent components to calculate for a complete description of the transport properties in the absence of a magnetic field. This will be used later as the simplest example which illustrates the principles on which the calculation of the components is based.

Another more general case, which can be used as the simplest example for discussing the phenomena associated with the action of a magnetic field, occurs if the magnetic field is applied parallel to a three- or four-fold axis of rotational symmetry of the solid. If this axis is taken as the 3-direction of a right-handed system of axes, then symmetry requires that for each tensor

$$L_{11}(\mathbf{B}) = L_{22}(\mathbf{B}); \quad L_{12}(\mathbf{B}) = -L_{21}(\mathbf{B}),$$
$$L_{13} = L_{31} = L_{23} = L_{32} = 0. \tag{3.5.8}$$

The extra information provided by the Onsager relations gives, for example

$$L_{12}{}^{(1)}(\mathbf{B}) = L_{21}{}^{(1)}(-\mathbf{B}) \tag{3.5.9}$$

so that

$$L_{12}{}^{(1)}(\mathbf{B}) = -L_{12}{}^{(1)}(-\mathbf{B}),$$

showing that it is an odd function of the magnetic field $\mathbf{B}$ and, in particular, vanishes for $\mathbf{B} = 0$. A similar behaviour is shown by $L_{12}{}^{(4)}(\mathbf{B})$, but not necessarily by $L_{12}{}^{(2)}(\mathbf{B})$ or $L_{12}{}^{(3)}(\mathbf{B})$. Further, since

$$L_{11}{}^{(1)}(\mathbf{B}) = L_{11}{}^{(1)}(-\mathbf{B}), \text{ etc.}; \quad L_{11}{}^{(4)}(\mathbf{B}) = L_{11}{}^{(4)}(-\mathbf{B}), \text{ etc.}, \tag{3.5.10}$$

then all the diagonal components of $L^{(1)}$ and $L^{(4)}$ are even functions of the magnetic field.

3.5.3 The Physical Interpretation of the Phenomenological Coefficients

Having discussed the general properties of the coefficients in equations (3.5.3), we turn to the discussion of their physical significance. For this purpose, it is desirable to express the equations in an alternative form which is particularly suitable for discussing various physical situations. The electric current density $\mathbf{i}$ in the solid is $-e\mathbf{j}$, where $-e$ is the electronic charge. We can thus introduce $\mathbf{i}$ instead of $\mathbf{j}$ into the equations. Then the term $\mathbf{grad}(\bar{\mu}/T)$ in the second equation can be expressed in terms of $\mathbf{i}$ and $\mathbf{grad}(1/T)$ from the first equation. Finally, expressing $\mathbf{grad}(\bar{\mu}/T)$ and $\mathbf{grad}(1/T)$ in terms of $\mathbf{grad}(\bar{\mu})$ and $\mathbf{grad}(T)$ leads to equations of the form

$$\mathbf{i} = \frac{1}{e}\sigma \cdot \mathbf{grad}\,\bar{\mu} - \sigma \cdot Q \cdot \mathbf{grad}\,T, \qquad (3.5.11a)$$

$$\mathbf{w} = \left(\pi - \frac{\bar{\mu}}{e}\right) \cdot \mathbf{i} - \kappa \cdot \mathbf{grad}\,T. \qquad (3.5.11b)$$

In these expressions, we have introduced four new second-order tensors σ, Q, π and κ in place of the $L^{(n)}$ of equations (3.5.3). These four new tensors can all be expressed in terms of the old set, by means of the relations

$$\sigma(\mathbf{B}) = \frac{e^2}{T}L^{(1)}(\mathbf{B}), \qquad (3.5.12a)$$

$$Q(\mathbf{B}) = \frac{\bar{\mu}}{eT} + \frac{1}{eT}(L^{(1)})^{-1} \cdot L^{(2)}(\mathbf{B}), \qquad (3.5.12b)$$

$$\pi(\mathbf{B}) = TQ(-\mathbf{B}), \qquad (3.5.12c)$$

$$\kappa(\mathbf{B}) = \frac{1}{T^2}L^{(4)}(\mathbf{B}) - \frac{1}{T}\left[\pi(\mathbf{B}) - \frac{\bar{\mu}}{e}\right] \cdot \sigma(\mathbf{B}) \cdot \left[TQ(\mathbf{B}) - \frac{\bar{\mu}}{e}\right], \qquad (3.5.12d)$$

where the Onsager relations have been used in deriving (3.5.12c).†

The reason for writing the equations in the alternative form (3.5.11) is that they are immediately applicable to two situations which are easily realizable in practice. These are (a) the isothermal condition,

---

† The reader who is not familiar with tensor notation and operation may follow the arguments here by taking all tensors to be scalar quantities.

and (b) the zero-current condition. The general equations are compli-cated but the main features can be brought out by using the simplest example which is realizable in practice. This is the example repre-sented by equations (3.5.7) where all tensors reduce to scalars. Then σ, Q, π and κ are all scalars and, from equation (3.5.12c),

$$\pi = TQ.$$

In the isothermal case, the equations of flow are

$$\mathbf{i} = \frac{1}{e}\sigma \, \mathbf{grad} \, \bar{\mu}, \qquad \mathbf{w} = \left(\pi - \frac{\bar{\mu}}{e}\right)\mathbf{i}. \tag{3.5.13}$$

The first of these equations expresses Ohm's law for the solid since the gradient of $\bar{\mu}$ is expressed in terms of the gradient of the external electrostatic potential ϕ by the equation

$$\mathbf{grad} \, \bar{\mu} = -e \, \mathbf{grad} \, \phi = e\mathscr{E}$$

where $\mathscr{E}$ is the electric field intensity. Thus, $\mathbf{i} = \sigma\mathscr{E}$ and σ is the *elec-trical conductivity* as ordinarily defined.

The second equation gives the energy flow in the presence of a current $\mathbf{i}$. The physical significance of the coefficient is thus the average energy carried per electron, the average being taken with respect to the current contributions of the electrons. The physical effects associa-ted with this expression appear in particular at a junction between two solids where there is a change in the value of π. The energy flow, under isothermal conditions is given by

$$\mathbf{w}_B = \left(\pi_B - \frac{\bar{\mu}_B}{e}\right)\mathbf{i}_B \quad \text{and} \quad \mathbf{w}_A = \left(\pi_A - \frac{\bar{\mu}_A}{e}\right)\mathbf{i}_A$$

on the two sides of the junction. If there is no divergence of the current, i.e. the two cross-sections are the same, we can write $\mathbf{i}_A = \mathbf{i}_B = \mathbf{i}$ and hence

$$\mathbf{w}_B - \mathbf{w}_A = (\pi_B - \pi_A)\mathbf{i} - \frac{1}{e}(\bar{\mu}_B - \bar{\mu}_A)\mathbf{i}. \tag{3.5.14}$$

The difference represents the rate at which energy is accumulating per unit area in the junction region. In the steady state this must be balanced by an external reservoir of heat which maintains the tem-perature of the junction at a constant value. Of the two terms occurring in the above expression, the second represents the difference in the energy flows arising as a result of any electrical resistance barrier at the junction. A perfect electrical contact, by definition, is one which gives continuity of the electrochemical potential across the barrier. For such a contact, the second term disappears and the first term is balanced by the external heat supply. This defines the *Peltier coefficient* for the junction as the difference between the parameter π for the two materials. Thus π may be called the absolute Peltier coefficient for a particular material.

The second case of interest is when the net current flow is zero. For the simple case discussed above, the first of equations (3.5.11) lead to

$$\frac{1}{e}\,\mathbf{grad}\,\bar{\mu} = Q\,\mathbf{grad}\,T. \tag{3.5.15}$$

This equation defines Q as the absolute *Seebeck coefficient* of the material. By integrating round a thermocouple circuit consisting of two materials A and B, the Seebeck coefficient Q_{AB} of the couple appears as the algebraic difference of Q_B and Q_A.

Finally, the second of equations (3.5.11), under conditions of zero current flow, gives

$$\mathbf{w} = -\kappa\,\mathbf{grad}\,T \tag{3.5.16}$$

as the relation between the energy flow and the temperature gradient under conditions of zero current flow. This is the physical condition which is met in defining the thermal conductivity of the solid and κ is the *thermal conductivity*.

Thus, in the simple example, we have been able to specify precisely conditions under which the four parameters σ, Q, π and κ can be measured. More correctly, the second and third of these cannot be measured directly for a particular solid but the difference between their values for two solids can be measured.

In the more general case, represented by equations (3.5.11) with the tensors possessing a general form, whose components are functions of the magnetic field acting on the solid, the two situations of zero temperature gradient and zero current flow still retain their usefulness in defining the physical significance of the components. It is natural to call σ the electrical conductivity tensor, Q the Seebeck tensor, π the Peltier tensor and κ the thermal conductivity tensor. In the presence of a magnetic field, the components of σ are related to effects such as the Hall effect and magnetoconductance effects, while the components of Q are related to the Nernst effect and the change of the Seebeck coefficient (as normally defined) with magnetic field. Similarly, the components of κ are related to the Righi–Leduc effect and the change of the thermal conductivity (as normally defined) in the presence of a magnetic field.

3.5.4. The Combined Transport Coefficients from Several Groups

The main aim of this section has been to give the framework within which the transport properties and, in particular, the thermal conductivity of a solid can be precisely defined. In succeeding parts of this book, the principles by which these properties can be calculated will be considered. A point which we wish to stress here is that the more detailed kinetic calculations lead, in the first place, to expressions for the coefficients $L_{ik}^{(n)}$ occurring in equations (3.5.1). To obtain the transport coefficients as normally required, it is necessary to apply the transformation equations (3.5.12) and, in particular, the last of these equations for the thermal conductivity.

This procedure has the following consequence, which is of considerable importance. The flows of electrons and of energy given in equation (3.5.1) and used in the subsequent discussion are those for the solid as a whole. In the more detailed kinetic theory, we have to consider the physical processes by which such flows can take place. For this purpose, we divide the solid up into groups and obtain expressions for the flows within each group. The total flows can then be expressed as the sum of the separate group flows. For each group, the electron and energy flows will be given by expressions analogous to equation (3.5.1) with the various coefficients $L_{ik}^{(n)}$ characteristic of that group. Since we are assuming common values of the thermodynamic parameters $\bar{\mu}$ and T for each group on a local basis, the $L_{ik}^{(n)}$ for the solid as a whole are obtained by summing the $L_{ik}^{(n)}$ for the various groups. Apart, however, from the electrical conductivity, which is directly related to $L^{(1)}$, the transport coefficients are not additive and it is necessary to calculate the $L_{ik}^{(n)}$ for the whole solid before applying the transformations (3.5.12). We shall see an example of this later in discussing the so-called bipolar effect on the thermal conductivity.

We may also stress once again that, in the above procedure, the Onsager relations (3.5.2) will not in general be applicable to the

$L_{ik}^{(n)}$ for the separate groups because these do not, in themselves constitute closed thermodynamic systems, but interact to some extent with other groups. Under certain conditions, however, it may be a good approximation to assume that the interactions are weak and that the Onsager relations apply to a particular group.

3.6 TRANSPORT PROCESSES IN SOLIDS—PRINCIPLES OF THE KINETIC THEORY

The problem of calculating the transport coefficients in solids has been shown in the preceding section to reduce to that of calculating the various coefficients $L_{ik}^{(n)}$ in equation (3.5.1) and, subsequently, using equations (3.5.12). In this section, we shall discuss the principles governing the calculation of the coefficients $L_{ik}^{(n)}$.

3.6.1 THE PROBABILITY DISTRIBUTION FUNCTION FOR ELECTRONS

In view of the very large number of electron and phonon quantum states present in any actual solid, these calculations must be based on the principles of statistical mechanics. These, in turn, are based on the realization that, for systems containing a very large number of particles, it is not possible to set up and solve the complete equations of motion for the system. There are two reasons for this. On the one hand, the system of equations is far too complex to be handled in practice. On the other hand, even if this could be done, the solutions would require a knowledge of the initial values of the appropriate co-ordinates of all the particles at some instant of time and such knowledge cannot be obtained in practice.

These difficulties are circumvented in statistical mechanics by calculating the most probable values of physical properties of the system. These are based on considerations of a so-called ensemble which consists of a large number of systems which all have the same structure and conform to the limited knowledge that is available for the system, but which otherwise may differ widely in the detailed assignment of co-ordinates to the individual particles. General considerations then show that the most probable values of physical properties calculated in this way become increasingly sharp, compared with other possible values, as the number of particles in the system increases. The probability of finding a system of the ensemble in any state which is other than very close to the most probable state becomes vanishingly small. The most probable values obtained in this way are assumed to correspond to the observed physical properties of an actual single system.

In this sense, we can define so-called *probability distribution functions* for the electrons and phonons in a solid. Considering the electrons for the present, we have seen that the quantum states are specified by their wave vector **k** and the band index n plus, of course, any further states, corresponding to bound electrons, which do not contribute directly to transport properties when occupied by electrons. Thus, we can define the most probable number of electron wave packets formed from **k** values within a particular band n, which, at a particular time t, have their mean positions within a small volume element **dr** enclosing a point with position vector **r** and have their mean **k** values situated within a small range about some **k** value (which may be described as a small volume element **dk** in **k** space). Clearly **dr** and **dk** in this context must be chosen so as to be sufficiently large that they can contain a reasonably large number of electrons. At the same time they must be sufficiently small that all the electrons for band n within them can be assumed to have the same basic properties and to be subject to the same external influence. Thus, for example, **dr** is sufficiently small that it includes no appreciable variation of electrostatic potential and temperature and **dk** is sufficiently small that all its electrons (in band n) can be assumed to have the same velocity and acceleration at a particular time. These restrictions, which are inherent in any statistical treatment, do not cause any difficulty in most practical situations.

From equation (3.3.10), the number of quantum states in the range **drdk** is **drdk**$/4\pi^3$ for each energy band, allowance being made for the fact that each **k** value corresponds to two quantum states because of the two possible values of the spin quantum number of an electron. Instead of talking about the number of electrons, it is preferable to define the most probable occupation of these states in terms of a function f such that the most probable number of electrons associated with the nth energy band in **drdk** at time t is given by

$$\frac{1}{4\pi^3}f(n, \mathbf{k}, \mathbf{r}, t)\mathbf{dr}\mathbf{dk}. \tag{3.6.1}$$

As indicated in this equation f is a function of position vector **r**, wave vector **k**, band index n and time.

3.6.2 The General Boltzmann Equation

The probability distribution function introduced in the above way is the same as the function which was introduced in Section 3.3.5 on the basis of the time average of the population of a particular quantum state.

As discussed above, we can take the expression (3.6.1) as giving the actual number of electrons in any solid of interest. All the electrons in the set are moving in the same way and are subject to the same external influences. Thus, if we follow the variation of the set with time, we can say that its total rate of change is due to the effect of collisions which cause electrons to be scattered out of and into the set. Denoting the effect of these collisions on f by $(\partial f/\partial t)_{\text{scatter}}$ we obtain the result that the total net rate of change of f with time is

$$\left(\frac{\mathrm{d}f}{\mathrm{d}t}\right)_{\text{tot}} = \left(\frac{\partial f}{\partial t}\right)_{\text{scatter}}. \tag{3.6.2}$$

On the other hand, we can write for the total change

$$\left(\frac{\mathrm{d}f}{\mathrm{d}t}\right)_{\text{tot}} = \frac{\partial f}{\partial \mathbf{k}} \cdot \frac{\partial \mathbf{k}}{\partial t} + \frac{\partial f}{\partial \mathbf{r}} \cdot \frac{\partial \mathbf{r}}{\partial t} + \left(\frac{\partial f}{\partial t}\right) \tag{3.6.3}$$

where, for each of the partial differentiations on the right-hand side the remaining variables are kept constant. In particular $(\delta f/\delta t)$ refers to the net rate of change of f with time for a fixed element $\mathrm{d}\mathbf{r}\mathrm{d}\mathbf{k}$. Combining these last two equations we obtain the so-called *Boltzmann equation* in general form

$$\left(\frac{\partial f}{\partial t}\right) = \left(\frac{\partial f}{\partial t}\right)_{\text{scatter}} - \frac{\partial f}{\partial \mathbf{k}} \cdot \dot{\mathbf{k}} - \frac{\partial f}{\partial \mathbf{r}} \cdot \dot{\mathbf{r}} \tag{3.6.4}$$

in which $\dot{\mathbf{k}}$ and $\dot{\mathbf{r}}$ refer to the rate of change with time of the wave vector and position vector for wave packets in the nth energy band.

The flows of electrons and energy associated with electrons in the nth band at the point $\mathbf{r}$ are given by the following integrals over the distribution

$$\mathbf{j}_n = \frac{1}{4\pi^3} \int \mathbf{v}f\,\mathrm{d}\mathbf{k}; \quad \mathbf{w}_n = \frac{1}{4\pi^3} \int E\mathbf{v}f\,\mathrm{d}\mathbf{k}, \tag{3.6.5}$$

where $\mathbf{v}$ and E are the velocity and energy associated with the state $(n, \mathbf{k})$. For steady-state conditions, these flows are independent of time and this requires that $(\partial f/\partial t)$ on the left-hand side of equation (3.6.4) should be zero. This is the physical situation of interest for discussing the transport processes along the lines of the preceding section and hence we shall usually be concerned with the steady-state Boltzmann equation in the form

$$\frac{\partial f}{\partial \mathbf{k}} \cdot \dot{\mathbf{k}} + \frac{\partial f}{\partial \mathbf{r}} \cdot \dot{\mathbf{r}} = \left(\frac{\partial f}{\partial t}\right)_{\text{scatter}}. \qquad (3.6.6)$$

Further, since the transport coefficients have been defined on the basis of equations (3.5.3), which express the flows as linear functions of the "forces", $\mathbf{grad}(\bar{\mu}/T)$ and $\mathbf{grad}(1/T)$, it is clear from equations (3.6.5) that the solution of the Boltzmann equation (3.6.6) is required to be a linear function of these forces also. For subsequent discussion it is convenient to write this solution in the form

$$f = f_0 - \frac{f_1 \partial f_0}{\partial E} \qquad (3.6.7)$$

where f_0 is the equilibrium distribution function corresponding to the local values of $\bar{\mu}$ and T and f_1 is a linear function of the forces, which in its most general form can be written

$$f_1 = \mathbf{\chi} \cdot \mathbf{grad}\left(\frac{\bar{\mu}}{T}\right) + \mathbf{\psi} \cdot \mathbf{grad}\left(\frac{1}{T}\right). \qquad (3.6.8)$$

The functions $\mathbf{\chi}$ and $\mathbf{\psi}$ are vector functions of position and of the magnetic field if present. They define, to the first order, the extent to which the occupational probability of the quantum state $(n, \mathbf{k})$ is affected by the driving forces.

Since the solution of the Boltzmann equation is required only to the first order in the driving forces, it is clear that, when equation (3.6.7) is substituted into equation (3.6.6), only those terms which are linear in the driving forces need be retained. We have seen earlier (equation 3.3.16) that the value of $\dot{\mathbf{k}}$ is given by

$$\dot{\mathbf{k}} = \frac{-e}{\hbar}\{-\mathbf{grad}\,\phi + \mathbf{v} \wedge \mathbf{B}\} \qquad (3.6.9)$$

where ϕ is the local value of the electrostatic potential, and $\mathbf{v}$ is the local velocity of wave packets corresponding to the state $(n, \mathbf{k})$ which is, of course, equal to $\dot{\mathbf{r}}$.

The term f_0 of equation (3.6.7), when put into equation (3.6.6), gives

$$\frac{\partial f_0}{\partial \mathbf{k}} = \frac{\partial f_0}{\partial E} \frac{\partial E}{\partial \mathbf{k}} = \hbar \mathbf{v} \frac{\partial f_0}{\partial E} \qquad (3.6.10)$$

since we have stressed that the derivative is taken for constant $\mathbf{r}$ and the only variation of f_0 with $\mathbf{k}$ is due to its variation with E. Remembering also that $(\partial f_0/\partial \mathbf{r})$ is to be taken for constant $\mathbf{k}$, we have

$$\frac{\partial f_0}{\partial \mathbf{r}} = \frac{\partial}{\partial \mathbf{r}} \left[\frac{1}{1 + \exp\left(\dfrac{E - \bar{\mu}}{kT}\right)} \right] = kT \frac{\partial f_0}{\partial E} \frac{\partial}{\partial \mathbf{r}} \left(\frac{E - \bar{\mu}}{kT} \right)_{\mathbf{k}=\text{const}}. \qquad (3.6.11)$$

In working out the last expression, the value of $(\partial E/\partial \mathbf{r})$ at constant $\mathbf{k}$ can be obtained if one remembers that the energy level scheme of the solid shifts in position (with respect to a common zero of energy) by the amount $-e\phi$. Hence,

$$\left(\frac{\partial E}{\partial \mathbf{r}} \right)_{\mathbf{k}} = -e \, \mathbf{grad} \, \phi. \qquad (3.6.12)$$

The remaining terms in equation (3.6.11) cause no difficulty. Thus, collecting the results of the last four equations together, we get a contribution to the left-hand side of the Boltzmann equation (3.6.6) which is linear in the driving forces and has the form

$$-T \frac{\partial f_0}{\partial E} \mathbf{v} \cdot \left[\mathbf{grad}\left(\frac{\bar{\mu}}{T} \right) - E \, \mathbf{grad}\left(\frac{1}{T} \right) \right]. \qquad (3.6.13)$$

This does not contain any magnetic field term since we have so far used only the f_0 part of equation (3.6.7) and this gives rise to a term containing $\mathbf{v} \cdot \mathbf{v} \wedge \mathbf{B}$ which is identically zero. Physically, this corresponds to the fact that a magnetic field does not by itself alter the equilibrium distribution since the electrons do not absorb energy from the field. To obtain the effect of the magnetic field term to an extent linear in the driving forces, it is necessary to use the second term in equation (3.6.7), which gives rise to a contribution involving the derivative of f_1 with respect to $\mathbf{k}$. The final form of the Boltzmann equation which is linear in the driving forces is

$$-T\frac{\partial f_0}{\partial E}\mathbf{v}\cdot\left[\mathbf{grad}\left(\frac{\bar{\mu}}{T}\right)-E\,\mathbf{grad}\left(\frac{1}{T}\right)\right]+\frac{e}{\hbar}\frac{\partial f_0}{\partial E}\mathbf{v}\wedge\mathbf{B}\cdot\frac{\partial f_1}{\partial\mathbf{k}}$$

$$=\left(\frac{\partial f}{\partial t}\right)_{\text{scatter}}. \tag{3.6.14}$$

The subsequent development of the treatment of this equation involves the setting up of an expression for $(\partial f/\partial t)_{\text{scatter}}$ on the basis of the physical processes responsible. One must then solve the equation for the unknown function or, more accurately, the functions χ and ψ which define f_1 through equation (3.6.8). The substitution of equation (3.6.8) in equation (3.6.14) and the subsequent identification of the various components leads to the equations which are simpler in form, viz.

$$Tv_i = \left(\frac{\partial\chi_i}{\partial t}\right)_{\text{scatter}} + \frac{e}{\hbar}\mathbf{v}\wedge\mathbf{B}\cdot\frac{\partial\chi_i}{\partial\mathbf{k}}, \tag{3.6.15a}$$

$$-TEv_i = \left(\frac{\partial\psi_i}{\partial t}\right)_{\text{scatter}} + \frac{e}{\hbar}\mathbf{v}\wedge\mathbf{B}\cdot\frac{\partial\psi_i}{\partial\mathbf{k}}. \tag{3.6.15b}$$

3.6.3 ENTROPY PRODUCTION IN THE ELECTRON SYSTEM

We shall discuss certain general properties associated with the collision term of the Boltzmann equation in the next section. It is useful at this point, however, to note the following physical feature associated with the Boltzmann equation in the absence of a magnetic field. (The situation with a magnetic field present is more complicated and has been discussed by Ziman (1956:3)).

In discussing the phenomenological theory of the flow of energy and charge, we saw that the basic procedure involved the calculation of the rate of internal entropy production in terms of conjugated fluxes and forces. This rate is given by (see Appendix 2, equation (A.2.19))

$$s = \mathbf{w}\cdot\mathbf{grad}\frac{1}{T} - \mathbf{j}\cdot\mathbf{grad}\left(\frac{\bar{\mu}}{T}\right). \tag{3.6.16}$$

If we express the energy flow $\mathbf{w}_e$ and the electron flow $\mathbf{j}$ in terms of the distribution function for the electron system, using equations (3.6.5), we find, for the contribution s_e, from the electron system, to s,

$$s_e = -\frac{1}{4\pi^3}\sum_n\int\frac{\partial f_0}{\partial E}\mathbf{v}\cdot\left[E\,\mathbf{grad}\left(\frac{1}{T}\right)-\mathbf{grad}\left(\frac{\bar{\mu}}{T}\right)\right]f_1\,d\mathbf{k}. \tag{3.6.17}$$

Comparison of this with the Boltzmann equation (3.6.14), without the magnetic term, shows that

$$s_e = -\frac{1}{4\pi^3 T} \sum_n \int f_1 \left(\frac{\partial f}{\partial t}\right)_{\text{scatter}} d\mathbf{k}. \qquad (3.6.18)$$

This shows clearly the connexion of s_e with the scattering processes. This result is of special interest in connexion with the so-called variational method of dealing with the Boltzmann equation which will be discussed in the section 3.7.2.

3.6.4 THE PHONON SYSTEM

So far, we have discussed the Boltzmann equation only for the electron system. The corresponding equation for the phonon system can be set up using the same general principles. The number of phonon quantum states associated with branch j of the vibrational spectrum in a volume element $d\mathbf{r}$ of ordinary space and a volume element $d\mathbf{q}$ of wave-vector space is $d\mathbf{r}d\mathbf{q}/8\pi^3$, there being no factor corresponding to the spin of the electrons. The most probable number of phonons in each of these states will be denoted by $\mathcal{N}$ so that the most probable number of phonon wave packets of branch j in $d\mathbf{r}d\mathbf{q}$ at time t is

$$\frac{1}{8\pi^3}\mathcal{N}(j, \mathbf{q}, \mathbf{r}, t) \, d\mathbf{r}d\mathbf{q}. \qquad (3.6.19)$$

By similar arguments to those in the discussion following the corresponding equation (3.6.1) for electrons, we find, for the steady-state condition (cf. equation 3.6.6)

$$\left(\frac{\partial \mathcal{N}}{\partial t}\right)_{\text{scatter}} = \frac{\partial \mathcal{N}}{\partial \mathbf{q}} \cdot \dot{\mathbf{q}} + \frac{\partial \mathcal{N}}{\partial \mathbf{r}} \cdot \dot{\mathbf{r}} \qquad (3.6.20)$$

where $\dot{\mathbf{q}}$ and $\dot{\mathbf{r}}$ refer to the rate of change with time of the mean $\mathbf{q}$ value and mean $\mathbf{r}$ value of a phonon wave packet in the quantum state $(j, \mathbf{q})$. Under the conditions of interest to us, however, the quantum-mechanical derivation of the mean of $\dot{\mathbf{q}}$ gives a value of zero. This corresponds to the physical fact that external forces and, in particular, electric fields, do not affect the vibrational motion of the atoms in a crystal, since they are negligible by comparison with the internal forces which govern these motions. Thus $\dot{\mathbf{q}}$ in equation (3.6.20) is zero and $\dot{\mathbf{r}}$ is given by equation (3.4.4), so that the Boltzmann equation for phonons is

$$\mathbf{v} \cdot \frac{\partial \mathcal{N}}{\partial \mathbf{r}} = \left(\frac{\partial \mathcal{N}}{\partial t}\right)_{\text{scatter}} \tag{3.6.21}$$

with

$$\mathbf{v}(j, \mathbf{q}) = \frac{\mathrm{d}}{\mathrm{d}\mathbf{q}}\omega(j, \mathbf{q}). \tag{3.6.22}$$

The flow of energy in the phonon system is

$$\mathbf{w}_p = \frac{1}{8\pi^3} \sum_j \int \hbar\omega(j, \mathbf{q})\mathcal{N}(j, \mathbf{q})\mathbf{v}(j, \mathbf{q}) \, \mathrm{d}\mathbf{q} \tag{3.6.23}$$

and we require this, and hence $\mathcal{N}$, to be a linear function of the driving forces. We write

$$\mathcal{N} = \mathcal{N}_0 - \mathcal{N}_1 \frac{\partial \mathcal{N}_0}{\partial(\hbar\omega)} \tag{3.6.24}$$

where $\mathcal{N}_0$ is the equilibrium phonon distribution corresponding to the local conditions and $\mathcal{N}_1$ is a linear function of the driving forces. Substituting this on the left-hand side of equation (3.6.21), we have the term

$$\mathbf{v} \cdot \frac{\partial \mathcal{N}_0}{\partial \mathbf{r}} = \mathbf{v} \cdot \mathbf{grad}\left[\exp\left(\frac{\hbar\omega}{kT}\right) - 1\right]^{-1} = T\hbar\omega\frac{\partial \mathcal{N}_0}{\partial(\hbar\omega)}\mathbf{v} \cdot \mathbf{grad}\left(\frac{1}{T}\right)$$

as the only term linear in the driving forces so that the Boltzmann equation is

$$T\hbar\omega\frac{\partial \mathcal{N}_0}{\partial(\hbar\omega)}\mathbf{v} \cdot \mathbf{grad}\left(\frac{1}{T}\right) = \left(\frac{\partial \mathcal{N}}{\partial t}\right)_{\text{scatter}}. \tag{3.6.25}$$

This is the analogue of equation (3.6.14) for the electron system.

We shall discuss this equation in more detail in Section 3.8 but, as in the corresponding electron case, we may note that the contribution to the rate of entropy production by the phonon system is

$$s_p = \mathbf{w}_p \cdot \mathbf{grad}\left(\frac{1}{T}\right) \tag{3.6.26}$$

and, using equation (3.6.23) for $\mathbf{w}_p$, it is found that

$$s_p = -\frac{1}{8\pi^3 T} \sum_j \int \mathcal{N}_1 \left(\frac{\partial \mathcal{N}_1}{\partial t}\right)_{\text{scatter}} d\mathbf{q}. \qquad (3.6.27)$$

3.7 FURTHER DISCUSSION OF THE BOLTZMANN EQUATION FOR ELECTRONS

3.7.1 THE SCATTERING OF ELECTRONS

The scattering term $(\partial f/\partial t)_{\text{scatter}}$ in the Boltzmann equation for electrons arises as a result of the presence in the crystal of departures from perfect periodicity of the potential field in which the electrons are moving. There are basically two ways in which such departures can arise. First, the thermal motion of the atoms causes a blurring of the potential and, secondly, there may be present localized imperfections, either crystalline defects or foreign atoms. A third possible source of scattering is the collision of electrons with each other, but we shall neglect this for the purposes of the present discussion.

The motion of the atoms, as we have seen, is described in terms of phonons and the scattering of electrons resulting from this process is described in terms of interactions between the electrons and phonons. A simple, yet physically realistic, way of looking at the scattering process is in terms of interaction between waves. This viewpoint has been discussed by Slater (1958:**7**). An electron wave having a wave vector $\mathbf{k}$ interacting with a phonon wave with a wave vector $\mathbf{q}$ results in the creation of an electron wave having a wave vector $\mathbf{k}'$ possessing a certain amplitude, with consequent modification of the amplitudes of the original waves. This picture, which is essentially the classical one of wave interference, in fact gives correctly one of the so-called *selectivn rules* for electron–phonon interaction, viz. that the wave vector of the scattered electron is either the sum or difference of the wave vectors of the interacting waves. In the correct quantum-mechanical treatment, the amplitudes of the waves are quantized. The scattering process is then described in terms of the probability per unit time that an electron wave packet with wave vector $\mathbf{k}$ will disappear from this state, as a result of interaction with a phonon wave packet of wave vector $\mathbf{q}$, and that a new electron wave packet will appear in a state $\mathbf{k}'$ where $\mathbf{k}' = \mathbf{k} \pm \mathbf{q}$. The classical change of amplitude of the phonon wave goes over into the quantum-mechanical statement that, in the process, a phonon either disappears or appears in a state with wave vector $\mathbf{q}$. A further feature of this process is the requirement of conservation of energy. If a phonon disappears from the state $(j, \mathbf{q})$ its energy is given to the electron and the final energy $E(n', \mathbf{k}')$ of the electron is related to the initial energy by

$$E(n', \mathbf{k}') = E(n, \mathbf{k}) + \hbar\omega(j, \mathbf{q}) \tag{3.7.1}$$

with

$$\mathbf{k}' = \mathbf{k} + \mathbf{q}.$$

For the process in which a phonon appears in $(j, \mathbf{q})$ the corresponding equations are

$$E(n', \mathbf{k}') = E(n, \mathbf{k}) - \hbar\omega(j, \mathbf{q}) \tag{3.7.2}$$

with

$$\mathbf{k}' = \mathbf{k} - \mathbf{q}.$$

The physical content of the quantum-mechanical treatment of the scattering process due to phonons is represented by a transition probability function $W_p(n, \mathbf{k}; n', \mathbf{k}')$. This gives the probability per unit time that an electron in the state $(n, \mathbf{k})$ will make a transition to the state $(n', \mathbf{k}')$ provided that this latter state is unoccupied. This last restriction is necessary to take account of the exclusion principle which prohibits such a transition if $(n', \mathbf{k}')$ is already occupied by an electron. The function W_p contains, among other factors, the number of phonons $\mathcal{N}(j, \mathbf{q})$ in the phonon quantum state $(j, \mathbf{q})$ this state being related to the electron quantum states by equation (3.7.1) or (3.7.2).

There is, thus, an inherent difficulty in obtaining a solution of the electron Boltzmann equation since the scattering term involves a knowledge of the corresponding equation for phonons. Similarly, this second equation cannot be solved until the electron distribution function is known. The two equations thus form a coupled system and, in principle, have to be solved simultaneously.

Although such a programme can be carried out, at least on an approximate basis, it is clearly involved, and we shall not pursue this aspect further. For a general review of the transport processes, and particularly for the electronic and thermal conductivities, it will be sufficient to consider the simpler case for which, in the electron scattering expression, the phonon distribution function can be taken to have its thermal equilibrium value. This assumption allows the electron Boltzmann equation to be solved independently of the corresponding phonon equation.

From the discussions of the preceding section (equations 3.6.16 and 3.6.26), it will be seen that this assumption is equivalent to assuming that the rates of entropy production in the electron and phonon systems are independent of each other, since both of these are associated with the departures of the corresponding distribution functions from equilibrium. Thus, in making our assumption, we are ignoring the effect of electron–phonon interactions in coupling entropy production in one system with entropy production in the other. The physical effects associated with such coupling are classified under the name of phonon-drag effects. Under certain conditions they have a marked influence on the Seebeck coefficient but, from the evidence available at the present time, it seems that their effect on the electrical and thermal conductivities is small in comparison with other processes.

The mathematical formulation of the assumption is that the transition probability $W_p(n, \mathbf{k}; n', \mathbf{k}')$ is the same as if the phonon distribution function were in equilibrium. This immediately gives one property of W_p, viz. that it contains a factor proportional to the absolute temperature T. This factor arises because, as would be expected on physical grounds, the transition probability function is proportional to the number of phonons in the associated phonon state. The majority of phonon modes interacting with electrons have energies which are very much less than kT at all except the very lowest temperatures. Thus, from equation (3.4.3), $\mathcal{N}_0 (j, \mathbf{q}) \fallingdotseq kT/\hbar\omega(j, \mathbf{q})$ for nearly all modes which interact with electrons. For the same reason, unless the bands n and n' overlap in energy, W_p is effectively zero unless $n = n'$, since the changes in energy given by equations (3.7.1) and (3.7.2) are much less than kT and the forbidden energy ranges are usually much greater than kT. For example, in semiconductors there are no direct transitions between the valence and conduction bands as a result of electron–phonon interactions under normal conditions.

Turning to the other main source of electron scattering, due to imperfections, this can also be specified in terms of a transition probability function $W_i(n, \mathbf{k}; n', \mathbf{k}')$. For the present, the only property of this function that we need to consider is that it should be expected, on physical grounds, to have the same value as for thermal equilibrium.

Combining the effects of phonon and imperfection scattering in the obvious way, by addition, we obtain a transition probability

7

$$W(n, \mathbf{k}; n', \mathbf{k}') = W_p + W_i \tag{3.7.3}$$

which is the same as for thermal equilibrium conditions. In terms of this function, the expression for $(\partial f/\partial t)_{\text{scatter}}$ is

$$\left(\frac{\partial f(n, \mathbf{k})}{\partial t}\right)_{\text{scatter}}$$

$$= \sum_{n'} \frac{1}{4\pi^3} \int \{f'(1-f)W(n', \mathbf{k}'; n, \mathbf{k}) - f(1-f')W(n, \mathbf{k}; n', \mathbf{k}')\} \, d\mathbf{k}'. \tag{3.7.4}$$

In this expression, the primed symbols refer to the state $(n', \mathbf{k}')$ and the unprimed to the state $(n, \mathbf{k})$. The two terms in eq. 3.7.4 refer, respectively, to the effect of electrons being scattered into and out of $(n, \mathbf{k})$. The factors $(1-f)$ are included take account of the exclusion principle and $d\mathbf{k}'$ is a volume element in $\mathbf{k}$ space surrounding the state $(n', \mathbf{k}')$.

In thermal equilibrium, the value of $(\partial f/\partial t)_{\text{scatter}}$ is zero and this is satisfied if, for every pair of states $(n, \mathbf{k})$, $(n', \mathbf{k}')$

$$V(n', \mathbf{k}'; n, \mathbf{k}) \equiv f_0'(1-f_0)W(n', \mathbf{k}'; n, \mathbf{k}),$$
$$= f_0(1-f_0')W(n, \mathbf{k}; n', \mathbf{k}'),$$
$$\equiv V(n, \mathbf{k}; n', \mathbf{k}'), \tag{3.7.5}$$

i.e. the function V is symmetrical in the parameters describing the two states. This is the mathematical formulation of the principle of microscopic reversibility which requires that, in the thermal equilibrium situation, the number of electrons scattered per unit time from one state to the other is the same as the number undergoing the reverse process.

Introducing the expression (3.6.7) for f into equation (3.7.4) and retaining only terms which are linear in the applied fields, i.e. linear in f_1, it is found with the help of the above results that

$$\left(\frac{\partial f}{\partial t}\right)_{\text{scatter}} = \frac{1}{kT} \sum_{n'} \frac{1}{4\pi^3} \int \{f_1' - f_1\} V(n, \mathbf{k}; n', \mathbf{k}') \, d\mathbf{k}', \tag{3.7.6}$$

where use has been made of the identity

$$\frac{\partial f_0}{\partial E} = \frac{-f_0(1-f_0)}{kT}. \tag{3.7.7}$$

3.7.2 THE RATE OF ENTROPY PRODUCTION AND THE VARIATIONAL METHOD OF SOLVING THE BOLTZMANN EQUATION

The expression (3.7.6) for the collision term has been made the starting point for a number of investigations of the properties of the solution of the Boltzmann equation. In particular Kohler (1941:2), using only the symmetry property of $V(n, \mathbf{k}; n', \mathbf{k}')$, showed that the solution must lead to expressions for the phenomenological coefficients $L_{ik}^{(n)}$ in equations (3.5.1) which satisfy the Onsager relations. Sondheimer (1956:4), using a similar approach, extended this proof to allow for the effect of the departure of the distribution functions from equilibrium, i.e. he considered the correct coupled equations. Kohler also established a variational theorem governing the solution of the Boltzmann equation. An account of this is given by Wilson (1953:2) and has been discussed more recently by Ziman (1956:3). Since the variational method is perhaps the most satisfactory way of dealing with the Boltzmann equation, apart, of course, from a direct solution, a brief account of it will be given here. For simplicity, we shall restrict ourselves to the case where there is no magnetic field present and refer the reader to the paper by Ziman for an account of the complications arising from the presence of a magnetic field.

We have seen (equation 3.6.17) that the rate of entropy production in the electron system is given by

$$s_e = -\frac{1}{4\pi^3} \sum_{n'} \int \frac{\partial f_0}{\partial E} \mathbf{v} \cdot \left(E \, \mathbf{grad} \, \frac{1}{T} - \mathbf{grad} \, \frac{\bar{\mu}}{T} \right) f_1 \, d\mathbf{k} \qquad (3.7.8)$$

and that the use of the Boltzmann equation allows this to be expressed in terms of $(\partial f/\partial t)_{\text{scatter}}$ in the form of equation (3.6.18). Using the form of $(\partial f/\partial t)_{\text{scatter}}$ given by equation (3.7.6), we obtain

$$s_e = -\frac{1}{4\pi^3 T} \sum_{n} \int f_1 \left(\frac{\partial f}{\partial t} \right)_{\text{scatter}} d\mathbf{k},$$

$$= -\frac{1}{(4\pi^3)^2 k T^2} \sum_{n} \sum_{n'} \int \int f_1 (f_1' - f_1) V(n, \mathbf{k}; n', \mathbf{k}') \, d\mathbf{k}' d\mathbf{k}. \qquad (3.7.9)$$

The symmetry of V with respect to primed and unprimed symbols and the fact that the double integrations and summations are taken over all quantum states, allows the interchange of primed and un-primed symbols in the integrand. By adding the two expressions, we find that

$$s_e = + \frac{1}{(4\pi^3)^2} \frac{1}{2kT^2} \sum_n \sum_{n'} \iint (f_1' - f_1)^2 V(n, \mathbf{k}; n', \mathbf{k}') \, d\mathbf{k}' d\mathbf{k} \quad (3.7.10)$$

which shows clearly that s_e is an essentially positive quantity, since the transition probabilities and other functions in equation (3.7.5) are positive so that V is positive. This result is to be expected in accordance with the phenomenological argument that the system is producing entropy in an attempt to reach equilibrium, where the entropy is, of course, a maximum.

Both expressions (3.7.10) and (3.7.8) can, in principle, be calculated if the function f_1 is known, since a knowledge of the function V is assumed. If f_1 is the correct solution of the Boltzmann equation, the two expressions must, of course, be equal to each other from the way in which they have been derived. It is, however, usually impossible to obtain a correct analytical solution of the Boltzmann equation.

It is in these circumstances that the variational theorem can be used. This theorem states that if we choose a function F which satisfies the condition that the two expressions for s_e, equations (3.7.8) and (3.7.10), calculated using F in place of f_1, are equal to each other, then the value of s_e so obtained is always less than, or equal to, the true value of s_e calculated using the correct solution f_1 of the Boltzmann equation. A proof of this theorem is given in Appendix 3. Physically, it corresponds to the fact that, in the presence of a given set of driving forces, the system is doing its utmost to oppose the effect of the driving forces and to get back to the equilibrium state by producing entropy at the maximum rate.

In the usual way of applying the variational method, physical arguments are used to make a guess at the general behaviour of the distribution function and the detailed quantitative behaviour is described in terms of parameters whose numerical values are adjusted on the basis of the variational theorem. It is reasonable to expect that the final results, for example, of the calculation of the transport coefficients, will be fairly close to the correct values. Since the mathematical techniques involved in this process are very much simpler than those required to obtain a solution of the Boltzmann equation, the variational method has been widely used in practice. To offset the gain in mathematical simplicity, there is, of course, the disadvantage that it is not generally possible to place any limits on the accuracy of the calculations.

3.7.3 The Relaxation Time Solution of the Boltzmann Equation

We have spent some time in discussing the principles of the variational method because, short of an accurate solution of the Boltzmann equation, it is probably the most satisfactory way of handling the problem of calculating the transport properties. It can be extended to include the effect of scattering by imperfections of various kinds in a straightforward way. It suffers, however, from the disadvantage that it does not usually give rise to general formulae, each situation being treated on its own.

An alternative approach, which has been used widely, allows an analytical solution of the Boltzmann equation to be obtained, and, thus leads to general formulae which give, for example, the temperature dependence of the transport properties. This approach is based on the same principles as the above but various assumptions are introduced in order to calculate the functional form of the transition probabilities.

A general discussion is complicated but the essential features are shown in considering the special case where the crystal has cubic symmetry and the band structure, for the particular band whose contribution to the transport properties is required, has the especially simple form given by equation (3.3.40) or (3.3.42), i.e. it is described by a single effective mass parameter. If the vibration spectrum of the solid is approximated by a Debye spectrum, the transition probabilities can be obtained by various other approximations. The form of $(\partial f / \partial t)_{\text{scatter}}$ can then be obtained by integration. Of the approximations, the most reliable one is probably the so-called *deformation potential method* introduced by Bardeen and Shockley (1950:3). The results lead to an expression for $(\partial f / \partial t)_{\text{scatter}}$, due to the effect of lattice vibrations, which has the form

$$\left(\frac{\partial f}{\partial t} \right)^{\text{phon}}_{\text{scatter}} = \frac{-(f - f_0)}{\tau} \tag{3.7.11}$$

where τ is the so-called *relaxation time*. In the theory, which is applicable to reasonably pure (non-degenerate) semiconductors, τ can be expressed in terms of fundamental parameters of the semiconductor, as

$$\tau = \frac{h^4}{8\pi^3}\left(\frac{\rho v_l^2}{kT}\right)\frac{1}{(2m_c)^{3/2}\Delta_1{}^2}(E-E_c)^{1/2} \qquad (3.7.12)$$

if equation (3.3.40) is applied. For equation (3.3.42), m_c is replaced by m_v and $(E-E_c)$ by (E_v-E). In the above equation ρ is the density, v_l is the velocity of longitudinal sound waves and Δ_1 is a parameter, called the deformation potential parameter, whose value can in principle be obtained from independent measurements. For a more detailed discussion of this procedure and of the complications that can arise in extending the treatment to more complicated band structures, the reader is referred to the review article by Blatt (1957:2) and to the paper by Herring and Vogt (1956:5).

For our present purposes it will be sufficient to deal with equation (3.7.12) in the form

$$\tau = \tau_0(E-E_c)^p \qquad (3.7.13)$$

where the index p has the value $-\frac{1}{2}$ for lattice scattering.

An approximate procedure applied to the other mechanism of scattering which is likely to be of importance in semiconductors, viz. scattering by charged impurity centres, also leads to an expression for $(\partial f/\partial t)^{\text{imp}}_{\text{scatter}}$ which has the same form as (3.7.11), with a value of τ given by

$$\tau_i = \tau_{i0}(E-E_c)^{3/2}. \qquad (3.7.14)$$

This is of the same form as equation (3.7.13) with $p = \frac{3}{2}$.

Although these expressions are often only approximate and apply strictly only to special cases, they do contain the essential features of the scattering processes. Since they lead to expressions for the transport properties in a comparatively simple form, they are widely used as an aid to interpreting the main features of these properties. The simplicity arises from the fact that use of equation (3.7.11), in the Boltzmann equation (3.6.14), gives a direct solution for the distribution function in the absence of a magnetic field. This solution is

$$f = f_0 + T\frac{\partial f_0}{\partial E}\tau\mathbf{v}\cdot\left[\mathbf{grad}\left(\frac{\bar{\mu}}{T}\right) - E\,\mathbf{grad}\left(\frac{1}{T}\right)\right] \qquad (3.7.15)$$

which we shall use later (Section 4.2) to obtain expressions for the transport properties.

3.8 FURTHER DISCUSSION OF THE BOLTZMANN EQUATION FOR PHONONS

The discussion of the scattering term in the Boltzmann equation for phonons, although following the same general lines as the corresponding term in the electron equation, is, unfortunately, more complicated. In our general discussion of phonons in Section 3.4 we pointed out that the so-called harmonic approximation, viz. that the forces acting on the atoms are linear functions of the displacements of the atoms from their mean positions, could never be completely accurate. Higher-order terms, although small, are always present and become more important as the amplitude of vibration of the atoms increases, i.e. as the temperature increases. The presence of such anharmonic terms gives rise to phonon scattering, and this must always occur to a greater or lesser extent in actual crystals.

Other processes which can give rise to phonon scattering may also be present in actual crystals, but they can, at least, in principle, be removed. Of greatest importance is the presence of imperfections of various kinds, either crystalline defects or foreign atoms. Another process which is important at low temperatures is associated with scattering at the surface of the solid. In solids which contain sufficient electrons, scattering of phonons by electrons, viz. the inverse of the process considered in the last section, has also to be taken into account.

3.8.1 PHONON–PHONON INTERACTIONS

The anharmonic terms, whose effect must always be considered, unfortunately require the most complicated analysis leading to mathematical equations which, because of their complexity, just cannot be solved accurately. It is in this sort of situation that the variational principle comes into its own and we shall indicate, in this section, how such a principle can be established.

It is first necessary to consider the description of the phonon-scattering processes. A useful classical way of looking at this, as in the corresponding electron case, is in terms of the interaction of waves. In the absence of any scattering processes (the ideal case which we considered in establishing the phonon concept), the lattice displacement waves do not interfere with each other and the amplitude of any one of them is constant with time. The anharmonic terms correspond to processes in which interference between two or more lattice waves can take place with a consequent change of amplitudes. In the simplest of such processes, two lattice waves with wave vectors $\mathbf{q}$ and $\mathbf{q}'$ interfere to give another wave with wave vector $\mathbf{q}''$. In the classical description of this process we would find that $\mathbf{q}''$ is either the sum or the difference of $\mathbf{q}$ and $\mathbf{q}'$ and that there is a relation between the wave amplitudes. In the quantum-mechanical description, the relation between the wave vectors still holds, but the amplitudes of the waves are quantized and the corresponding description is in terms of the change in the phonon occupation of the modes $\mathbf{q}$, $\mathbf{q}'$ and $\mathbf{q}''$.

Some general results of the quantum-mechanical treatment of phonon transition processes may be quoted here although no attempt will be made to derive them. In any process, the number of phonons in a mode can change only by ± 1. The probability of processes in which the number of phonons in a mode $(j, \mathbf{q})$ decreases by unity contains a factor $\mathcal{N}(j, \mathbf{q})$, i.e. it is proportional to the number of phonons in the mode *before* the process occurs. On the other hand, the probability of processes in which the number of phonons in $(j, \mathbf{q})$ changes from $\mathcal{N}$ to $(\mathcal{N}+1)$ contains a factor $(\mathcal{N}+1)$, i.e. it is proportional to the number of phonons in the state *after* the process occurs. These are standard results which arise from the quantum-mechanical treatment of the harmonic oscillator.

The result of the quantum-mechanical treatment, applied to the simplest type of anharmonic process, is to give a description in which phonons disappear from the states $(j, \mathbf{q})$, $(j', \mathbf{q}')$ and, simultaneously, a phonon appears in the state $(j'', \mathbf{q}'')$. This process may be described by saying that two phonons combine (or interfere) to produce a third phonon. It is governed by the so-called selection rules.

$$\hbar\omega'' = \hbar\omega + \hbar\omega', \qquad (3.8.1a)$$

$$\mathbf{q}'' = \mathbf{q} + \mathbf{q}' + 2\pi\boldsymbol{\tau}. \qquad (3.8.1b)$$

The first of these describes the conservation of energy for the process. The second is the equivalent of the condition that the wave vector of the produced wave is the sum of the wave vectors of the interfering waves. It is, however, modified by the fact that, for the waves in a crystal lattice, addition of a factor $2\pi\boldsymbol{\tau}$, where $\boldsymbol{\tau}$ is any vector of the reciprocal lattice, does not give a new wave as it would if the waves were propagating through a continuum. In the case of a lattice, such a wave is equivalent in all its physical contents to the original one.

This is the basis which allows us to describe all the normal modes of the lattice in terms of wave vectors lying within the first Brillouin zone. If we wish to retain this description which, although not essential, is extremely desirable for mathematical purposes, we have to re-interpret the situation in which $(\mathbf{q} + \mathbf{q}')$ lies outside the Brillouin zone in terms of a wave vector $\mathbf{q}''$ lying inside this zone. This wave vector is given by equation (3.8.1b), where the reciprocal lattice vector $\boldsymbol{\tau}$ is defined uniquely by the fact that all three wave vectors lie within the first Brillouin zone. It is possible, of course, for $\boldsymbol{\tau}$ to be zero, and this will generally be the case when either $\mathbf{q}$, or $\mathbf{q}'$, or both, are small.

From the discussion above, the rate at which processes governed by the rules (3.8.1) occur has the general form

$$\mathcal{N}\mathcal{N}'(\mathcal{N}'' + 1)M(\mathbf{q}, \mathbf{q}'; \mathbf{q}'') \qquad (3.8.2)$$

where, for simplicity in notation, the branch parameters j, j' and j'' will be assumed from now on to be included in the corresponding wave vectors. The intrinsic transition probability $M(\mathbf{q}, \mathbf{q}'; \mathbf{q}'')$ is zero unless the relations (3.8.1) are satisfied between the states $\mathbf{q}$, $\mathbf{q}'$ and $\mathbf{q}''$.

The reverse of the above process must always be physically possible. This can be described as the splitting of a phonon $\mathbf{q}''$ into two phonons $\mathbf{q}$ and $\mathbf{q}'$. The rate at which this occurs has the form

$$(\mathcal{N} + 1)(\mathcal{N}' + 1)\mathcal{N}''M(\mathbf{q}''; \mathbf{q}, \mathbf{q}') \qquad (3.8.3)$$

where $M(\mathbf{q}''; \mathbf{q}, \mathbf{q}')$ is again zero unless the relations (3.8.1) are satisfied.

In thermal equilibrium, by the principle of detailed balancing, the processes (3.8.2) and (3.8.3) must be proceeding at the same rate. This rate is

$$\begin{aligned} U(\mathbf{q}, \mathbf{q}'; \mathbf{q}'') &= \mathcal{N}_0\mathcal{N}_0'(\mathcal{N}_0'' + 1)M(\mathbf{q}, \mathbf{q}'; \mathbf{q}'') \\ &= (\mathcal{N}_0 + 1)(\mathcal{N}_0' + 1)\mathcal{N}_0''M(\mathbf{q}''; \mathbf{q}, \mathbf{q}'). \qquad (3.8.4) \end{aligned}$$

The function $U(\mathbf{q}, \mathbf{q}'; \mathbf{q}'')$ represents the rate at which phonons are entering and leaving the state $\mathbf{q}$ in thermal equilibrium, as a result of interactions involving the states $\mathbf{q}$, $\mathbf{q}'$ and $\mathbf{q}''$ which are related by the selection rules (3.8.1). Since these processes possess the property that every time a phonon leaves $\mathbf{q}$ one also leaves $\mathbf{q}'$ and that every time a phonon enters $\mathbf{q}$ one also enters $\mathbf{q}'$, it is clear that $U(\mathbf{q}, \mathbf{q}'; \mathbf{q}'')$ is also the rate at which phonons are entering and leaving the state $\mathbf{q}'$ in thermal equilibrium, due to the same processes. In other words, the processes are symmetrical in $\mathbf{q}$ and $\mathbf{q}'$ and whatever the form of the function U it must also possess this symmetry, i.e. that interchanging $\mathbf{q}$ and $\mathbf{q}'$ leaves its value unaltered. In mathematical terms

$$U(\mathbf{q}, \mathbf{q}'; \mathbf{q}'') = U(\mathbf{q}', \mathbf{q}; \mathbf{q}''). \qquad (3.8.5)$$

We can now obtain the formal expression for the rate of change of the phonon population of the state $(j, \mathbf{q})$ due to processes of the above type. This contains four terms:

(a) A term of the form of equation (3.8.3) with a positive sign, integrated over all $\mathbf{q}'$ and $\mathbf{q}''$ and summed over branches (remembering that the function M is zero unless equations (3.8.1) are satisfied). This represents the rate at which phonons are entering $\mathbf{q}$ due to a splitting of phonons in $\mathbf{q}''$.

(b) A term of the form of equation (3.8.2), integrated over $\mathbf{q}'$ and $\mathbf{q}''$ with a negative sign giving the rate at which phonons are leaving $\mathbf{q}$ due to the process inverse to (a), viz. combination of $\mathbf{q}$ and $\mathbf{q}'$.

(c) A term with a positive sign giving the effect of processes in which phonons in $\mathbf{q}'$ and $\mathbf{q}''$ combine to give $\mathbf{q}$. This is of the same form as equation (3.8.2) with a rearrangement of variables, viz.

$$\mathcal{N}'\mathcal{N}''(\mathcal{N}+1)M(\mathbf{q}', \mathbf{q}''; \mathbf{q}). \qquad (3.8.6)$$

(In this expression M is zero unless $\mathbf{q} = \mathbf{q}'+\mathbf{q}''$ and $\omega = \omega'+\omega''$.) Integrating this over all $\mathbf{q}'$ and $\mathbf{q}''$ counts each process twice, so that the resultant integral has to be divided by 2.

(d) A term with a negative sign, which is the inverse to (c) in which a phonon in $\mathbf{q}$ splits to give phonons in $\mathbf{q}'$ and $\mathbf{q}''$. This is of the form (cf. equation 3.8.3)

$$\mathcal{N}(\mathcal{N}'+1)(\mathcal{N}''+1)M(\mathbf{q}; \mathbf{q}', \mathbf{q}''). \qquad (3.8.7)$$

When these expressions are written down, they can be simplified by using the expression (cf. equation 3.6.24).

$$\mathcal{N} = \mathcal{N}_0 - \mathcal{N}_1 \frac{\partial \mathcal{N}_0}{\partial(\hbar\omega)} \qquad (3.8.8)$$

and the identity

$$\frac{\partial \mathcal{N}_0}{\partial(\hbar\omega)} = -\frac{1}{kT}\mathcal{N}_0(1+\mathcal{N}_0). \qquad (3.8.9)$$

Use of equation (3.8.4) for the function U then leads to

$$\left(\frac{\partial \mathcal{N}}{\partial t}\right)^{\text{phon}}_{\text{scatter}} = \frac{1}{(8\pi^3)^2 kT} \int\int (\mathcal{N}_1'' - \mathcal{N}_1' - \mathcal{N}_1) U(\mathbf{q}, \mathbf{q}'; \mathbf{q}'') \, d\mathbf{q}'d\mathbf{q}'' +$$

$$+ \frac{1}{(8\pi^3)^2} \frac{1}{2kT} \int\int (\mathcal{N}_1' + \mathcal{N}_1'' - \mathcal{N}_1) U(\mathbf{q}', \mathbf{q}''; \mathbf{q}) \, d\mathbf{q}'d\mathbf{q}'' \quad (3.8.10)$$

where we have omitted to indicate specifically the sum over branches. The factors $1/(8\pi^3)^2$ are included since $d\mathbf{q}', d\mathbf{q}''$ are regarded as volume elements in $\mathbf{q}$ space.

3.8.2 ENTROPY PRODUCTION AND THE VARIATIONAL PRINCIPLE FOR PHONON–PHONON INTERACTIONS

Referring back to equation (3.6.27), we can now obtain the contribution of the anharmonic process to the rate of entropy production in the phonon system. This involves multiplying equation (3.8.10) throughout by $\mathcal{N}_1$ and integrating over all $\mathbf{q}$. This gives integrals which are taken over all variables $\mathbf{q}$, $\mathbf{q}'$ and $\mathbf{q}''$ equally so that the variables can be rearranged. In particular, the second part of equation (3.8.10) gives rise to a term which can be rearranged to give (ignoring the non-essential features)

$$\iiint \mathcal{N}_1''(\mathcal{N}_1 + \mathcal{N}_1' - \mathcal{N}_1'') U(\mathbf{q}, \mathbf{q}'; \mathbf{q}'') \, d\mathbf{q}d\mathbf{q}'d\mathbf{q}''. \quad (3.8.11)$$

This may be combined with the first term and the expression for the contribution $s_p^{(\text{an})}$ to s_p is

$$s_p^{(\text{an})} = -\frac{1}{(8\pi^3)^3 kT^2} \int\int\int (\mathcal{N}_1'' - \mathcal{N}_1' - \mathcal{N}_1)\left(\mathcal{N}_1 - \frac{\mathcal{N}_1''}{2}\right) \times$$
$$\times U(\mathbf{q}, \mathbf{q}'; \mathbf{q}'') \, d\mathbf{q}d\mathbf{q}'d\mathbf{q}''. \quad (3.8.12)$$

The symmetry of the function U with respect to $\mathbf{q}$ and $\mathbf{q}'$ (equation 3.8.5) allows us to interchange primed and unprimed symbols in this expression. By adding the two expressions for $s_p^{(\text{an})}$ we then obtain

$$s_p^{(\text{an})} = +\frac{1}{(8\pi^3)^3 2kT^2} \int\int\int (\mathcal{N}_1'' - \mathcal{N}_1' - \mathcal{N}_1)^2 \times$$
$$\times U(\mathbf{q}, \mathbf{q}'; \mathbf{q}'') \, d\mathbf{q}d\mathbf{q}'d\mathbf{q}''. \quad (3.8.13)$$

This is analogous to equation (3.7.10) for the electron case and yields the expected result that the rate of entropy production by the scattering process must be positive, since the function U is essentially positive (or zero if $\mathbf{q}'' \neq \mathbf{q} + \mathbf{q}'$, $\omega'' \neq \omega + \omega'$).

The expression (3.6.26) for the entropy production in the phonon system becomes

$$s_p = \mathbf{w}_p \cdot \mathbf{grad} \frac{1}{T} = \frac{1}{8\pi^3} \int \hbar\omega \mathcal{N} \mathbf{v} \cdot \mathbf{grad} \frac{1}{T} \, d\mathbf{q}$$

$$= -\frac{1}{8\pi^3} \int \hbar\omega \mathcal{N}_1 \frac{\partial \mathcal{N}_0}{\partial(\hbar\omega)} \mathbf{v} \cdot \mathbf{grad} \frac{1}{T} \, d\mathbf{q} \qquad (3.8.14)$$

and, if the anharmonic processes are the only ones responsible for phonon scattering, the two expressions (3.8.13) and (3.8.14) must be equal to each other, being related by the Boltzmann equation.

The proof of the variational principle governing the above equations can be obtained using similar principles to those used in the electron case (Appendix 2). Restricting ourselves, for the present, to the case where the anharmonic terms are the only ones to be considered, the principle in its general form states that

$$s_{p,s}(R)s_p(\mathcal{N}_1) - s_{pf}{}^2(R) \geqslant 0. \qquad (3.8.15)$$

Here $s_{p,s}(R)$ (subscript s for scatter) is given by expression (3.8.13) calculated using a trial function R in place of $\mathcal{N}_1$ and $s_{p,f}(R)$ (subscript f for field) is given by expression (3.8.14) similarly calculated. Both expressions are, of course, equal if $\mathcal{N}_1$ the correct solution of the Boltzmann equation is used, i.e.

$$s_{p,s}(\mathcal{N}_1) = s_{p,f}(\mathcal{N}_1) \equiv s_p(\mathcal{N}_1). \qquad (3.8.16)$$

If the trial function R is adjusted so as to satisfy the same condition, i.e.

$$s_{p,s}(R) = s_{p,f}(R) \qquad (3.8.17)$$

then, from equation (3.8.15), both of these are less than the true value of s_p (since $s_{p,s}$ must be positive). Thus, the best trial function is obtained by maximizing $s_{p,s}(R)$ (or $s_{p,f}(R)$) subject to the above condition.

An alternative approach, which is simpler from a mathematical point of view is to use equation (3.8.15) together with (3.8.16) in the form

$$s_{p,s}(R)/s_{pf}{}^2(R) \geqslant 1/s_p(\mathcal{N}_1) \equiv s_{p,s}(\mathcal{N}_1)/s_{p,f}{}^2(\mathcal{N}_1). \qquad (3.8.18)$$

This avoids the use of the subsidiary condition (3.8.17) and clearly implies choosing the trial function R so that the expression on the left-hand side is a minimum. From the very nature of the expressions, this minimum value cannot be negative.

3.8.3 NORMAL AND UMKLAPP PROCESSES

For the case where the lattice properties can be calculated without any reference to the electron system, the variational method leads directly to an estimate of the lattice thermal conductivity. The left-hand side of equation (3.8.18), when minimized, is the best estimate of $1/s_p$, the reciprocal of the entropy production and will always be greater than the true value of $1/s_p$. However, since

$$s_p = \mathbf{w}_p \cdot \mathbf{grad}\frac{1}{T} = T^2 \kappa_L \left(\mathbf{grad}\frac{1}{T}\right)^2 \qquad (3.8.19)$$

(where κ_L is assumed to be a scalar), we have directly an estimate of $1/\kappa_L$ which, in the circumstances, will always be greater than the true value.

This approach has been used by Ziman (1956:**3**) to demonstrate a particular property of the anharmonic processes which was first pointed out by Peierls. Going back to the selection rule (3.8.1b), let us consider those processes for which $\boldsymbol{\tau}$ is zero, i.e. when $\mathbf{q}, \mathbf{q}'$ and their sum all lie within the first Brillouin zone. For such processes, we can find, by direct inspection, the trial function

$$R = \mathbf{q} \cdot \boldsymbol{\lambda} \qquad (3.8.20)$$

where $\boldsymbol{\lambda}$ is a vector function proportional to $\mathbf{grad}(1/T)$ and is independent of the phonon state. For this trial function, the value of $s_{p,s}(R)$, calculated from equation (3.8.13), is zero since

$$R'' - R' - R = \boldsymbol{\lambda} \cdot (\mathbf{q}'' - \mathbf{q}' - \mathbf{q}) \qquad (3.8.21)$$

and, for the processes considered, this is zero from the selection rules. On the other hand, $s_{p,f}(R)$ is not, in general, zero so that, using equation (3.8.18) we have found a trial function which gives $1/s_p$ its minimum possible value, i.e. zero. This must therefore be the correct solution of the Boltzmann equation for the above type of scattering process and clearly gives a value of zero for $1/\kappa_L$, i.e. corresponds to infinite thermal conductivity.

This result gives rise to one of the main complications of the theory of lattice thermal conductivity, since it implies that the simplest type of phonon interactions arising from anharmonic terms do not influence the thermal conductivity directly. The processes of interaction in which the total wave vector is conserved ($\mathbf{q}'' = \mathbf{q}+\mathbf{q}'$) are called N-processes (*normal* processes). It is worth while giving an alternative discussion in physical terms of why such processes are associated with infinite thermal conductivity. If we look at equation (3.6.23) we can see that the expression for the flow of energy is zero if N_1 is symmetrical on inverting $\mathbf{q}$ through the origin. This is because the vibration spectrum is symmetrical and the velocity $\mathbf{v} = d\omega/d\mathbf{q}$ is, therefore, antisymmetrical. Conversely, $\mathbf{w}_p$ is non-zero if N_1 is not symmetrical. The same arguments apply to the sum of $\mathbf{q}$ values over the phonon distribution, viz.

$$\int N_1 \mathbf{q} \, d\mathbf{q}. \tag{3.8.22}$$

Thus, if a distribution is set up for which this sum is non-zero, by applying a temperature gradient and subsequently removing it, there will be an energy flow so long as the sum (3.8.22) is non-zero. However, this sum is unaltered by N-processes, from their definition, and, thus, energy will continue to flow even in the absence of a temperature gradient, if N-processes are the only ones governing the interaction between phonons. This corresponds to an infinite thermal conductivity.

This result concerning N-processes is the source of one of the chief difficulties in the theory of lattice thermal conduction. Although it is necessary to consider alternative processes in order to obtain a finite thermal conductivity, the N-processes would be expected to be the dominant type of phonon–phonon interaction, particularly at low temperatures where the phonons present in the solid are those corresponding to small values of $|\mathbf{q}|$, i.e. of long wavelength. They therefore have an effect on the lattice thermal conductivity which is indirect in the sense that they redistribute phonons among the different modes and these phonons are then scattered by other processes.

At sufficiently high temperatures phonons will be present in modes of larger $|\mathbf{q}|$ values and the possibility of processes in which the sum of the wave vectors of two interacting phonons lies outside the first

Brillouin zone will be increased. These processes are called *umklapp* processes (*U*-processes) and correspond to non-zero values of τ in the selection rule (3.8.1b). For such processes, the wave vector is not conserved and a finite thermal conductivity results. Clearly, the thermal conductivity associated with these processes decreases with increasing temperature since the probability of *U*-processes then increases.

It is to be expected that the two types, *N*- and *U*-processes, are the dominant ones associated with the effect of anharmonic forces. In principle, it is possible for higher-order effects to occur in which interaction takes place involving simultaneous changes of occupation of four-phonon modes. Although such mechanisms have been invoked from time to time in order to explain certain experimental measurements, the evidence that such processes are important is very dubious.

3.8.4 THE SCATTERING OF PHONONS BY POINT IMPERFECTIONS

Apart from the anharmonic effects, which must be present in any crystal, the most important effect on the lattice thermal conductivity is due to the presence of imperfections in most actual solids. The type of imperfection which gives rise to scattering can again be discussed on the basis of wave motion. In a continuous medium the propagation of a displacement wave is governed by a second-order differential equation which involves the elastic constants of the medium and its density. Any discontinuities in one or both of these properties gives rise to a scattering of the wave, with the formation of a scattered wave and modification of the amplitude of the incident wave. In a lattice the elastic constants are replaced by the interatomic forces and the density by the masses of the atoms. Any discontinuities in these will give rise to a situation in which the phonon population of a mode $(j, \mathbf{q})$ is altered with a simultaneous alteration in the phonon population of a mode $(j', \mathbf{q}')$.

Thus, phonon scattering will occur as a result of any type of imperfection which modifies the local interatomic forces or the local mass of atoms. One or both of these properties is possessed by practically every type of imperfection.

Among the numerous types of imperfection, one stands out because of its comparative simplicity. This is associated with the presence of naturally occurring isotopes in many chemical species. In crystals containing such species, different isotopes possess different atomic masses so that there are local fluctuations in the density of the medium which can give rise to phonon scattering. The simplicity of this type of imperfection is that the local interatomic forces are not altered by its presence.

Other types of point imperfection usually affect both the local density and interatomic forces. These include atoms of a different chemical species from those of the parent crystal. They may lie either on substitutional or interstitial sites of the parent lattice. Crystalline defects such as vacant lattice sites are also included in this category. More extended defects may also be responsible for phonon scattering. Chief among these are the crystalline defects known as dislocations.

The general treatment of imperfections follows similar lines to those discussed previously for the anharmonic phonon terms and for electron scattering. The processes involve two phonon modes and, for a process in which a phonon disappears from $(j, \mathbf{q})$ and one appears in $(j', \mathbf{q}')$ the corresponding rate at which this occurs has the general form

$$\mathcal{N}(\mathcal{N}' + 1)M_i(\mathbf{q}, \mathbf{q}') \qquad (3.8.23)$$

where, as previously, we assume the branch parameters to be included. Taking the inverse process into account, we obtain for thermal equilibrium,

$$\begin{aligned}
U_i(\mathbf{q}, \mathbf{q}') &\equiv \mathcal{N}_0(\mathcal{N}_0' + 1)M_i(\mathbf{q}, \mathbf{q}') \\
&= (\mathcal{N}_0 + 1)\mathcal{N}_0' M_i(\mathbf{q}', \mathbf{q}) \equiv U_i(\mathbf{q}', \mathbf{q}). \qquad (3.8.24)
\end{aligned}$$

Proceeding on the same lines as previously, we find

$$\left(\frac{\partial \mathcal{N}}{\partial t}\right)^{\text{imp}}_{\text{scatter}} = \frac{1}{8\pi^3 kT} \int (\mathcal{N}_1' - \mathcal{N}_1) U_i(\mathbf{q}, \mathbf{q}') \, \mathrm{d}\mathbf{q}' \qquad (3.8.25)$$

which is similar in form to the corresponding electron equation (3.7.6).

Taking into account the anharmonic terms which must also be present, it is a simple matter to show that the rate of entropy production due to the combined scattering processes is

$$s_{p,s}(\mathcal{N}_1) = s_{p,s}^{(\text{an})}(\mathcal{N}_1) + s_{p,s}^{(\text{imp})}(\mathcal{N}_1) \qquad (3.8.26)$$

where $s_{p,s}^{(\text{an})}$ is given by equation (3.8.13) and

$$s_{p,s}^{(\text{imp})}(N_1) = \frac{1}{(8\pi^3 2 kT^2)} \int\int (\mathcal{N}_1' - \mathcal{N}_1)^2 U_i(\mathbf{q}, \mathbf{q}') \, \mathrm{d}\mathbf{q}\mathrm{d}\mathbf{q}'. \qquad (3.8.27)$$

The expression (3.8.26) must be equal to the alternative expression $s_{p,f}(\mathcal{N}_1)$ given by equation (3.8.14), where $\mathcal{N}_1$ is the true solution of the Boltzmann equation. The variational principle is not affected by the presence of two terms in $s_{p,s}$ since both of these possess the basic requirements for the principle to hold of being positive and symmetrical in $\mathbf{q}$ and $\mathbf{q}'$. Equation (3.8.18) then takes the form

$$\frac{1}{s_{p,f}{}^2(R)}[s_{p,s}{}^{(\mathrm{an})}(R) + s_{p,s}{}^{(\mathrm{imp})}(R)]$$

$$> \frac{1}{s_{p,f}{}^2(\mathcal{N}_1)}[s_{p,s}{}^{(\mathrm{an})}(\mathcal{N}_1) + s_{p,s}{}^{(\mathrm{imp})}(\mathcal{N}_1)]$$

$$\equiv \frac{1}{s_p(\mathcal{N}_1)} \equiv \frac{1}{\kappa_L T^2 [\mathbf{grad}(1/T)]^2} \qquad (3.8.28)$$

for a trial function R. Thus, the first term in this expression always leads to an upper estimate of $1/\kappa_L$ and the best trial function is obtained by minimizing the expression.

This approach to the problem of obtaining the thermal conductivity has been used by Ziman (1956:**3**) to discuss the extra thermal resistance due to imperfections. For this case, the effect of the imperfections on the phonon distribution is small compared with the anharmonic processes, provided that the concentration is sufficiently small. For low temperatures, we know that, in the limit of zero imperfection concentration, the anharmonic terms produce a distribution of the form of equation (3.8.20), since we showed that this led to the extreme value of zero for $1/\kappa_L$. Thus, for small concentrations of imperfections, at temperatures low enough for U-processes to be unimportant, it is reasonable to expect that the same function can be used to estimate the effect of imperfection scattering. Accordingly, in the expression (3.8.28), the trial function $R = \boldsymbol{\lambda} \cdot \mathbf{q}$ can be used. This, of course, gives zero for $s_{p,s}{}^{(\mathrm{an})}(R)$ and the value of $s_{p,s}{}^{(\mathrm{imp})}(R)$ leads directly to an estimate of $1/\kappa_L$ associated with imperfections.

8

Chapter 4

THE ELECTRONIC PART OF THE THERMAL CONDUCTIVITY IN SEMICONDUCTORS

OUR object in this chapter is to discuss the main features of the contribution of the free charge carriers in semiconductors to the transport properties and, in particular, to the thermal conductivity. We shall also compare the theoretical results with the available experimental evidence. It will be evident from the previous chapter that a completely rigorous theoretical discussion would be very complicated. For the purposes of a general survey, the only simplification of any value is that based on the relaxation time approximation discussed in Section 3.7.3, with the use of the associated simplified form of band structure. This allows general formulae to be obtained, for the main transport properties, which certainly show the main features of these properties, although it would be dangerous to rely too heavily on the quantitative predictions. Since, however, in many semiconductors, the parameters which are required for more detailed calculations are not known, such formulae remain the best available.

The electronic thermal conductivity considered by itself does not provide much useful information. It is necessary to relate it to the other main transport properties, particularly the electrical conductivity. Taking the various situations that can occur in semiconductors in increasing order of complexity, we shall first consider the predictions of the simple model for the case where there is no magnetic field. We also suppose that only one band of the semiconductor is making an effective contribution to the transport processes (Section 4.1); this is the case for all semiconductors at sufficiently low temperatures and corresponds to extrinsic conduction. At sufficiently high temperatures, the semiconductor becomes intrinsic and both the conduction and the valence bands make comparable contributions. This leads to a marked effect on the electronic component of the thermal conductivity which is discussed in Section 4.2. In Section 4.3, we give an outline of the experimental results for semiconductors having an appreciable electronic thermal conductivity. Then, in Section 4.4, we discuss briefly the effect of a magnetic field with particular reference to its application in the separation of the lattice and electronic components of the thermal conductivity.

4.1 THE ELECTRONIC COMPONENT OF THE THERMAL CONDUCTIVITY FOR AN EXTRINSIC SEMICONDUCTOR

In this section, we shall obtain the formulae for the transport properties for a semiconductor in which the only contributions come from a single band which is defined in terms of a single effective mass. We assume that the scattering processes can be defined in terms of a relaxation time. The relation between the energy and wave vector will be taken as

$$E(\mathbf{k}) = E_c + \frac{\hbar^2 k^2}{2m_c} \qquad (4.1.1)$$

corresponding to the simplest model for the conduction band whose minimum energy is E_c. The relaxation time τ will be taken to have the form

$$\tau = \tau_0 (E - E_c)^p \qquad (4.1.2)$$

where we have seen in Section 3.7 that for lattice scattering $p = -\frac{1}{2}$ and $\tau_0 \propto 1/T$, while for ionized-impurity scattering $p = \frac{3}{2}$ and τ_0 does not depend on T explicitly.

The formulae for the transport coefficients $L_{ik}^{(n)}$ of equation (3.5.1), subject to the above assumptions, can be obtained directly from the results of Section 3.7. The solution of the Boltzmann equation in the absence of a magnetic field is (cf. equation 3.7.15)

$$f = f_0 + T \frac{\partial f_0}{\partial E} \tau \, \mathbf{v} \cdot \left[\mathbf{grad} \left(\frac{\bar{\mu}}{T} \right) - E \, \mathbf{grad} \left(\frac{1}{T} \right) \right]. \qquad (4.1.3)$$

The components of the flows of charge and energy in the electron system are, therefore, given by

$$-j_i = -\frac{1}{4\pi^3} \int v_i f \, d\mathbf{k}$$

$$= -\frac{T}{4\pi^3} \sum_{j=1}^{3} \left\{ \int \tau v_i v_j \frac{\partial f_0}{\partial E} \, d\mathbf{k} \right\} \frac{\partial}{\partial x_j}\left(\frac{\mu}{T}\right) +$$

$$+ \frac{T}{4\pi^3} \sum_{j} \left\{ \int E\tau v_i v_j \frac{\partial f_0}{\partial E} \, d\mathbf{k} \right\} \frac{\partial}{\partial x_j}\left(\frac{1}{T}\right), \quad (4.1.4a)$$

and

$$(w_e)_i = \frac{1}{4\pi^3} \int E v_i f \, d\mathbf{k}$$

$$= \frac{T}{4\pi^3} \sum_{j} \left\{ \int E\tau v_i v_j \frac{\partial f_0}{\partial E} \, d\mathbf{k} \right\} \frac{\partial}{\partial x_j}\left(\frac{\mu}{T}\right) -$$

$$- \frac{T}{4\pi^3} \sum_{j} \left\{ \int E^2 \tau v_i v_j \frac{\partial f_0}{\partial E} \, d\mathbf{k} \right\} \frac{\partial}{\partial x_j}\left(\frac{1}{T}\right). \quad (4.1.4b)$$

These equations are in a form which is directly comparable with that of equations (3.5.1), and the phenomenological coefficients $L_{ik}^{(n)}$ can all be expressed in terms of integrals of the form

$$I_{ij}^{(s)} = \frac{T}{4\pi^3} \int E^s \tau v_i v_j \frac{\partial f_0}{\partial E} \, d\mathbf{k}. \quad (4.1.5)$$

Thus,

$$L_{ij}^{(1)} = -I_{ij}^{(0)}, \qquad L_{ij}^{(2)} = L_{ij}^{(3)} = I_{ij}^{(1)}, \qquad L_{ij}^{(4)} = -I_{ij}^{(2)}. \quad (4.1.6)$$

The evaluation of the integrals $I^{(s)}$ is straightforward. Since

$$v_i = \frac{1}{\hbar}\frac{\partial E}{\partial k_i} = \frac{\hbar k_i}{m_c}$$

from equation (4.1.1), and since E and, therefore, τ depend only on the modulus k of $\mathbf{k}$, the obvious way of proceeding is to transform to spherical polar co-ordinates in space by writing

$$k_1 = k \sin\theta \cos\phi, \qquad k_2 = k \sin\theta \sin\phi,$$
$$k_3 = k \cos\theta, \qquad d\mathbf{k} = k^2 \sin\theta \, dk d\theta d\phi. \quad (4.1.7)$$

The integration over the angular co-ordinates to obtain $I^{(s)}$ involves only the part $v_i v_j$. The integral is zero unless $i = j$ where it becomes $4\pi/3$ independently of i. Thus, as expected on physical grounds, since we have taken conditions appropriate to an isotropic solid, the tensors $L^{(n)}$ reduce to scalars, with the diagonal components all equal and the non-diagonal components zero.

The remaining integration over the modulus k of $\mathbf{k}$ can be changed to an integral over the variable

$$\epsilon = (E - E_c) = \frac{\hbar^2 k^2}{2 m_c} \tag{4.1.8}$$

i.e. to the energy relative to the band edge. It is then found that

$$I_{ii}{}^{(s)} = \frac{1}{m_c} \left(\frac{2 m_c}{\hbar^2} \right)^{3/2} \frac{T}{3\pi^2} \tau_0 \int_0^\infty (E_c + \epsilon)^s \epsilon^{(p+3/2)} \frac{\partial f_0}{\partial \epsilon} \, d\epsilon. \tag{4.1.9}$$

These integrals reduce to the consideration of the integrals

$$K_s = -\frac{1}{m_c} \left(\frac{2 m_c}{\hbar^2} \right)^{3/2} \frac{T}{3\pi^2} \tau_0 \int \epsilon^s \epsilon^{(p+3/2)} \frac{\partial f_0}{\partial \epsilon} \, d\epsilon \tag{4.1.10}$$

obtained by expanding the factor $(E_c + \epsilon)^s$ in equation (4.1.9) and in which a minus sign is introduced for simplicity in subsequent discussion, since the factor $\partial f_0 / \partial \epsilon$ is essentially negative. This factor falls off very rapidly as ϵ increases and the upper limit of the integral may be taken as infinity for all practical purposes. An integration by parts then gives

$$\int_0^\infty \epsilon^{(s+p+3/2)} \frac{\partial f_0}{\partial \epsilon} \, d\epsilon = -(s+p+\tfrac{3}{2}) \int_0^\infty \epsilon^{(s+p+1/2)} f_0 \, d\epsilon. \tag{4.1.11}$$

Changing the variable from ϵ to the dimensionless variable x equal to ϵ/kT and introducing the dimensionless parameter

$$\eta = \left(\frac{\bar{\mu} - E_c}{kT} \right), \tag{4.1.12}$$

we have

$$f_0 = [\exp(x - \eta) + 1]^{-1}.$$

The integral in equation (4.1.11) is

$$-(s+p+\tfrac{3}{2})(kT)^{(s+p+3/2)} F_{(s+p+1/2)}(\eta) \tag{4.1.13}$$

where

$$F_r(\eta) = \int_0^\infty \frac{x^r}{1+e^{x-\eta}}\,\mathrm{d}x \qquad (4.1.14)$$

is the so-called *Fermi–Dirac integral* of order r.

Thus, collecting all the results together, we obtain

$$\begin{aligned}
L_{ii}^{(1)} &= K_0, \\
L_{ii}^{(2)} &= L_{ii}^{(3)} = -(E_c K_0 + K_1), \\
L_{ii}^{(4)} &= E_c^2 K_0 + 2E_c K_1 + K_2,
\end{aligned} \qquad (4.1.15)$$

where

$$K_s = \frac{\tau_0}{m_c}\frac{T}{3\pi^2}\left(\frac{2m_c kT}{\hbar^2}\right)^{3/2}(s+p+\tfrac{3}{2})(kT)^{(s+p)}F_{(s+p+1/2)}(\eta). \quad (4.1.16)$$

The final task is to relate the $L^{(n)}$ coefficients to the transport parameters as normally measured, viz. the electrical conductivity σ, the Seebeck coefficient Q, the Peltier coefficient π, and the electronic thermal conductivity κ_e. In the simple case considered here, all these quantities are scalars and, from equations (3.5.12),

$$\sigma = \frac{e^2}{T}L_{ii}^{(1)} = \frac{e^2}{T}K_0, \qquad (4.1.17a)$$

$$\begin{aligned}
Q &= \frac{\bar\mu}{eT} + \frac{1}{eT}\frac{L_{ii}^{(2)}}{L_{ii}^{(1)}} = \frac{1}{eT}\left[\bar\mu - \frac{(E_c K_0 + K_1)}{K_0}\right] \\
&= \frac{k}{e}\left[\eta - \frac{K_1}{kT K_0}\right],
\end{aligned} \qquad (4.1.17b)$$

$$\pi = TQ, \qquad (4.1.17c)$$

$$\begin{aligned}
\kappa_e &= \frac{1}{T^2}L_{ii}^{(4)} - \frac{1}{T}\sigma\left(\pi - \frac{\bar\mu}{e}\right)^2 \\
&= \frac{K_0}{T^2}\left(\frac{K_2 K_0 - K_1^2}{K_0^2}\right).
\end{aligned} \qquad (4.1.17d)$$

The second and fourth of these expressions have been put into forms which involve the ratios of K_1/K_0 and K_2/K_0 since it is clear from equation (4.1.16) that these ratios are very much simpler than the integrals themselves. Thus, for example,

$$\frac{K_1}{K_0} = kT\frac{(p+\tfrac{5}{2})F_{(p+3/2)}(\eta)}{(p+\tfrac{3}{2})F_{(p+1/2)}(\eta)}. \tag{4.1.18}$$

Using the similar expression for K_2/K_0 we obtain

$$\frac{\kappa_e}{\sigma T} = \frac{k^2}{e^2}\left\{\frac{(p+\tfrac{7}{2})(p+\tfrac{3}{2})F_{(p+5/2)}F_{(p+1/2)}-(p+\tfrac{5}{2})^2F^2_{(p+3/2)}}{(p+\tfrac{3}{2})^2F^2_{(p+1/2)}}\right\}. \tag{4.1.19}$$

The ratio on the right-hand side of this equation is a numerical parameter whose value depends on p and η. This parameter is called the *Lorenz number* and will be denoted by the symbol L.

A second physically measurable quantity, which depends on the same parameters p and η is given directly by the Seebeck coefficient Q. From equation (4.1.17b) we have

$$Q = \frac{k}{e}\left\{\eta - \frac{(p+\tfrac{5}{2})F_{(p+3/2)}(\eta)}{(p+\tfrac{3}{2})F_{(p+1/2)}(\eta)}\right\} \tag{4.1.20}$$

A discussion of the Fermi–Dirac integrals $F_r(\eta)$ is given in Appendix 4. In general, they have to be obtained numerically but there are two limiting cases where they can be expressed in simplified form. The first of these occurs when η is large and negative, i.e. when the Fermi level is well below the minimum energy of the conduction band. Then, in the expression (4.1.14), the factor $[1+\exp(x-\eta)]^{-1}$ can be replaced, without appreciable loss of accuracy, by $\exp(\eta-x)$. This corresponds to the assumption of a Maxwell–Boltzmann distribution function f_0 equal to $\exp(\eta)\exp(-E/kT)$ for the equilibrium distribution function. This approximation is said to refer to a *non-degenerate* system of electrons and leads to the result

$$F_r(\eta) = \exp(\eta)\int_0^\infty x^n \exp(-x)\,dx = \exp(\eta)\Gamma(r+1) \tag{4.1.21}$$

where $\Gamma(r)$ is the gamma function of r. This function possesses the property

$$\Gamma(r+1) = r\,\Gamma(r). \tag{4.1.22}$$

Clearly $\Gamma(1) = 1$, so, when r is an integer, $\Gamma(r+1) = r!$. Another useful value is

$$\Gamma(\tfrac{1}{2}) = (\pi)^{1/2} \tag{4.1.23}$$

which, in conjunction with equation (4.1.22) leads directly to values of $\Gamma(r)$ when r is a half-integer.

In practice, the approximation (4.1.21) is very accurate when $\eta < -4$ and is 95 per cent accurate when $\eta = -2$. When this approximation holds, the expressions (4.1.19) and (4.1.20) simplify to

$$\frac{\kappa_e}{\sigma T} = L = \frac{k^2}{e^2}(p + \tfrac{5}{2}) \qquad (4.1.24)$$

and

$$Q = \frac{k}{e}[\eta - (p + \tfrac{5}{2})]. \qquad (4.1.25)$$

It is useful to remember, in conjunction with these formulae, the numerical value of k/e which is 86·4 μV/°K. The sign of the Seebeck coefficient is, of course, negative, in accordance with the convention implicit in the original definition of Q.

Equation (4.1.24) for the electronic thermal conductivity is of limited interest in practice since, when η is large and negative, the probability of occupation of the states in the conduction band is low, so that the total density of carriers is low. Thus, the electrical conductivity σ is small and in general κ_e is small. The actual value of κ_e depends on the mobility μ of the charge carriers as well as on their number. For most of the semiconductors which have been investigated, the value of κ_e under non-degenerate conditions turns out to be only a negligible fraction of the lattice component of the thermal conductivity κ_L.

The second limiting case, that of complete degeneracy, occurs when η is large and positive. Under this condition, corresponding to the Fermi level being well above the minimum energy of the band, the Fermi–Dirac function can be expressed in a series of descending powers of η in the form

$$F_r(\eta) = \frac{\eta^{r+1}}{(r+1)} + r\eta^{r-1}\frac{\pi^2}{6} + r(r-1)(r-2)\eta^{r-3}\frac{7\pi^4}{360} + \ldots. \quad (4.1.26)$$

The terms of this series converge rapidly for large values of η. Use of this expression gives the dominant term in equation (4.1.19) as

$$\frac{\kappa_e}{\sigma T} = L = \frac{\pi^2}{3}\left(\frac{k}{e}\right)^2 \qquad (4.1.27)$$

which is a constant, independent of both p and η. The physical significance of this result is to be found in the form of the Fermi–Dirac function f_0 which is appreciably different from zero or unity only in a narrow range of energy around the Fermi level. By equation (3.3.21), the contribution to the entropy is zero for states where $f = 0$ or 1. Thus, it is only the states very close to the Fermi level which make an appreciable contribution to the transport properties and, to a good approximation, the energy dependence of the relaxation time can be ignored over this small interval.

For values of the Fermi level between the two extremes discussed above, the numerical value of the Lorenz number varies in a way which can be obtained from numerical values of the integrals in equation (4.1.19), which, of course, implies a knowledge of the parameters p and η. For semiconductors, the position of the Fermi level with respect to the conduction band in the extrinsic range is a complicated function of temperature and impurity concentration. As the position of the Fermi level varies, so also do the relative contributions of the various scattering processes. If the simple model, employed so far, is to be used at all realistically it is necessary to allow for the fact that the appropriate value of p may vary with η. Some guide to the way in which this occurs can be obtained from the behaviour of the Seebeck coefficient and also, if known, the temperature dependence of the mobility μ. This is defined by the equation

$$\sigma = ne\mu \qquad (4.1.28)$$

where n is the number of carriers taking part in the conduction process. For the simple model

$$n = \frac{1}{4\pi^3} \int f_0 \, d\mathbf{k} = \frac{1}{6\pi^2}\left(\frac{2m_c kT}{\hbar^2}\right)^{3/2} F_{1/2}(\eta). \qquad (4.1.29)$$

Thus, with σ given by equation (4.1.17a), we obtain

$$\mu = \frac{2e\tau_0}{m_c}(p + \tfrac{3}{2})(kT)^p \frac{F_{p+1/2}(\eta)}{F_{1/2}(\eta)} \qquad (4.1.30)$$

in which the dominant temperature dependence is given by the factor $(kT)^p$ and, of course, the temperature dependence of τ_0. For simple lattice scattering μ has a $T^{-3/2}$ dependence while for ionized-impurity scattering it has approximately a $T^{3/2}$ dependence.

The straightforward way of applying the above result to semiconductors, in practice, is to consider the variations of the total thermal conductivity of a particular semiconducting material as a function of its electrical conductivity. The electrical conductivity can be varied, at a particular temperature, by varying the impurity concentration of the semiconductor. On the basis of the preceding considerations we can write

$$\kappa = \kappa_L(T) + \kappa_e = \kappa_L(T) + L\sigma T. \qquad (4.1.31)$$

Thus, by measuring the electrical and thermal conductivities at a particular temperature, for specimens of different impurity content leading to different electrical conductivities, we can obtain some information about the unknown parameters in this equation. Some care is necessary, however, in the way in which this is done. In particular, the theory of the lattice component of the thermal conductivity developed in the next chapter shows that this is affected by the presence of impurities. It is affected also, in principle, by the presence of free charge carriers. Both these effects lead to the conclusion that the value of κ_L for high impurity concentrations (high σ values) should be less than for low concentrations, although, in the circumstances for which equation (4.1.31) has any useful application, the difference is likely to be small. For samples with low impurity concentrations (low σ values) the dominant scattering mechanism is that associated with the lattice vibrations and, on the theory discussed above, the corresponding value of L is $2k^2/e^2$. By extrapolating this part of the curve back to zero electrical conductivity the value of $\kappa_L(T)$ at the particular temperature can be obtained. The application of these ideas to specific cases is described in Section 4.3.

For many semiconductors, the above procedure to obtain the lattice thermal conductivity is unnecessary since they can be prepared in a sufficiently pure form for the second term in equation (4.1.31) to be completely negligible in comparison with the first, over a wide range of temperature. This is the case for semiconductors such as silicon and germanium and certain of the simpler compound semiconductors such as indium antimonide. There is, however, a class of semiconductors which has been studied particularly with reference to possible applications in thermoelectric cooling and generation. Semiconductors in this class have a very low value of the lattice thermal conductivity. Furthermore, they cannot usually be prepared in an electrically pure state, so that the electrical conductivity is high. For both these reasons, in such materials, the second term in equation (4.1.31) is comparable with the first and the procedure outlined above is the most direct one for separating out the two contributions to the thermal conductivity.

The foregoing discussion has been restricted to the case where the only band contributing to the transport properties is the conduction band of the semiconductor with the simple form given by equation (4.1.1). More elaborate band structures are known to exist in practice and one type, in particular, may be mentioned here. This is the so-called *many-valley* band structure in which the conduction band has a number of equivalent minima situated at points in **k** space which are related to each other through the crystal symmetry. The simple example considered previously is a particular case of this more general situation. Around each minimum energy position, the energy may still be expressed as a quadratic function of the wave vector but, instead of the surfaces of constant energy being spheres, they become ellipsoids. The treatment given above has to be modified to take this feature into account. In particular, the single relaxation time used in the theory, has to be extended and different relaxation times may apply for different crystallographic directions. The formulae for such cases become very complicated. In one simple case however equations (4.1.19) and (4.1.20) are unaltered. This occurs when the various relaxation times all have the same energy dependence. This is likely to be the case when the dominant scattering mechanism is associated with the lattice vibrations but almost certainly fails for other mechanisms, particularly for ionized-impurity scattering. For further discussion of this problem the reader is referred to the paper by Herring and Vogt (1956:5).

Finally, we may indicate the corresponding results for an extrinsic *p*-type semiconductor, i.e. where the band contributing to the transport properties is the valence band. In this case, as is well known, in contrast to the above approach, attention is focused on the relatively few unoccupied quantum states whose energies lie close to the maximum energy of the band. This is permissible because of the symmetry of the expression for the entropy of a system of particles obeying Fermi–Dirac statistics in f and $(1-f)$. The transport properties are associated with the production of entropy and, if $f = 1$ for all states, the entropy is zero, just as it is for an empty band in which $f = 0$ for all states. Thus, for a nearly full band, the entropy production in the presence of external fields is associated with those relatively few states for which $(1-f)$ is appreciably different from zero. Most of the states, for which $f = 1$, make no contribution.

The valence band is assumed to have the simple form

$$E = E_v - \frac{\hbar^2 k^2}{2m_v} = E_v - \epsilon' \tag{4.1.32}$$

where E_v is the maximum energy of the valence band. Thus, using the distribution function for the vacant levels $g = (1-f)$, we write

$$g = g_0 + g_1 \tag{4.1.33}$$

where

$$g_0 = 1 - f_0 = \cfrac{1}{1 + \exp\left(\cfrac{\bar{\mu} - E}{kT}\right)} = \cfrac{1}{1 + \exp\left(\cfrac{\epsilon'}{kT} - \theta\right)} \tag{4.1.34}$$

with

$$\theta = \left(\frac{E_v - \bar{\mu}}{kT}\right).$$

We can set up a Boltzmann equation for g and it is well known that we can calculate the transport properties of the band as though the vacant levels were occupied by positively charged particles called positive holes, the contribution of the other levels being neglected. The corresponding Boltzmann equation for holes is thus of a similar form to that for electrons except that $-e$ is replaced by e. If the scattering term is expressed in terms of a "hole" relaxation time and this is taken to have the form

$$\tau' = \tau_0' \epsilon'^{p'}, \tag{4.1.35}$$

then the Boltzmann equation can be solved and the flow of holes and energy can be obtained by integrating over ϵ'. The integrals can all be expressed in terms of integrals K_s' defined as ($c f$ equation 4.1.16)

$$K_s' = \frac{\tau_0'}{m_v} \frac{T}{3\pi^2} \left(\frac{2m_v kT}{\hbar^2}\right)^{3/2} (s + p' + \tfrac{3}{2})(kT)^{s+p'} F_{s+p'+1/2}(\theta). \tag{4.1.36}$$

Thus, the transport properties σ, Q, π and κ_e are given by equations of the form (4.1.17) with the appropriate K_s' replacing K_s and with the sign of e changed wherever it occurs. We eventually obtain

$$\sigma_v = \frac{e^2}{T} K_0'(\theta), \tag{4.1.37a}$$

$$Q_v = \frac{k}{e}\left\{-\theta + \frac{(p' + \tfrac{5}{2}) F_{(p'+3/2)}}{(p' + \tfrac{3}{2}) F_{(p'+1/2)}}\right\}, \tag{4.1.37b}$$

$$\left(\frac{\kappa_e}{\sigma T}\right)_v = L_v$$
$$= \frac{k^2}{e^2}\left\{\frac{(p' + \tfrac{7}{2})(p' + \tfrac{3}{2}) F_{(p'+5/2)} F_{(p'+1/2)} - (p' + \tfrac{5}{2})^2 F^2_{(p'+3/2)}}{(p' + \tfrac{3}{2})^2 F^2_{(p'+1/2)}}\right\}. \tag{4.1.37c}$$

in which the subscript v is used to indicate the association with the valence band and all the Fermi–Dirac functions are functions of the argument θ. As previously, these formulae become simpler when θ is large and negative, which physically corresponds to the Fermi level $\bar{\mu}$ being well above the maximum energy E_v of the valence band. The main difference between this and the case for the conduction band is that the Seebeck coefficient is positive whereas previously it was negative. There is no change of sign of the first and third of the above expressions, for σ and L respectively.

4.2 TRANSPORT PROCESSES IN AN INTRINSIC SEMICONDUCTOR

The formulae of the preceding section apply when only one band is making an effective contribution to the transport properties. As we have seen, this implies that the Fermi level $\bar{\mu}$ is much closer to one band than to any other, so that the distribution function f is either zero or unity except over part of this one band. Since this function changes from zero to unity over an energy interval governed by the value of kT, it follows in general that, at sufficiently high temperatures, more than one band will contribute to the transport properties. A typical semiconductor is extrinsic at low temperatures, with only either the conduction or valence band making a contribution, but, as the temperature is raised to some value which is determined primarily by the separation in energy of the two bands, the other band starts to make an effective contribution.

It is a very simple matter to obtain the formulae for the transport properties in this situation. The basic principle is that the vector flows of charge and of energy in the two bands are additive to give the total flow of charge and energy. Thus, if we take the phenomenological equations in the form given by expressions (3.5.11), we have for one band

$$\mathbf{i}_1 = \frac{1}{e}\sigma_1 \cdot \mathbf{grad}\,\bar{\mu} - \sigma_1 \cdot Q_1 \cdot \mathbf{grad}\,T, \qquad (4.2.1\text{a})$$

$$\mathbf{w}_1 = \left(\pi_1 - \frac{\bar{\mu}}{e}\right) \cdot \mathbf{i}_1 - \kappa_1 \cdot \mathbf{grad}\,T. \qquad (4.2.1\text{b})$$

There are similar equations (with the subscript 2) for the second band and we have seen how to calculate the appropriate coefficients for each band separately. The total current flow $\mathbf{i}$ and the total energy flow $\mathbf{w}$ are given by

$$\mathbf{i} = \mathbf{i}_1 + \mathbf{i}_2, \qquad \mathbf{w} = \mathbf{w}_1 + \mathbf{w}_2. \tag{4.2.2}$$

The expressions obtained by substituting equations (4.2.1) into (4.2.2) have to be manipulated so as to obtain them in the form

$$\mathbf{i} = \frac{1}{e}\sigma \cdot \mathbf{grad}\,\bar{\mu} - \sigma \cdot Q \cdot \mathbf{grad}\,T, \qquad (4.2.3a)$$

$$\mathbf{w} = \left(\pi - \frac{\bar{\mu}}{e}\right) \cdot \mathbf{i} - \kappa \cdot \mathbf{grad}\,T. \tag{4.2.3b}$$

The coefficients σ, Q, π and κ in these expressions then give the electrical conductivity, Seebeck coefficient, Peltier coefficient and electronic thermal conductivity, for the overall system when both bands are contributing, in terms of the coefficients for each band separately. In general, this process has to be done by tensor manipulation of the equations, but, if we restrict ourselves to the case of no magnetic field and to cubic symmetry, the algebra becomes much simpler. Since this example illustrates the essential features we shall restrict the discussion of this case, noting, however, that the formulae for transport processes of non-isotropic bodies in the presence of a magnetic field, when two or more bands are contributing, can be obtained by the same principles.

Using equation (4.2.1a) and the corresponding equation for band 2, we obtain

$$\mathbf{i} = \mathbf{i}_1 + \mathbf{i}_2 = \frac{1}{e}(\sigma_1 + \sigma_2)\,\mathbf{grad}\,\bar{\mu} - $$
$$- (\sigma_1 Q_1 + \sigma_2 Q_2)\,\mathbf{grad}\,T. \tag{4.2.4}$$

This equation is already of the required form corresponding to equation (4.2.3a) and gives directly

$$\sigma = \sigma_1 + \sigma_2, \tag{4.2.5}$$

$$\sigma Q = \sigma_1 Q_1 + \sigma_2 Q_2. \tag{4.2.6}$$

Thus, the total electrical conductivity and Seebeck coefficient are obtained. The total flow of energy is

$$\mathbf{w} = \mathbf{w_1} + \mathbf{w_2} = \left(\pi_1 - \frac{\bar{\mu}}{e}\right)\mathbf{i_1} + \left(\pi_2 - \frac{\bar{\mu}}{e}\right)\mathbf{i_2} - (\kappa_1 + \kappa_2)\,\mathbf{grad}\,T. \quad (4.2.7)$$

We can eliminate the terms in $\mathbf{i_1}$ and $\mathbf{i_2}$ by expressing them in terms of equation (4.2.1a) and then eliminating the resultant term in $\mathbf{grad}\,\bar{\mu}$ by use of equation (4.2.3a). This process yields

$$\mathbf{w} = \left\{\left(\frac{\sigma_1\pi_1 + \sigma_2\pi_2}{\sigma}\right) - \frac{\bar{\mu}}{e}\right\}\mathbf{i} - $$
$$- \left\{\kappa_1 + \kappa_2 + \frac{\sigma_1\sigma_2}{\sigma}(\pi_2 - \pi_1)(Q_2 - Q_1)\right\}\mathbf{grad}\,T \quad (4.2.8)$$

which is directly comparable with equation (4.2.3b) and gives

$$\sigma\pi = \sigma_1\pi_1 + \sigma_2\pi_2, \quad (4.2.9)$$

$$\kappa = \kappa_1 + \kappa_2 + \frac{\sigma_1\sigma_2}{(\sigma_1 + \sigma_2)}T(Q_2 - Q_1)^2. \quad (4.2.10)$$

In the last expression we have made use of the relation (3.5.12c). We must stress that the derivation applies only to the electronic component of the thermal conductivity. Equation (4.2.10) shows that the overall electronic thermal conductivity contains an extra term over and above that obtained by the straightforward addition of the separate contributions of the two bands. To see the magnitude of this effect let us consider the case where the two bands concerned are the conduction and valence bands, using the simple model of these bands discussed in the last section. If subscript 1 refers to the conduction band and 2 refers to the valence band, we have, by use of equations (4.1.20) and (4.1.37b),

$$Q_2 - Q_1 = \frac{k}{e}\left\{-\theta + r_2 - \eta + r_1\right\}$$
$$= \frac{k}{e}\left\{r_2 + r_1 - \left(\frac{E_v - \bar{\mu} + \bar{\mu} - E_c}{kT}\right)\right\}$$
$$= \frac{k}{e}\left\{r_2 + r_1 + \frac{E_G}{kT}\right\} \quad (4.2.11)$$

where r_2 and r_1 are dimensionless positive parameters depending on the scattering processes in the valence and the conduction bands and the position of the Fermi level with respect to these bands. The positive quantity E_G equal to $(E_c - E_v)$ is the separation in energy between the minimum of the conduction band and the maximum of the valence band. We have seen that, for both bands to contribute, the Fermi level must be at comparable separations from both bands. Thus, if the band separation is more than a few times kT, it follows that we can use the non-degenerate approximations for both bands in the intrinsic range. Also, since two-band conduction occurs at fairly high temperatures, lattice scattering tends to predominate so that r_1 and r_2 are both of the order of 2. Thus, if we write

$$\kappa_1 = L_1 \sigma_1 T, \qquad \kappa_2 = L_2 \sigma_2 T$$

where we expect L_1 and L_2 to be of the order of $2k^2/e^2$ we obtain for the total Lorenz number

$$L = \frac{\kappa}{\sigma T} \eqsim \frac{2k^2}{e^2} + \frac{k^2}{e^2} \frac{\sigma_1 \sigma_2}{(\sigma_1 + \sigma_2)^2} \left[4 + \frac{E_G}{kT} \right]^2. \qquad (4.2.12)$$

It is clear that, if the separate contributions σ_1 and σ_2 to the electrical conductivity are comparable in magnitude, then the second term can be very much larger than the first.

The physical processes behind this extra contribution to the electronic component of the thermal conductivity are fairly evident. An essential part of the above argument is that we have used the same value of the electrochemical potential $\bar{\mu}$ and temperature T for both the valence and conduction bands, thus implying that they are in mutual equilibrium with each other at all times. Since the densities n_c and n_v of electrons and holes both depend on the value of the electrochemical potential, they are not independent of each other and at any particular temperature there is a relation between them, required by the fact that they both have a common electrochemical potential. This relation is obtained by eliminating the electrochemical potential $\bar{\mu}$ from the equations (cf. equation (4.1.29)),

$$n_c = \frac{1}{6\pi^2} \left(\frac{2m_c kT}{\hbar^2} \right)^{3/2} F_{1/2}(\eta),$$

$$n_v = \frac{1}{6\pi^2} \left(\frac{2m_v kT}{\hbar^2} \right)^{3/2} F_{1/2}(\theta).$$

When the non-degenerate approximation can be used, this elimination is very simple, since then

$$F_{1/2}(\eta) = \Gamma(\tfrac{3}{2}) \exp(\eta) = \frac{\sqrt{\pi}}{2} \exp\left(\frac{\bar{\mu} - E_c}{kT}\right),$$

$$F_{1/2}(\theta) = \Gamma(\tfrac{3}{2}) \exp(\theta) = \frac{\sqrt{\pi}}{2} \exp\left(\frac{E_v - \bar{\mu}}{kT}\right). \tag{4.2.13}$$

Thus,

$$n_c n_v = \frac{1}{144\pi^3}\left(\frac{2kT}{\hbar^2}\right)^{3/2} (m_c m_v)^{3/2} \exp\left(\frac{-E_G}{kT}\right). \tag{4.2.14}$$

In the presence of a temperature gradient, this relation must hold at each point. Thus, as electrons and holes move from the hot end of the specimen to the cold end under the influence of the temperature gradient, the tendency for them to concentrate at the cold end is counteracted by their recombination (i.e. the electrons fall into the vacant levels of the valence band). In this process energy is given up to the surroundings. Thus, over and above the normal direct transport of energy by the carriers, there is the process of creation of electron–hole pairs at the hot end (absorbing energy from the source of heat), movement of the carriers down the temperature gradient and recombination at the cold end. This gives rise to the transport of ionization energy which is the source of the extra term appearing in equation (4.2.10) and (4.2.12). Heat transfer by this means is sometimes referred to as *bipolar thermodiffusion* (1955:**6**).

4.3 DETERMINATION OF THE ELECTRONIC COMPONENT OF THE THERMAL CONDUCTIVITY

4.3.1 EXTRINSIC SEMICONDUCTORS

It is evident from, for example, equation (4.1.24) that the electronic component of the thermal conductivity in an extrinsic semiconductor is only important when the ratio of the electrical conductivity to the lattice component of the thermal conductivity is of the order of $10^5\,°\mathrm{C}\,\Omega^{-1}\,\mathrm{W}^{-1}$ or greater. It may be shown that this condition only holds for materials having a high ratio of carrier mobility to lattice thermal conductivity† (i.e. good thermoelectric materials)

---

† To be precise, it is the factor $(\mu/\kappa_L)(m^*/m)^{3/2}$ which should be high (see Appendix 1).

unless, of course, we restrict ourselves to highly degenerate semiconductors. It is not surprising, therefore, that the first real studies of the electronic thermal conductivity in semiconductors were carried out on lead telluride and bismuth telluride, the two best compounds for thermoelectric applications. Similar work has since been reported by Hashimoto (1958:8) for bismuth selenide. It has been necessary to take into account the heat conduction by the charge carriers in a

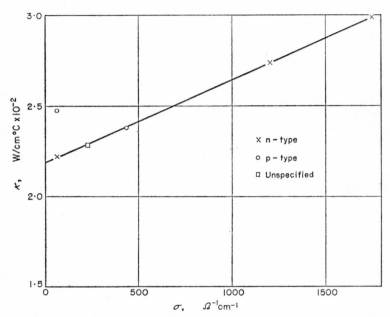

FIG. 4.3.1. Thermal conductivity plotted against electrical conductivity for lead telluride at room temperature [after Devyatkova (1957:4)].

number of other cases; for example, the measurements of Stuckes (1957:3) on indium antimonide, of Hockings (1959:6) on silver antimony telluride and of Devyatkova et al. (1959:7) on tellurium may be mentioned. However, in all these latter cases it has been impossible to obtain any useful information on the detailed variation of the electronic thermal conductivity over a wide range of electrical conductivities because of either a high lattice thermal conductivity or an insufficient carrier mobility. Instead, the magnitude of the heat conductivity due to the charge carriers has been estimated theoretically [from equation (4.1.24) with $p = -\frac{1}{2}$] and this value subtracted from the total thermal conductivity in order to obtain the lattice component. We shall thus confine our attention in this section to the work on lead telluride, bismuth telluride and bismuth selenide.

The most useful measurements on lead telluride, PbTe, have been carried out by Devyatkova (1957:4). The electrical conductivity of the samples which she used covered the range 60 to 1740 $\Omega^{-1}\,cm^{-1}$ at room temperature. Her experimental results are shown in Fig. 4.3.1 in which the thermal conductivity at 300°K is plotted against the electrical conductivity. The experimental points for all the samples, except one which had been given an abnormal heat treatment, lie on a straight line. Devyatkova therefore felt justified in expressing the thermal conductivity as the sum of a constant lattice component equal to 0·022 W $cm^{-1}\,°C^{-1}$, and an electronic component κ_e which is directly proportional to the electrical conductivity σ. The constant of proportionality was found to be very close to $2(k/e)^2T$. On the basis of this evidence it appears that the value of p for lead telluride is $-\frac{1}{2}$, this corresponding to acoustical-mode lattice scattering of the charge carriers.

The above calculation is of considerable importance. When p is equal to $-\frac{1}{2}$ it is expected that the carrier mobility should be proportional to $T^{-3/2}$. However, measurements on lead telluride near room temperature show that the carrier mobilities for both electrons and holes are more nearly proportional to $T^{-5/2}$ than to $T^{-3/2}$. It has been suggested that the rapid variation of mobility with temperature is due to optical-mode scattering; thus, the variation of thermal conductivity with electrical conductivity obtained by Devyatkova is rather surprising.

Gershtein et al. (1957:5) have shown that Devyatkova's results can be reconciled with the variation of mobility with temperature if one assumes that the charge carriers are predominantly scattered, not by single phonons, but by two phonons simultaneously. Under these conditions the mobility is proportional to T^{p-2} so, if p equals $-\frac{1}{2}$, μ varies as $T^{-5/2}$. Two-phonon collisions can become more likely than single-phonon collisions because a much wider range of phonons can take part in the former processes.

There is one point of criticism which must be made against the above interpretation of Devyatkova's measurements. The Seebeck coefficient of the sample of lead telluride with the highest electrical conductivity cannot be much more than 150 μV °C^{-1}. Thus, if p equals $-\frac{1}{2}$

we expect, from equation (4.1.20), that the Fermi level should lie a distance of approximately kT inside the conduction band. For this sample, therefore, classical statistics are quite inapplicable and, in fact, an electronic thermal conductivity equal to about $2 \cdot 3 (k/e)^2 \sigma T$ might have been expected. It is clear that results from a rather larger number of measurements are desirable before it can be said with conviction

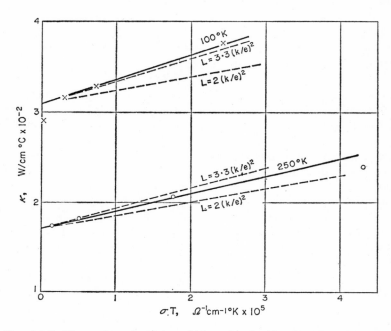

FIG. 4.3.2. Thermal conductivity of bismuth selenide plotted against the product of electrical conductivity and absolute temperature [after Hashimoto (1958:8)].

that the variation of thermal conductivity with electrical conductivity really supports the hypothesis that the carriers in lead telluride are involved in two-phonon collisions.

Hashimoto's results for bismuth selenide, Bi_2Se_3, are shown in Fig. 4.3.2. His measurements covered the temperature range from 100 to 250°K but only the results at the extreme ends of this range are shown in the diagram. There is some advantage to be gained from plotting the thermal conductivity κ against the product σT since, at least for non-degenerate material, we expect a family of straight lines, corresponding to different temperatures, all of the same slope. The intercept of each line with the axis of K should then give the lattice component of the thermal conductivity. The broken lines in Fig. 4.3.2 show the slopes to be expected for the two cases of non-degeneracy, with p equal

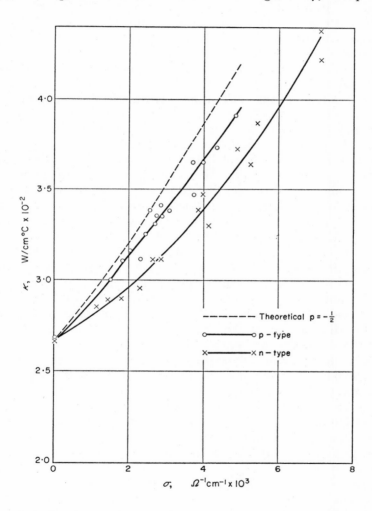

Fig. 4.3.3. Thermal conductivity plotted against electrical conductivity for bismuth telluride at 150°K (1958:9).

to $-\frac{1}{2}$, and complete degeneracy, respectively. It is interesting that at 100°K the results obtained by Hashimoto seem to lie on a line with a slope corresponding to the degenerate case while at 250°K the slope of the experimental plot lies half way between the two limits. Here, of course, as for the case of lead telluride, it would be desirable to have results from a considerably greater number of samples.

Goldsmid's measurements on bismuth telluride, Bi_2Te_3, cannot be interpreted in quite so straightforward a manner (1958:9). His experimental results at 150°K are given in Fig. 4.3.3 in which the thermal conductivity is plotted against the electrical conductivity. A noticeable feature which will be discussed in the next paragraph is that the results for p-type samples are clearly distinguishable from those for n-type samples. It should be noted that simultaneous measurements were made of the Seebeck coefficient and it was, therefore, possible to estimate the position of the Fermi level in each case.

The broken line in Fig. 4.3.3 corresponds to the assumption that p is equal to $-\frac{1}{2}$. The experimental curves for both types of material lie below this curve. However, the variation of mobility with temperature in bismuth telluride is significantly different from the simple $T^{-3/2}$ law. Assuming that μ is proportional to T^{p-1} the experimental mobility variation between 150 and 300°K can best be fitted with values of p equal to about -0.9 for p-type material and -0.7 for n-type material (1958:10). Such values of p do not, of course, correspond to any simple scattering law but, surprisingly enough, the thermal conductivity results for p-type bismuth telluride can be fitted remarkably well on the assumption that p equals -0.9. The results for n-type bismuth telluride cannot, however, be interpreted in this way; one would have to assume an appreciably larger negative value for p in this case. It is, therefore, a reasonable supposition that the low values for the thermal conductivity of n-type material are due to the fact that the lattice component is significantly less than for p-type material. This leads us to the conclusion that the halogen atoms, and in particular those of iodine, which are introduced as donor centres in the n-type samples, must have a large effective cross-section for the scattering of phonons. Further evidence on this point will be given in the next section.

All the experiments which have been described in this section have been aimed at separating the total thermal conductivity into its lattice and electronic components. In each case the thermal conductivity has been plotted against the electrical conductivity (or σT)

and the results extrapolated to zero electrical conductivity. We have seen that such plots need not be linear; in fact, we must expect them to be curved since, if a wide range of electrical conductivity is to be covered, some samples, at least, must be partially degenerate. If the two components of the thermal conductivity are to be separated in this simple fashion, all the samples must be extrinsic; the particular behaviour of the thermal conductivity in intrinsic semiconductors is dealt with in the next sub-section.

4.3.2 INTRINSIC SEMICONDUCTORS

It has been shown in Section 4.2 that the Lorenz number of a semiconductor rises, sometimes by an order of magnitude, when it becomes intrinsic. The transport of heat by bipolar thermodiffusion is most easily demonstrated, in the region of room temperature, for semiconductors with a small energy gap; then, even when the semiconductor is intrinsic, its electrical conductivity is relatively high.

Fig. 4.3.4 shows how the character of the results for bismuth telluride, which were plotted in Fig. 4.3.3 for a temperature of 150°K, changes when the measurements are carried out at 300°K. Once again thermal conductivity has been plotted against the electrical conductivity. When the electrical conductivity exceeds, say, 1000 Ω^{-1} cm^{-1} the experimental data for p-type bismuth telluride can be fitted by supposing that κ_e is given by equation (4.1.24) with p again equal to -0.9. In this case, also, the lower values of the thermal conductivity for n-type material can be explained on the basis that the phonons are appreciably scattered by the donor impurities. However, as the electrical conductivity is reduced below about 500 Ω^{-1} cm^{-1}, the thermal conductivity shows an upward trend and reaches approximately the same value for *intrinsic* material with an electrical conductivity of about 140 Ω^{-1} cm^{-1} as it does for *extrinsic* material with a conductivity of nearly 2000 Ω^{-1} cm^{-1}.

It is, of course, rather difficult to estimate the lattice component of the thermal conductivity for bismuth telluride at 300°K from the results given in Fig. 4.3.4 since it is necessary to extrapolate the curves for extrinsic material over a fairly wide range in order to obtain the intercept with the ordinate axis. However, it has been thought reasonable to accept a value of 0.0157 W cm^{-1} °C^{-1} for the lattice thermal conductivity; the electronic component for the intrinsic material is then found to be 0·0071 W cm⁻¹ °C⁻¹. This is 12·8 times the value of the electronic component which would be expected if the electronic heat conduction were due solely to the transport of kinetic energy by

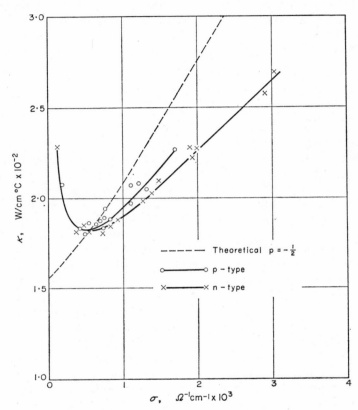

FIG. 4.3.4. Thermal conductivity plotted against electrical conductivity for bismuth telluride at 300°K (1958:9).

the charge carriers. We find that this large electronic thermal conductivity can be explained by the use of equation (4.2.12), in which the effect of bipolar thermodiffusion is included, if we assume the energy gap is about 0·15 eV. This forbidden band width is, in fact, close to the values obtained from infrared transmission measurements and from the variation of electrical conductivity with temperature in the intrinsic range.

The increase in thermal conductivity, as bismuth telluride becomes intrinsic, was first reported in 1956 (1956:1). However, two years previously Busch and Schneider (1954:3) had reported a similar effect in indium antimonide. The electronic thermal conductivity for intrinsic material was said to be a hundred times greater than the value expected from the transport of kinetic energy. It has not been found possible to repeat these observations and it must be concluded that the Lorenz number for intrinsic indium antimonide is never appreciably greater than that for extrinsic material. The reason that the bipolar contribution is so small in indium antimonide is easily seen. It is proportional to $\sigma_1\sigma_2/\sigma^2$ which, in the intrinsic region, is equal to $\mu_c\mu_v/(\mu_c+\mu_v)^2$. For a material like bismuth telluride, in which there is not much difference between μ_c and μ_v this ratio has a value of about 1/4. However, in indium antimonide b, equal to μ_c/μ_v, is about 100 so that $\mu_c\mu_v/(\mu_c+\mu_v)^2$ is approximately 1/100. In general it may be stated that the effect of bipolar thermodiffusion is small in semiconductors which have a large mobility ratio.

It is worth while considering the results which Kettel (1959:8) obtained for germanium. Figure 4.3.5 shows the thermal conductivity of this semiconductor plotted against the reciprocal of the absolute temperature. The electrical conductivity is also shown. The measurements were made on two samples, one of which was intrinsic over the whole temperature range (subscript i) while the other was highly doped with an acceptor concentration of $1\cdot1 \times 10^{18}$ cm^{-3} (subscript p). For values of $1/T$ in excess of 17×10^{-4} °C^{-1} the thermal conductivities of both samples were found to lie on a straight line passing through the origin. At the corresponding temperatures, the electronic component of the thermal conductivity in germanium is negligible and the lattice component is, at least approximately, inversely proportional to the absolute temperature.

For temperatures in excess of about 600°K, the thermal conductivity of the intrinsic sample started to rise above the value expected from the simple $1/T$ law; it reached a minimum value at about 650°K and then increased to a value of about $0\cdot4$ W cm^{-1} °C^{-1} at 1000°K. This was twice the value predicted for the lattice component. If the difference between the two values is taken to be the electronic component, we find the corresponding Lorenz number to be about 66 k^2/e^2. Kettel found this to be four times the value of the Lorenz number to be expected from equation (4.2.12) using estimates of the energy gap and mobility ratio based on Morin and Maita's work (1954:4). These estimates may not be wholly accurate but it is difficult to see how they can be sufficiently in error to explain the discrepancy between theory and experiment. It appears, therefore, that part of the increase in the thermal conductivity of germanium at elevated temperatures must be explained in a different way. Kettel showed that transfer of heat by infrared radiation could not account for the observed effect. His

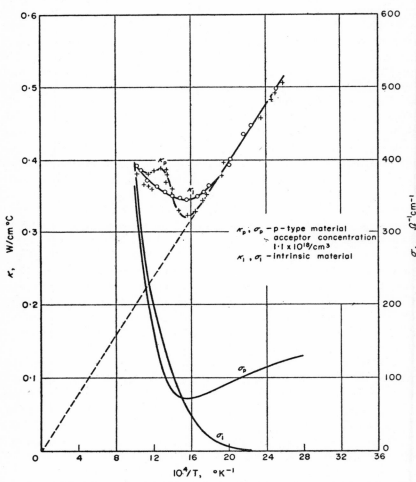

FIG. 4.3.5. Thermal and electrical conductivity of germanium plotted against the reciprocal of the absolute temperature [after Kettel (1959:8)].

suggestion, that it is due to the transport of excitons, is reasonable although it is not definitely established.

The peculiar behaviour shown by Kettel's p-type sample is rather interesting. At 650°K, it has a lower thermal conductivity than the intrinsic sample due to the relatively small contribution from the bipolar thermodiffusion effect. However, at about 800°K the thermal conductivity of the p-type sample reached a maximum which was appreciably in excess of the value for the intrinsic material. This phenomenon is easily explained. For a semiconductor in which the mobility ratio b is significantly greater than unity, the Lorenz number reaches its maximum value, not in the intrinsic range when it is proportional to $b/(1+b)^2$, but for material with the concentration of holes exceeding that of electrons such that the electron and hole contributions to the electrical conductivity are equal. $\sigma_1\sigma_2/(\sigma_1+\sigma_2)^2$ reaches its maximum value of $1/4$ when σ_1 equals σ_2. Kettel showed that the thermal conductivity of the p-type germanium exceeded that for the intrinsic material by the greatest amount at precisely the temperature for which the electrons and holes made equal contributions to the electrical conductivity.

4.4 THE EFFECT OF A MAGNETIC FIELD

The change in thermal resistance on the application of a magnetic field (*magnetothermal resistance* effect) has been studied for a number of metals since it can be used, in principle, to separate out any appreciable lattice component from the total thermal conductivity. Under the action of a magnetic field the thermal conductivity is given by

$$\kappa(\mathbf{B}) = \kappa_L + L(\mathbf{B})\sigma(\mathbf{B})T \tag{4.4.1}$$

where κ_L is unaffected by the field but the Lorenz number $L(\mathbf{B})$ and the electrical conductivity $\sigma(\mathbf{B})$ are both field dependent. It would, of course, be a simple matter to separate the two components of the thermal conductivity if the Lorenz number were independent of the presence of a magnetic field. However, even if magnetothermal resistance measurements cannot yield the value of the electronic thermal conductivity directly, they can assist in its calculation by throwing some light on the scattering law for the charge carriers.

In semiconductors the lattice component of the thermal conductivity is generally so much greater than the electronic component that the change in thermal resistance on the application of a magnetic field is negligible. Steele (1957:**6**) showed that there was no measurable magnetothermal resistance effect for germanium. He did, however, demonstrate an appreciable *magnetothermoelectric* effect and pointed out that this is also related to the scattering process for the charge carriers.

4.4.1 Expressions for the Changes of Seebeck Coefficient and Thermal Conductivity in a Magnetic Field

We shall not spend time in deriving the equations which describe the magnetothermoelectric and magnetothermal resistance effects; these equations will merely be quoted. The same model as that used in Section 4.1 is assumed. The solution of the Boltzmann equation in the presence of a weak magnetic field then gives (1953:**2**)

$$\frac{\sigma \Delta Q}{\Delta \sigma} \doteqdot \mp \frac{k}{e} \left\{ \frac{(2p+5)F_{p+3/2}}{(2p+3)F_{p+1/2}} - \frac{(6p+5)F_{3p+3/2}}{(6p-3)F_{3p+1/2}} \right\}, \qquad (4.4.2)$$

where the negative sign applies for *n*-type material and the positive sign for *p*-type material. ΔQ is the change of Seebeck coefficient due to the magnetic field, and $\Delta \sigma$ is the change of electrical conductivity under the same field, but in the absence of any lateral electric field. Because of this latter condition, $\Delta \sigma$ is related to the measured change of resistivity $\Delta \rho$ by

$$-\frac{\Delta \sigma}{\sigma} = \frac{\Delta \rho}{\rho} + \frac{R^2 B^2}{\rho^2} \qquad (4.4.3)$$

where R is the Hall coefficient. Equation (4.4.2) is only approximate since it does not take into account the Nernst effect. The transverse temperature gradient and magnetic field together produce a longitudinal voltage which must be added to the thermoelectric voltage.

The expression for the magnetothermal resistance effect is

$$\frac{\Delta \kappa}{\Delta \sigma} \doteqdot \frac{k^2}{e^2} T \left\{ \frac{(6p+7)F_{3p+5/2}}{(6p+3)F_{3p+1/2}} + \frac{(2p+5)^2 F^2_{p+3/2}}{(2p+3)^2 F^2_{p+1/2}} - \right.$$
$$\left. - 2\frac{(6p+5)(2p+5)F_{3p+3/2}F_{p+3/2}}{(6p+3)(2p+3)F_{3p+1/2}F_{p+1/2}} \right\}, \qquad (4.4.4)$$

where $\Delta\kappa$ is the change of thermal conductivity under the magnetic field. Equation (4.4.4) is also only an approximation since it should contain additional terms related to the Ettingshausen and Righi–Leduc effects. A longitudinal temperature gradient arises because of the action of the magnetic field with a transverse electric field or temperature gradient. Plots of the bracketed terms in equations (4.4.2) and (4.4.4) as functions of the Fermi potential, over a range of values of p, and expressions for the additional terms in these equations have been given by Bowley et al. (1958:**11**).

Equations (4.4.2) and (4.4.4) can be expressed much more simply if classical statistics may be employed. However, the classical expression for the magnetothermal resistance effect is of no practical use since the effect can only be observed in at least partially degenerate material.

The sign of the magnetothermoelectric effect is closely related to the scattering law. The change in Q is of the same sign as Q if p is negative and opposite in sign if p is positive. Quantitatively, if the Seebeck coefficient and its change in a magnetic field have been measured, equations (4.1.20) and (4.4.2) may be used to obtain both the value of p and that of the reduced Fermi potential η. This method of obtaining the parameters which are needed in calculating the Lorenz number is attractive since the experimental procedure is quite simple.

The magnetothermal resistance is not quite so simply related to the scattering parameter p. Whereas κ_e/σ increases continuously with p, $\Delta\kappa/\Delta\sigma$ has a minimum value for p lying between 0 and $-\frac{1}{2}$. Thus, in general, there may be two pairs of values for p and η for a given magnitude of the magnetothermal resistance effect. This effect is probably more useful in checking the parameters yielded by magnetothermoelectric measurements than in giving these parameters directly.

4.4.2 EXPERIMENTAL RESULTS

It is clear that the magnetothermal resistance effect must always be negligible in semiconductors having a high lattice thermal conductivity or a low electrical conductivity. Even for the semiconductor bismuth telluride, the increase in the thermal resistivity on the application of a field of 10 kilo-oersted amounted to only a few per cent. However, the measurements on bismuth telluride led to some interesting conclusions (1958:**11**) and they will be outlined here.

The apparatus for magnetothermal resistance measurements is illustrated in Fig. 4.4.1. Since the effect was so small it was desirable to keep the temperature of the copper heat sink as steady as possible and to reach equilibrium as quickly as possible after applying the field. Thus, the whole specimen chamber was immersed in liquid nitrogen and measurements were carried out only at this temperature. Also the thermal capacity of the heater was kept as small as possible and

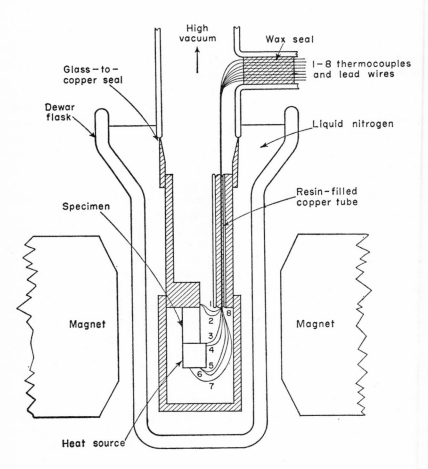

Fig. 4.4.1. Apparatus for measurement of magnetothermal resistance (1958:**11**).

the specimen had a ratio of length to width of no more than 2 : 1. The latter condition introduced the possibility of spurious end-effects (1957:7) but no such effects were found to occur in this particular experiment. Apart from the special features mentioned above, the apparatus did not differ essentially from one for the absolute measurement of the thermal conductivity of a moderate heat conductor. It was used simultaneously for the determination of the Seebeck coefficient and the magnetothermoelectric effect. In order to interpret the results it was necessary, in addition, to measure the electrical conductivity and its change in a magnetic field (*magnetoresistance* effect) and the Hall coefficient. The measurements were made on two undoped p-type samples of bismuth telluride and on three n-type samples doped with varying amounts of iodine.

Certain general features were apparent. The ratio of $\Delta\kappa$ to $\Delta\sigma$ was found to be independent of magnetic field strength B even when the magnetoresistance effects were no longer quadratic in B, as expected from simple low-field theory. Similarly, the ratio ΔQ to $\Delta\sigma$ was found to be constant as the field was increased. It was, therefore, considered that the low-field theory could be used in interpreting the results.

The magnetothermoelectric measurements allowed estimates of the reduced Fermi potential η (or θ) and the parameter p or (p') to be made for all the samples. The two p-type samples were found to have θ equal to 4, while η lay between 2 and 12 for the n-type samples. Clearly, classical statistics could not be employed. In all cases p (or p') was found to be negative and of the order $-\frac{1}{2}$, i.e. the theoretical value for acoustical-mode lattice scattering in a simple semiconductor. This result is remarkable in view of the low temperature (77°K) and the high impurity concentration, particularly for the most heavily-doped n-type sample. The negative value of p (or p') indicates that impurity scattering could not have made a major contribution in any of the samples studied. The absence of impurity scattering is related to the very high dielectric constant (1958:12) which localizes the field of the impurity ions.

The magnetothermal resistance experiments did not give such clear-cut information but, qualitatively, they supported the magneto-thermoelectric measurements. It was, therefore, thought reasonable to use the parameters, determined from the latter measurements, in calculating the electronic component of the thermal conductivity. The lattice component of bismuth telluride, obtained by subtracting the calculated electronic component from the total thermal conductivity, was found to fall steeply on the addition of iodine. This was in good agreement with the experiments mentioned in Section 4.3.1.

Chapter 5

THE LATTICE COMPONENT OF THE
THERMAL CONDUCTIVITY

OUR object in this chapter is to discuss the theoretical aspects of the basic processes governing the lattice component of the thermal conductivity in semiconductors and to compare the formulae that have been proposed with the available experimental evidence. We shall concentrate on the physics of these processes leaving the more complex mathematical details to be studied, if required, from the original articles.

The basic processes which affect the lattice component of the thermal conductivity under all conditions are those associated with the presence of anharmonic effects in the vibrational motion of the atoms. Correspondingly, the basic problem in the theoretical calculations is to obtain a satisfactory description of these processes, both as regards their direct effect on the lattice thermal conductivity and their indirect effect through interaction with other processes. The calculation of such effects is essential before we can begin to make reasonably accurate predictions of the thermal conductivity under general conditions.

Let us consider what information we would like to have in order to obtain a satisfactory theory of the anharmonic effects. Basically, it would be necessary to know how the restoring force on an atom in the solid varies with the displacement of the atom from its mean position. The principal contribution to this force is harmonic and is directly proportional to the displacement. The anharmonic contributions are much smaller but we have to know these with considerable accuracy since, as we have seen, the lattice thermal conductivity is not affected by the harmonic contributions.

The prospects of being able to obtain these contributions with the required accuracy from theoretical calculations of the forces between atoms, must remain poor for a long time. Apart from certain extreme types of crystal, such as the alkali halides and crystals of the rare-gas elements, the calculations of the interatomic forces that have been made are of low accuracy and it is not possible to sort out the anharmonic contributions with reasonable reliability in any crystals. In such circumstances, the only procedure that can be adopted is to attempt to obtain these terms from physical measurements. The lattice thermal resistivity due to the anharmonic contributions might then be related to other physical properties of the solid which also depend on these contributions although probably in a different way.

The most relevant of such other physical properties is the relation between the components of a stress applied to the crystal and the components of the resultant strain. This relation is defined by the elastic constants of the crystal. Interpreting these on an atomic scale it is clear that if the restoring force on an atom were proportional to the displacement, i.e. if the force were harmonic, then the elastic constants would be true constants and independent of the strain.

This, in fact, is the case, to an accuracy which is sufficient for most practical purposes, when the strains are small. In actual crystals, however, for larger strains, the anharmonic contributions become appreciable and their effect on the overall mechanical properties leads to a departure from the generalized form of Hooke's law which states that there is a linear relation between stress and strain. Thus, for large strains, the elastic "constants" of the crystal are in fact not constant, but vary with strain. The parameters which describe this variation are called the *third-order elastic constants*. Since the elastic properties of solids can be measured very precisely it appears possible in principle to determine the third-order elastic constants accurately enough to allow the anharmonic contributions to the interatomic forces to be obtained. Such a procedure would seem to offer the best prospects of obtaining a satisfactory theory of the lattice thermal conductivity.

Unfortunately, although estimates of the third-order elastic constants have been made for a few materials, the necessary measurements have not been made with the required accuracy for the vast majority of solids. In the absence of such direct information, the current theories relate the lattice thermal resistivity due to anharmonic processes, to the variation of the thermal expansion of the solid with temperature. This latter property also depends on the anharmonic contributions to the interatomic forces since part of the energy taken up in supplying heat to the solid is stored as increased potential energy resulting from the change in the distance between the atoms. Making considerable simplifications to the theory, the effect can be described in terms of a single parameter called the *Gruneisen constant*. This parameter can in principle be measured reasonably accurately for a particular solid but it is unfortunately true that it gives us only one piece of information about the anharmonic forces. Also the predictions of the simple theory of thermal expansion using a single parameter are not always in good agreement with experiment. Thus, in the ensuing discussion it should be borne in mind that the theories of the lattice thermal conductivity, using the Gruneisen parameter to estimate the effects of the anharmonic forces, are not quantitatively reliable. Their main use is in determining what physical properties are important and in comparing different materials.

The most extensive calculation of the lattice thermal conductivity due to anharmonic processes was carried out by Leibfried and Schlömann (1954:5). They used a variational method, the principles of which have been discussed in Section 3.8. The results of these calculations are discussed in detail in Section 5.2.1. The predictions agree well with the variation of the thermal conductivity with temperature observed in actual crystals under appropriate conditions and with the variation of the thermal conductivity from one type of crystal to another.

Next in order of importance to the anharmonic processes, in the theory of the lattice thermal conductivity, are the effects associated with the presence of structural imperfections in the lattice. These become increasingly important at low temperatures since the influence of umklapp processes falls off very rapidly with a decrease in temperature. The main difficulty in this problem is the estimation of the effects of the anharmonic N-processes. Although we have seen that these processes do not contribute directly to the thermal conductivity, they do have an important indirect influence in exchanging phonons between the various modes and hence on the overall scattering. This problem has been recently treated by Berman *et al.* (1959:9) again using a variational method. We shall discuss the results of this and other methods in Section 5.2.2.

Although the variational method has been reasonably successful in dealing with the above problems, it is unfortunately true that the principles involved are not easy to visualize physically. The more simple concept of assigning a mean free path to the phonons, in line with the ideas used in the kinetic theory of gases, provides a more direct physical picture and has been widely used. It is, however, necessary to be careful in applying this concept too freely. For this reason, we shall start by giving a discussion of the mean free path approach in Section 5.1. In the subsequent sections we shall discuss the various formulae for the thermal conductivity under different conditions and compare these with the experimental results on semiconductors.

5.1 THE MEAN FREE PATH CONCEPT FOR PHONONS

To make things as simple as possible we shall assume that we have to deal with an isotropic crystal. This property will be reflected in the phonon spectrum. Thus, for a particular branch of this spectrum, the phonons lying in a frequency interval ω to $\omega + \delta\omega$ will be within a spherical shell in $\mathbf{q}$ space of radius q and thickness δq, where q is the magnitude of $\mathbf{q}$. All such phonons will have the same magnitude of velocity $v(\mathbf{q})$ although, of course, the velocities $\mathbf{v}$ will be directed in different orientations.

To discuss the effect of collisions we make the simplifying assumption that phonons in the shell persist, on the average, for a time $\tau(q)$ after which they take part in interaction processes. Alternatively, we may say that the average distance travelled between interaction processes is $l(q) = v\tau$ this being a definition of the mean free path l. We now have to make a basic assumption about the interaction processes, viz. that they restore local thermal equilibrium to the phonon distribution, corresponding to the local conditions at the point where the interaction takes place. This assumption certainly embodies the main features that we expect for an interaction process in that it results in the local production of entropy and so tends to restore the local thermal equilibrium distribution. It must be remembered, however, that it does not apply to the so-called N-processes, which we have seen do not restore equilibrium. For the present, we shall ignore this complication and return to a discussion of its effects later. Meanwhile, let us see what the assumption leads to in other cases where this complication does not arise, at least to the same extent.

The number of phonons (per unit volume) in the shell for thermal equilibrium is

$$n(\omega, T) = \mathcal{N}_0(\omega, T)g(\omega)\,\mathrm{d}\omega, \tag{5.1.1}$$

where $\mathcal{N}_0$ is the thermal equilibrium distribution function and $g(\omega)$ is the density-of-states energy distribution for the branch considered.

Taking a temperature gradient in the x direction, consider a surface element of unit area normal to the x axis in the plane $x = x_1$. We wish to calculate the energy flow per unit time across this surface element. Phonons which cross this element do so in all directions, i.e. they are moving in directions specified by $0 < \theta < \pi$, where θ is the angle which the velocity $\mathbf{v}$ of the phonons makes with the positive x direction. Consider the phonons corresponding to a particular value of θ in the range θ to $\theta + \delta\theta$. Then our assumption regarding the interaction processes leads to the result that the number of such phonons corresponds to the equilibrium number of phonons with θ values in this range associated with the x co-ordinate $x_1 - \Delta x$, where $\Delta x = l\cos\theta$. (At this latter position these phonons were, on the average, previously involved in an interaction process.) The number of such phonons is

$$n(\omega, T - \Delta T)\frac{\sin\theta}{2}\delta\theta = -\left(\frac{\partial n}{\partial T}\right)\Delta T\frac{\sin\theta}{2}\partial\theta, \qquad (5.1.2)$$

where

$$\Delta T = \left(\frac{\partial T}{\partial x}\right)\Delta x = \left(\frac{\partial T}{\partial x}\right)l\cos\theta.$$

Each of these phonons transports an amount of energy per unit time across the surface element equal to $\hbar\omega v\cos\theta$. Multiplying equation (5.1.2) by this factor and integrating from $\theta = 0$ to $\theta = \pi$, we find that the contribution of the phonons, in the shell $d\omega$ of the branch considered, to the energy flow in the x direction is

$$\Delta w = -\left(\frac{\partial T}{\partial x}\right)\left(\frac{\partial n}{\partial T}\right)_{x=x_1}\frac{\hbar\omega v l}{3}. \qquad (5.1.3)$$

Since $n\hbar\omega$ is the contribution to the total energy, this can be written as

$$\Delta w = -\left(\frac{\partial T}{\partial x}\right)\frac{v l \Delta C_v}{3}$$

where ΔC_v is the contribution to the lattice specific heat from the shell. The total energy flow is obtained by integrating this expression over the shells and summing over all branches. This leads to the expression for the thermal conductivity,

$$\kappa_L = \tfrac{1}{3} \sum_j \int \Delta C_v(j,q)\, v(j,q) l(j,q) \; \mathrm{d}q. \qquad (5.1.4)$$

For the Debye model of the spectrum, v is independent of q and ΔC_v is proportional to q^2.

It is natural to define the overall average mean free path of phonons $\bar{l}$ by the relation

$$\kappa_L = \tfrac{1}{3} C_v \bar{v} \bar{l} \qquad (5.1.5)$$

where C_v is the total specific heat per unit volume of the lattice and $\bar{v}$ is an average velocity of phonons, which is related to the average velocity of sound waves in the solid.

The equations (5.1.4) and (5.1.5) form the simplest way of expressing the thermal conductivity but are subject to the limitation already discussed, viz. that they do not take into account the effect of N-processes. This limitation shows up, in particular, when attempts are made to apply the formula to the case of scattering by point imperfections. In this case the mean free path is proportional to q^{-4} so that for long waves, as q tends to zero, the expression (5.1.4) becomes infinite.

5.2 FORMULAE FOR THE LATTICE THERMAL CONDUCTIVITY

5.2.1 PERFECT CRYSTALS

It is natural to start by considering the lattice thermal conductivity of a crystal which contains no imperfections. In this case, we have seen that the phonon–phonon interactions, which are most important in limiting the thermal conductivity, are the three-phonon umklapp processes.

As already mentioned, the theory of thermal conductivity, as limited by umklapp processes, has been investigated by Leibfried and Schlömann (1954:5). They used the variational approach and related the anharmonic forces to other physical properties of the solid. Their final result gave the formula for the lattice thermal conductivity in the form

$$\kappa_L = \kappa_0 \, f\!\left(\frac{\theta_D}{T}\right) \qquad (5.2.1)$$

in which θ_D is the Debye temperature of the solid, T the absolute temperature, and κ_0 is the thermal conductivity at the Debye temperature. Thus $f(\theta_D/T) = 1$ for $T = \theta_D$. For other values of T,

$$f\left(\frac{\theta_D}{T}\right) \fallingdotseq \frac{\theta_D}{T} \qquad \text{when } T > \theta_D, \qquad (5.2.2)$$

$$f\left(\frac{\theta_D}{T}\right) \fallingdotseq \left(\frac{T}{\theta_D}\right)^3 \exp\left(\frac{\theta_D}{bT}\right) \qquad \text{when } T \ll \theta_D, \qquad (5.2.3)$$

where b is a numerical parameter, not given accurately by the theory.

These expressions give the dependence on temperature of the lattice thermal conductivity and, in principle, allow this to be determined over a large temperature range from measurements at one particular temperature. They predict that, at temperatures well above the Debye temperature, the lattice thermal conductivity will be proportional to $1/T$. As the temperature is lowered, the conductivity should be increasingly larger than the value obtained by extrapolating a $1/T$ law from high temperatures, eventually being dominated by the exponential term at temperatures well below the Debye temperature. Thus, the thermal conductivity should increase very rapidly with decreasing temperature in this range.

This temperature dependence of κ_L when dominated by U-processes, was originally predicted by Peierls (1929:1) using general arguments. In particular, on the basis of Peierls' discussion, the appearance of the exponential term in equation (5.2.3) is a consequence of the fact that, in order for umklapp scattering to occur, the two phonons which interact to produce a third phonon (with wave vector outside the first Brillouin zone) must themselves have wave vectors extending about half-way towards the edge of the zone. On the simple Debye model, the energy of such phonons is given by $\hbar\omega = k\theta_D/2$, i.e. half the maximum energy. The number of such phonons is proportional to $[\exp(\theta_D/2T) - 1]^{-1}$ and when $T \ll \theta_D$ this is equal to $\exp(-\theta_D/2T)$. The rate at which U-processes occur, therefore, contains this factor and so does the corresponding value of the thermal resistivity. This argument gives an estimate of the factor b in equation (5.2.3) as being of the order of 2, its actual value being determined by the details of the energy spectrum and the structure of the Brillouin zone. In particular, it should have about the same value in materials with similar types of chemical binding and crystallographic structures.

As the temperature is lowered, the above theory predicts that the thermal conductivity should become rapidly larger, eventually tending to infinity at the absolute zero. In actual crystals, even though they may be structurally perfect, this tendency will be halted at some point as a result of the finite size of the crystal. The mathematical formulation of the properties of phonons in a crystal is based on simplified boundary conditions which effectively assume that the crystal is of infinite extent (more correctly, that it is one unit in an infinite periodic sequence). The effect of departures from this assumption in actual crystals, is to induce transitions between the phonon states of the ideal infinite crystal and, thus, to give a finite thermal conductivity. Such boundary scattering effects can be neglected when other very much stronger sources of scattering are present and, in particular, if the only other source is umklapp scattering, they can be neglected at high temperatures. As the temperature is lowered, however, umklapp scattering becomes progressively weaker and eventually boundary scattering predominates.

An estimate of the relative importance of boundary scattering and umklapp scattering can be obtained on the basis of the mean free path concept. The overall mean free path (as defined by equation 5.1.5) associated with umklapp scattering can be obtained by the use of equations (5.2.1) to (5.2.3). At low temperatures, the overall mean free path $\bar{l}_u$ associated with umklapp scattering is dominated by the factor $\exp(\theta_D/bT)$; this increases rapidly as the temperature decreases. As a working rule we expect that the effect of boundary scattering should become comparable with the effect of umklapp scattering when $\bar{l}_u$ becomes comparable with the geometrical dimensions of the crystal since the latter determine the mean free path $\bar{l}_b$ associated with boundary scattering. As the temperature is lowered further, boundary scattering must become increasingly predominant. The general features of the thermal conductivity are then described by equation (5.1.4) with the use of a constant mean free path, independent of $\mathbf{q}$ and j, whose value is determined by the geometrical dimensions of the crystal and which should, in fact, be of the same order as these dimensions.

In a more refined argument, we would anticipate, on the basis of the mean free path concept, that the conditions under which phonons are scattered at the surface, would play some part in determining the contribution of boundary scattering. If, for example, phonons tend to suffer specular reflections at the surfaces, the overall rate of increase of entropy in the phonon system must be less than if they are scattered randomly. In this case, therefore, the effect of boundary scattering on the thermal conductivity must be smaller, other processes being comparable. To obtain diffuse or random scattering at the surface would require surface irregularities with dimensions of the order of the phonon wavelengths. We anticipate that boundary scattering effects should be most efficient in limiting the thermal conductivity in crystals whose surfaces have been, for example, sandblasted or otherwise made irregular.

The first quantitative treatment of boundary scattering was given by Casimir (1938:**1**) who, assumed effectively, that scattering at the surface leads to local equilibrium, i.e. corresponds to maximum entropy production in the phonon system. His formula for the thermal conductivity, as limited by boundary scattering, is

$$\kappa_L = \tfrac{1}{3}(\sum_j C_j v_j)\bar{l_b} \qquad (5.2.4)$$

where C_j and v_j are, respectively, the contribution to the specific heat and the velocity of phonons of branch j of the vibration spectrum. This is of the form predicted by the above arguments. The value of $\bar{l_b}$ was given as $2R$ for a specimen of circular cross-section with a radius R, and as $1\cdot12D$ for a specimen of square cross-section of side D.

Since, at low temperatures, the contribution to the specific heat of the various branches tends to follow a T^3 law, equation (5.2.4) predicts that the thermal conductivity should follow the same law, when boundary scattering is predominant over other processes.

A more detailed theory of boundary scattering, taking into account the effects of finite length of the crystal and differing surface conditions has been given by Berman *et al.* (1953:**3**). They found that the mean free path $\bar{l_b}$ should decrease slowly with increasing temperature.

To summarize the preceding discussion, we expect that the lattice thermal conductivity of a crystal containing no imperfections will possess the general features shown in Fig. 5.2.1. At high temperatures it follows a $1/T$ law, increases more rapidly than this as the temperature is lowered below the Debye temperature and reaches a maximum at some temperature, below which it decreases, approaching a T^3 law as T tends to $0°K$. Apart from the effect of imperfections, which we shall discuss shortly, these features of the temperature dependence should be common to all crystals.

There is still the important question of the relative magnitude of the thermal conductivity for different crystals. On the basis of the theory of Leibfried and Schlömann the value of κ_0 in equation (5.2.1) is

$$\kappa_0 = \frac{24}{10}(4)^{1/3}\left(\frac{k}{h}\right)^3 \frac{M\delta\theta_D^2}{\gamma^2}. \tag{5.2.5}$$

Here k is Boltzmann's constant, h is Planck's constant, M is the mass per atom, δ^3 is the volume occupied per atom, θ_D is the Debye temperature, and γ is the Gruneisen parameter of the solid which can,

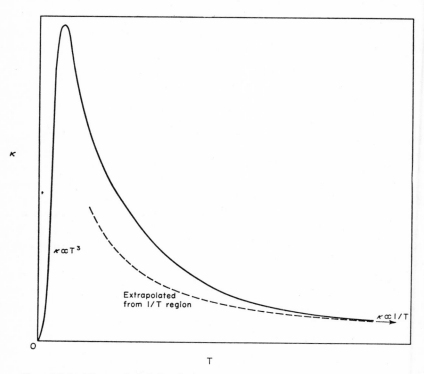

Fig. 5.2.1. Theoretical behaviour of thermal conductivity for a perfect crystal of finite size.

in principle, be obtained from thermal expansion data and contains the effect of the anharmonic forces. This formula was derived for a crystal composed of a single element. For compound materials, the factor M can be replaced, to a first approximation, by the average mass per atom and δ^3 by the average volume per atom. In view of the approximations which have to be made in the theory, the numerical values appearing in the formula cannot be regarded as reliable but the formula does show the approximate relation of the lattice thermal conductivity to other properties of the crystal.

Use of equation (5.2.5) in equation (5.2.1) leads to a high temperature ($T > \theta_D$) formula for the lattice thermal conductivity.

$$\kappa_L = \frac{24}{10}(4)^{1/3}\left(\frac{k}{h}\right)^3 \frac{M\delta\theta_D^3}{\gamma^2 T}. \tag{5.2.6}$$

There have been several other derivations of the numerical value of κ_L in this temperature range. Dugdale and Macdonald (1955:7) suggested the formula

$$\kappa_L = \frac{r_0\bar{v}}{3\chi\gamma^2 T}, \tag{5.2.7}$$

where r_0 is the distance between nearest neighbours, $\bar{v}$ is the velocity of sound and χ is the compressibility. Lawson (1957:8) and White and Woods (1958:13) have given other alternative forms, and have discussed the relationship between these showing that they are essentially equivalent and merely relate the lattice thermal conductivity to different properties. For example, on the simple Debye model, the Debye temperature can be related to $\bar{v}$ and to r_0 by the relation

$$\frac{k\theta_D}{h} = \frac{\bar{v}}{2r_0}. \tag{5.2.8}$$

In turn, $\bar{v}$ can be related to the density ρ and compressibility χ by

$$\bar{v} = (\rho\chi)^{-1/2} \tag{5.2.9}$$

and the density ρ is obviously given by

$$\rho = \frac{M}{\delta^3}. \tag{5.2.10}$$

Use of these formulae allows equation (5.2.6) to go over into equation (5.2.7) apart from a slight change in the numerical factor.

A third alternative form given by Lawson (1957:8) is obtained by using equation (5.2.9) to eliminate $\bar{v}$ in equation (5.2.7),

$$\kappa_L = \frac{r_0}{3\rho^{1/2}\chi^{3/2}\gamma^2 T}. \tag{5.2.11}$$

This equation was the starting point of a paper by Keyes (1959:**10**) in which he proceeded to use the *Lindemann melting rule* to eliminate the compressibility χ in favour of the melting temperature T_m of the solid. The melting rule (1910:**1**) is based on the hypothesis that melting takes place when the amplitude of the thermal vibrations of the atoms reaches some fraction ϵ of the interatomic distance, this fraction being the same for all solids. Keyes arrived at the formula

$$\kappa_L T = \frac{B T_m^{3/2} \rho^{2/3}}{A^{7/6}}, \tag{5.2.12}$$

where

$$B = \frac{R^{3/2}}{3\gamma^2 \epsilon^3 N_L^{1/3}}.$$

R is the gas constant, A is the atomic weight, N_L is Loschmidt's number and the remaining symbols have been defined previously. Keyes argued that the factor B in equation (5.2.12) did not vary very much from one solid to another. Suppose that $\kappa_L T$ is measured in W/cm, T_m in °K and ρ in g/cm³. Then, if B is assumed to be of the order of 1/30, the formula is satisfied, to within an order of magnitude, for a wide range of different types of crystal in which the overall variation of $\kappa_L T$ is over four orders of magnitude.

As expected from the approach used in the above arguments, the formulae, in general, are more reliable for comparing the thermal conductivities of materials belonging to similar crystal classes. For example, equation (5.2.12), with a value of B equal to 0·13, is much better for describing crystals in which the binding is predominantly covalent, while for ionic-type solids a much lower value of B of the order of 0·015 gives agreement to within a factor of 3 over two orders of magnitude of $\kappa_L T$. The value of B giving the best fit for the semiconductors shown in Fig. 5.2.2 is 0·06.

The departures of the values of $\kappa_L T$ from those predicted by equation (5.2.12), for a given class of compounds, were shown by Keyes to possess a systematic trend when the ratio of the masses of the different types of atoms in the solid is taken into account. The effect of altering this mass ratio in otherwise structurally similar crystals was noted by Eucken and Kuhn (1928:**1**) in a study of the thermal conductivity of a number of alkali halide crystals. A theoretical explanation of the effect was suggested by Blackman (1935:**2**), who investigated the conditions under which umklapp scattering could take place in a one-dimensional lattice consisting of two different types of atom. Black-man showed that, as the ratio of the masses of the two types of atom is altered from unity, then the conditions for umklapp processes involving

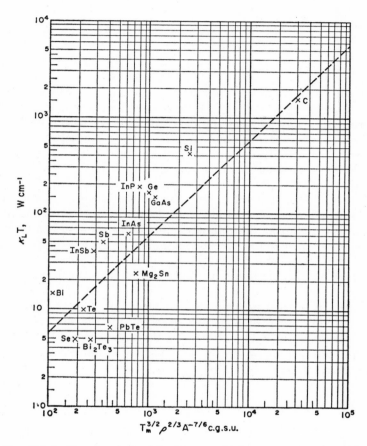

Fig. 5.2.2. Keyes' relationship between high-temperature thermal con-ductivity and melting point for a number of semiconductors.

an acoustic phonon and an optical phonon become more easily satis-fied. When the mass ratio is unity, the conditions for U-processes of this type cannot be satisfied but, as the mass ratio changes, the number of such possible processes at first increases. It reaches a maximum at some value of the ratio, which Blackman estimated to be about three, and then drops again rapidly to zero. Thus, the thermal conductivity should show a similar trend, over and above that due to U-processes involving only acoustic phonons (or only optical phonons), decreasing as the mass ratio alters from unity over a limited range. Such a trend was, in fact, observed by Keyes.

5.2.2 IMPERFECT CRYSTALS AT LOW TEMPERATURES

In introducing in the last sub-section a comparison of the experimental results with theoretical formulae, it must be remembered that, so far, these formulae apply in principle only to crystals which are structurally perfect. In practice, however, it is very difficult to prepare crystals which even approach this ideal and most crystals on which measurements have been made contain numbers of different types of imperfections, which can affect the thermal conductivity. We shall proceed to consider the effect of such imperfections. The general conclusion which emerges is that the high temperature lattice thermal conductivity tends to be dominated by umklapp processes so that the above theory is expected to have some significance. At low temperatures, however, the effect of imperfections, if the concentration is large enough, may be the predominant factor in limiting the thermal conductivity.

In general, when considering the scattering of phonons by imperfections, it is necessary in principle to allow for the fact that other scattering processes may be going on at the same time. This is shown clearly, for example, if we use the last part of equation (3.8.28) and write the thermal conductivity in the form

$$\frac{1}{\kappa_L T^2 \left(\mathbf{grad}\dfrac{1}{T}\right)^2} = \frac{1}{s_{p,f}{}^2}[s_{p,s}{}^{(\text{an})} + s_{p,s}{}^{(\text{imp})}], \qquad (5.2.13)$$

where $s_{p,f}$ is the entropy production calculated from the field term of the Boltzmann equation and $s_{p,s}{}^{(\text{an})}$ and $s_{p,s}{}^{(\text{imp})}$ are the rates of entropy production due to scattering by anharmonic processes and imperfections, respectively. All of these depend on the form of the phonon distribution function. If, however, one type of scattering process is much stronger than (another in the sense that the corresponding rate of entropy production is dominant) then this process dominates the form of the distribution function. For example, in a crystal containing a small concentration of imperfections, we expect that the thermal conductivity would still be dominated by anharmonic processes. In this case, the field term $s_{p,f}$ in the above equation can be taken to be the same as its value in the absence of any imperfections and the equation can be written in the alternative form

$$\frac{1}{\kappa} = \frac{1}{\kappa_{an}} + \frac{1}{\kappa_{imp}}, \tag{5.2.14}$$

where κ is the total thermal conductivity and κ_{an} is the thermal conductivity that would be measured in the absence of any imperfections. This equation clearly loses its validity when the effect of scattering by imperfections is comparable with the effect of scattering by anharmonic processes, and is strictly valid only in the limit of small concentrations of imperfections.

The quantity $1/\kappa_{imp}$ in equation (5.2.14) is obtained by considering the extra scattering due to the imperfections. The most important types of imperfections in practice are point imperfections where the effect of the imperfection is confined to a volume which is of the same order as the average volume per atom. If we forget, for the time being, that we are dealing with a crystal lattice, the scattering due to such point imperfections can be obtained on the basis of a classical formula due to Rayleigh (1896:1). He investigated the following problem. An elastic wave, characterized by a certain wavelength and velocity, is propagating through a medium possessing uniform properties and encounters a small region where the properties differ from the bulk. The criterion of smallness is expressed in terms of the wavelength of the incident wave. If the region is of linear dimensions c, we must have $c/\lambda \ll 1$.

Rayleigh showed that the ratio of transmitted to incident energy for the wave depended on the inverse fourth power of the wavelength, on the dimensions of the region and on the differences between the compressibilities and densities of the region and the bulk medium. Defining the scattering cross-section σ, so that σ multiplied by the energy density of the incident wave is the amount of energy lost by the wave, the formula for σ is

$$\sigma \propto c^6 q^4 \left[\frac{\Delta\chi}{\chi} + \frac{\Delta\rho}{\rho} \right]^2, \tag{5.2.15}$$

where $q = 2\pi/\lambda$ is the magnitude of the wave vector, $\Delta\chi$ and $\Delta\rho$ are the deviations of the compressibility and density of the region from the bulk values, χ and ρ.

Although this formula was derived for a continuous medium, we would expect that the same physical content would hold for the elastic waves (or normal modes) in a crystal lattice, at least for those whose wavelength is large compared with the dimensions of a unit cell. For such waves the discrete nature of the lattice is not important. Since the normal modes of long wavelength are the only ones which are present at low temperatures, we should be able to write the scattering cross-section associated with a point imperfection at low temperatures, for a mode of wave vector $\mathbf{q}$, as a modified form of equation (5.2.15), viz.

$$\sigma(\mathbf{q}) = C V_0^2 S^2 q^4. \tag{5.2.16}$$

Here C is a numerical constant, V_0 is the effective volume over which the point imperfection influences the elastic properties and density and S^2 is a positive dimensionless factor describing the net effect of the imperfection in producing local variations in these quantities.

When there is a concentration $\mathcal{N}_i$ of imperfections per unit volume, the total cross-section can be obtained by simple addition, provided that the concentration is small enough so that the distance between imperfections is large compared with the wavelength. Thus, the cross-section is $\mathcal{N}_i\sigma(q)$ per unit volume and, if we take this volume to be a unit cube, then, in travelling unit distance, $\mathcal{N}_i\sigma(q)$ is the fraction of energy lost by the incident wave. The definition of the mean free path $l(q)$ leads to the conclusion that this is the distance travelled when the fraction of energy lost is unity. Thus, we can obtain the mean free path as

$$l(q) = \frac{1}{\mathcal{N}_i\sigma(q)}. \tag{5.2.17}$$

The form of this result is not altered when we go through the process of quantizing the lattice waves and expressing the energy in terms of the phonon occupation, and we can write the mean free path for phonons of wave vector $\mathbf{q}$, when limited by point imperfections, as

$$l_i(\mathbf{q}) = \frac{q^{-4}}{A}, \tag{5.2.18}$$

where

$$A = C V_0^2 S^2 \mathcal{N}_i. \tag{5.2.19}$$

With more than one type of imperfection, A is the sum of a number of terms of the type in equation (5.2.19).

Since the mean free path concept is fairly well defined for impurity scattering, it would seem that the expression (5.2.18) could be substituted into equation (5.1.4) for the thermal conductivity and the integral evaluated. There is, however, a basic difficulty in this process in that the integral diverges at the long wavelength limit ($q = 0$) owing to the q^{-4} dependence of $l_i(q)$. It is necessary to take into account the fact that, below a certain value of q the effective mean free path of phonons will be limited by processes other than point-defect scattering so that the divergence for long waves is removed. Boundary scattering is one such process, but a more important effect is that associated with three-phonon N-processes, involving modes of very long wavelength and modes of shorter wavelength. Physically, such processes result in the transfer of phonons from the former modes to the latter where they can be scattered by point imperfections and give a finite thermal conductivity. Thus the very long wavelength modes have an "effective mean free path" determined by the rate at which phonons are exchanged between them and shorter wavelength modes and this removes the divergence of the resulting expression for the thermal conductivity.

A treatment, based on a Debye model for the vibration spectrum and taking such effects into account was given by Klemens (1951:**1**), who assumed that the phonons with wave vector **q**, such that $q < kT/\hbar\bar{v}$ where $\bar{v}$ is the velocity of sound, all have the same effective mean free path. He arrived at the formula

$$\kappa_{imp} = \frac{0{\cdot}90\ h\bar{v}^2}{4\pi^3\ AT}, \tag{5.2.20}$$

where A is the factor in equation (5.2.19).

A formula which is more satisfactory for small concentrations has been given by Ziman (1956:**3**), who, as mentioned previously, used the variational approach. He argued that, for small concentrations of imperfections, the form of the distribution function was dominated by phonon–phonon interactions and was thus able to calculate the term κ^{imp} in equation (5.2.14) using the appropriate transition probability. Ziman's formula, valid for small concentrations of point imperfections at low temperatures is, in a form analogous to equation (5.2.20),

$$\kappa_{imp} = \frac{1}{60(4\pi^3)} \frac{h\bar{v}^2}{AT}.$$

(5.2.21)

This formula differs by a numerical factor of 54 from that of Klemens. Although the variational method leads to a value of the thermal conductivity which is lower than the true value by an amount which cannot be specified exactly, the reasoning behind the derivation of equation (5.2.21) indicates that this should be fairly accurate at the limit of small concentrations of point imperfections.

The simplest type of point defect for a theoretical treatment arises from the fact that many elements in their natural state consist of two or more different isotopes. The simplicity is associated with the fact that, although the presence of atoms with different masses gives rise to local density fluctuations, there are no local fluctuations in the elastic properties since the interatomic force constants are unaltered. There is, however, an additional complication because the relative abundances of different isotopes in a particular element are usually comparable with each other and it is, therefore, necessary to extend the above discussion to the case of large concentrations of imperfections.

This can be done for isotope imperfections along the following lines (1956:6). When the only difference introduced by the point defect is one of local density, the formula for the cross-section, equation (5.2.16), taking into account the polarization of the phonons, has the form

$$\sigma(q) = \frac{1}{4\pi} V_0^2 \left(\frac{\delta\rho}{\rho}\right)^2 q^4.$$

(5.2.22)

If we introduce the local variation in mass δM equal to $V_0 \delta\rho$ this becomes

$$\sigma(q) = \frac{(\delta M)^2 q^4}{4\pi\rho^2},$$

(5.2.23)

in which δM is the difference between the mass actually present and the mass that would be present in the same volume if the density ρ were uniform.

Consider now a solid consisting of two different isotopic species of masses M_1 and M_2 and suppose that the concentrations of these are cN and $(1-c)N$, respectively, where N is the total number of atoms per unit volume. We regard the medium as possessing an overall average density ρ equal to $N\bar{M}$ where

$$\bar{M} = cM_1 + (1-c)M_2. \qquad (5.2.24)$$

The mean free path is then given by (cf. equation (5.2.17))

$$\frac{1}{l(q)} = \frac{q^4 N}{4\pi\rho^2}[c\delta M_1{}^2 + (1-c)\delta M_2{}^2], \qquad (5.2.25)$$

where

$$\delta M_1 = M_1 - \bar{M}, \qquad \delta M_2 = M_2 - \bar{M}.$$

This leads to

$$\frac{1}{l(q)} = \frac{q^4 c(1-c)(M_2 - M_1)^2}{4\pi N\bar{M}^2} \qquad (5.2.26)$$

as an estimate of the reciprocal mean free path. Since, in general, $(M_2 - M_1)$ is very much less than M_1 (or M_2), $\bar{M}$ does not vary strongly with c and the dominant dependence on concentration is given by the factor $c(1-c)$. The generalization to several isotopes is given by Berman, Foster and Ziman (1956:6).

This mean free path is of the same form as that given by equation (5.2.18), with a particular value of A which can be calculated and then substituted into either of the expressions (5.2.20) or (5.2.21) to give the appropriate contribution to the thermal conductivity. It is more useful to use the inverse of these formulae since equation (5.2.14) states that it is the thermal resistivities which are additive, at least for small concentrations. The Klemens formula, equation (5.2.20), leads to

$$W_{\text{imp}} = \frac{1}{\kappa_{\text{imp}}} = \frac{\pi^2}{0 \cdot 90} \frac{c(1-c)(M_2 - M_1)^2 T}{N h \bar{v}^2 \bar{M}^2} \qquad (5.2.27)$$

and the Ziman formula (5.2.21) to a similar equation with a numerical factor some fifty-four times larger. It must be remembered that the Ziman formula, from the nature of its derivation, applies only to small concentrations where c is close to zero. Further, the relation (5.2.14) can only be expected to apply when the effect of imperfection scattering is small compared with the effect of the anharmonic processes. Thus, a direct comparison of the experimentally observed thermal resistivity of solids containing different isotopic species with these formulae would not be expected to give quantitatively accurate results. Such a comparison was made by Toxen (1958:**14**) who found that the observed thermal resistivities of a number of solids were very much larger than expected on the basis of Klemens' formula (5.2.27) for small concentrations of imperfections (isotopes) (i.e. they were more consistent with the variational formula). For large concentrations Toxen found that the discrepancy tended to go in the opposite direction.

A considerable amount of light on the origin of these deviations from the predictions of the simple approach discussed above has been provided by a recent paper by Berman *et al.* (1959:**9**). In this work, the thermal conductivity of single crystals of lithium fluoride, containing various relative concentrations of the lithium isotopes Li^6 and Li^7, was measured between 10°K and 90°K. The first important result obtained from this work was the experimental verification of the Ziman variational formula for small concentrations, i.e. the formula

$$W_i = 60\pi^2 \frac{c(1-c)(M_2-M_1)^2 T}{N h \bar{v}^2 \bar{M}^2}$$

was found to fit the experimental results as $c \to 0$. However, deviations from this formula were observed with increasing c. In fact, the limiting case was deduced by an extrapolation of the experimental results and, for example, with $c(1-c)$ equal to 0·05 the thermal resistivity predicted by the above equation was some three times larger than the observed value. The discrepancy increased still further with increasing values of $c(1-c)$. Thus, the second important result was that, for appreciable concentrations of imperfections, the actual thermal resistivity rises with increasing concentration very much less rapidly than would be given by a factor $c(1-c)$. This trend is in line with that deduced by Toxen (1958:**14**) from less precise data.

This result was explained by Berman *et al.* using an extension of the variational method which allowed for the fact that, at large concentrations of imperfections, the form of the phonon distribution function could not be expected to be dominated by anharmonic processes as was assumed for the case of small concentrations. The more natural assumption was made that the form of the distribution function for long-wavelength phonons is still dominated by such processes, since imperfection scattering is weak for such phonons, but, above some wavelength, the distribution function goes over into a form dominated by imperfection scattering. The wavelength at which this occurs was taken as an arbitrary parameter which, in the final calculations, was adjusted to give the extreme value of the variational expression.

The results of this analysis expressed the ratio of the theoretical thermal conductivity at low temperatures to the quantity κ_{imp} given by equation (5.2.21), i.e. the value determined by the variational method in the limit of small concentrations. Thus, the factor by which the actual thermal conductivity departs from the simple formula (5.2.21), could be determined numerically. This factor was plotted in terms of a parameter x which is a very complicated function of a number of parameters of the solid. The expression for x given by Berman *et al.* is

$$x = \frac{\theta_D}{T} \frac{\lambda_0}{\lambda_i{}^0}. \tag{5.2.29}$$

Taking the mean free path for imperfection scattering in the form of equation (5.2.18), viz.

$$l_i(\mathbf{q}) = \frac{1}{Aq^4},$$

the parameter $\lambda_i{}^0$ is given by

$$\lambda_i{}^0 = \frac{\left(\dfrac{4\pi}{3}\right)^{1/3}}{192\pi^7 N^{4/3} A}, \tag{5.2.30}$$

where N is the number of atoms per unit volume. For the case of isotope scattering, with two types of isotopes, A is obtained comparing equations (5.2.26) and (5.2.18).

The other parameter λ_0 in equation (5.2.29) is a measure of the relative effective contribution of anharmonic processes determined from the Leibfried–Schlömann theory of these processes. Its value, as given by this theory, is

$$\lambda_0 = \frac{k\theta_D}{\hbar^2 N} \frac{M}{\gamma^2} \tag{5.2.31}$$

where the symbols have already been defined following equation (5.2.5). In the absence of experimental values of the parameters appearing in this equation, λ_0 can be estimated from the high temperature thermal conductivity, e.g. from equation (5.2.6).

To summarize this rather complicated discussion, the thermal conductivity of a crystal containing point imperfections at low temperatures is in general determined by a combination of scattering due to both the anharmonic processes and the imperfections. (We assume that the temperature, although low, is sufficiently high for boundary scattering to be neglected.) The expected behaviour of the thermal conductivity varies in a complicated way with the relative influence of the two processes. For zero contribution (to the entropy production) from imperfections, it should follow a law of the form of equation (5.2.3) determined by umklapp scattering; we call this value of the thermal conductivity κ_u. Then, with imperfections present, in such small concentrations that their effect is very small compared with that of the anharmonic processes, we should find that the total thermal conductivity is given by

$$\frac{1}{\kappa_L} = \frac{1}{\kappa_u} + \frac{1}{\kappa_i}$$

with κ_i given by equation (5.2.21), where the factor A is proportional to a factor $c(1-c)$. In the range of very small c, $c(1-c)$ can be replaced by c. For most solids, however, this equation does not hold because the relative influence of imperfection scattering, either through the presence of natural isotopes or accidental imperfections, tends to predominate over the anharmonic processes The thermal conductivity in this case is *not* determined by ignoring the factor $1/\kappa_u$ in the above equation and using equation (5.2.21) to determine κ_i. Instead the right-hand side of equation (5.2.21) has to be multiplied by a numerical factor (greater than unity) which can be determined from the theoretical curve given by Berman *et al.* (1959:9). A useful general rule is that this factor is given approximately by $0.042x^{1/2}$ over a range of x values from 10^4 to 10^7. Although this theory was developed especially to consider isotope scattering, its conclusions should remain unaltered in principle for other types of point imperfection, making the necessary allowance in the factor in equation (5.2.30) and elsewhere.

5.2.3 IMPERFECT CRYSTALS AT HIGH TEMPERATURES

The discussion of imperfect crystals at low temperatures given in the last section, although complicated, is based on fairly sound assumptions The confidence which can be placed on these assumptions is directly related to the fact that it is the phonons of long wavelength which are predominant in the transport processes. The probability of the presence of phonons whose wavelength is of the same order of magnitude as the lattice constant is very small at low temperatures.

As the temperature is raised, however, phonons of short wavelength become increasingly numerous. The presence of such phonons complicates the theory of thermal conductivity in a number of ways. In the first place, even for perfect crystals, the Debye approximation to the vibration spectrum becomes less applicable. The basic assumption of this approximation is that there is no dispersion of the phonons in a particular branch of the vibration spectrum, i.e. that the frequency is a linear function of the magnitude of the wave vector, so that all phonons in the branch have the same group velocity. Although this is certainly a good approximation for the acoustic modes of long wavelength which are important at low temperatures, it becomes worse as the wavelength is reduced (see for example the vibration spectrum for germanium given by Brockhouse and Iyengar (1958:**15**)). It is in fact a general rule that the slope of the ω vs. q curves must vanish on crossing the boundary of the first Brillouin zone. Exceptions to this rule arise only in very special cases from symmetry considerations. As a result, the group velocity of phonons of a particular branch tends to decrease as the wavelength decreases, becoming zero as the wave vector approaches the boundary of the first Brillouin zone. Although the specific heat, for which the Debye theory was formulated, is relatively insensitive to the presence of such dispersion, it is to be expected that the thermal conductivity, which depends directly on the group velocity, should be considerably influenced. In their variational calculation of the effect of umklapp processes, Leibfried and Schlömann allowed for the effect of dispersion using a frequency–wave vector relationship derived from a simple nearest neighbour interaction between atoms. The parameters describing the dispersion were related to the Debye temperature of the solid as deduced from specific heat data.

A second important effect, which affects the theory of imperfect crystals is that we cannot expect the Rayleigh formula, equation (5.2.18) to hold for short-wavelength phonons. There appears to be no simple formula of the same type for phonons whose wavelength is comparable with the linear dimensions of the region over which a point imperfection exercises its influence. General considerations indicate that the cross-section tends to become independent of wavelength under such conditions but there is obviously a wide transition region between this extreme case and that given by equation (5.2.18). Apart from some largely empirical relations, the only theories which attempt to describe the effect of point imperfections at high temperatures are those given by Ambegaokar (1959:**11**) and Klemens (1960:**3**). The former is concerned with the case of small concentrations and the latter with large concentrations, but in fact both theories can be combined as we shall show below. It should be mentioned that there are in fact very few reliable experimental results available for comparison with theory. The main source comes from the thermal conductivity of alloy systems and will be discussed in Section 5.4.

The theories of Ambegaokar and Klemens mentioned above are based on the use of a Debye spectrum and the formula (5.2.18) for the mean free path. Although we have already stated that these become less applicable for short-wavelength phonons, it is easy to see that using them both together leads to a situation in which errors tend to cancel. In particular, whether or not equation (5.2.18) is valid for short-wavelength phonons, it is clear that, in the presence of imperfections, the mean free path of such phonons will be very small. Thus, the calculated thermal conductivity will be relatively insensitive to whatever assumptions are made about the vibration spectrum for such phonons. This will be particularly true for large concentrations of imperfections. We can, therefore, use the Debye spectrum, which is applicable to the long-wavelength phonons, with the confidence that it does not matter too much that it describes the frequency–wave vector relationship rather poorly for short-wavelength phonons.

We next introduce an expression for the mean free path corresponding to umklapp scattering which, at high temperatures, together with imperfection scattering, are the most important processes. The form of the expression used by both the above authors is

$$l_u \propto q^{-2}.$$

On the basis of the Debye approximation, the relaxation times τ_i for imperfection scattering and τ_u for umklapp scattering have the forms

$$\frac{1}{\tau_i} = A'\omega^4, \qquad \frac{1}{\tau_u} = B\omega^2 \qquad (5.2.32)$$

where ω, equal to $\bar{v}q$, is the angular frequency, $\bar{v}$ being an average velocity of sound. Since we express the relaxation time τ as $l/\bar{v}$, we note that

$$A' = A\bar{v}^{-3} \qquad (5.2.33)$$

where A is defined by equation (5.2.19).

The final step is to obtain an overall relaxation time τ, taking both processes into account, from the relation

$$\frac{1}{\tau} = \frac{1}{\tau_i} + \frac{1}{\tau_u}. \tag{5.2.34}$$

This overall relaxation time can then be used in the expression (5.1.4) to give the thermal conductivity. Putting l equal to $\tau\bar{v}$, transforming to an integral over ω $(= \bar{v}q)$, and using the high-temperature form for specific heat contribution of the modes between ω and $\omega + d\omega$, gives the formula

$$\kappa_L = \frac{k}{2\pi^2\bar{v}B} \int_0^{\omega_D} \frac{d\omega}{1 + (A'/B)\omega^2}, \tag{5.2.35}$$

in which k is Boltzmann's constant and ω_D is the maximum frequency on the basis of the Debye model. This leads to

$$\kappa_L = \frac{k}{2\pi^2\bar{v}} \frac{\omega_0}{B} \tan^{-1}\left(\frac{\omega_D}{\omega_0}\right), \tag{5.2.36}$$

where $\omega_0^2 = B/A'$. The quantity ω_0 has the dimensions of frequency; equations (5.2.32) show that it is the frequency at which the relaxation times due to the two processes are equal. For small concentrations of imperfections, A' is small and ω_0 may be greater than ω_D. In this case ω_0 does not correspond to an actual frequency in the solid.

The thermal conductivity κ_u in the absence of imperfections is obtained from equation (5.2.35) by putting A' equal to zero. Then

$$\kappa_u = \frac{k\omega_D}{2\pi^2\bar{v}B}. \tag{5.2.37}$$

The combination of the last two equations gives the formula

$$\kappa_L = \kappa_u \frac{\omega_0}{\omega_D} \tan^{-1}\left(\frac{\omega_D}{\omega_0}\right). \tag{5.2.38}$$

On the basis of this formula, a knowledge of ω_0 enables us to predict the ratio of the thermal conductivity in the presence of imperfections to that in the absence of such imperfections. The value of ω_0/ω_D is given by

$$\frac{\omega_0{}^2}{\omega_D{}^2} = \frac{B}{A'\omega_D{}^2} = \frac{k}{2\pi^2\bar{v}\kappa_u\omega_D A'}, \qquad (5.2.39)$$

using equation (5.2.37). Thus, assuming that κ_u is known, we still have to find the value of A'. This gives us ω_0/ω_D and we can then find κ_L from equation (5.2.38).

As discussed in the preceding sub-section, the value of A' $(= A\bar{v}^{-3})$ can be obtained in a fairly unambiguous way when the imperfections scatter phonons as a result of the local change in density. The other effect of imperfections may be to introduce local variations in the elastic properties by altering the interatomic force strengths. There are certain cases in which we would expect the former effect to predominate over the latter.

The first case we shall consider is that treated by Ambegaokar (1959:11) who obtained an expression for the thermal resistance due to isotopes at high temperatures. Since isotopes scatter only by virtue of the variation in mass, the factor A' can be obtained directly. For the simplest case, where there are only two isotopic species of masses M_1 and M_2 with concentrations c and $(1-c)$, respectively, the mean free path is given by equation (5.2.26). Re-expressing this equation in terms of τ $(= l/\bar{v})$ and ω $(= q\bar{v})$ and comparing the result with the first of equations (5.2.32) gives

$$A' = \frac{c(1-c)}{4\pi\bar{v}^3\mathcal{N}}\frac{(M_2-M_1)^2}{\bar{M}^2}. \qquad (5.2.40)$$

The generalization of this equation when there are more than two kinds of isotopic species is

$$A' = \frac{\sum\limits_{i} x_i(M_i-\bar{M})^2}{4\pi\bar{v}^3\mathcal{N}\bar{M}^2}, \qquad (5.2.41)$$

where x_i is the relative concentration of atoms of mass M_i, $\mathcal{N}$ is the number of atoms per unit volume and $\bar{M}$ is the mean mass per atom defined by

$$\bar{M} = \sum\limits_{i} x_iM_i.$$

In all cases of interest, the scattering due to the presence of isotopes at high temperatures is small compared with that due to umklapp processes. This leads to consideration of an alternative form of equation (5.2.38) when $\omega_D \ll \omega_0$. This condition will be satisfied (due to the small value of A') when the effect of imperfections is small. For small values of ω_D/ω_0, the quantity $\tan^{-1}(\omega_D/\omega_0)$ in equation (5.2.38) can be expanded as a power series in ω_D/ω_0 giving the result

$$\kappa_L = \kappa_u \left[1 - \frac{1}{3} \frac{\omega_D^2}{\omega_0^2} \right]. \tag{5.2.42}$$

Inversion of this formula shows that the isotopes lead to a thermal resistivity higher than that to be expected in the absence of isotopes by an amount

$$W_i = \frac{\omega_D^2}{3\kappa_u \omega_0^2}. \tag{5.2.43}$$

From equation (5.2.39), this has the alternative form

$$W_i = \frac{2}{3} \frac{\pi^2 \bar{v} \omega_D A'}{k} = \frac{2\pi^2 \bar{v} \theta_D A'}{3\hbar} \tag{5.2.44}$$

where θ_D equal to $\hbar\omega_D/k$ is the Debye temperature. This formula, with A' given by equation (5.2.41) is equivalent to that derived by Ambegaokar and used by him to calculate the isotope scattering at high temperatures in germanium. We note that the extra thermal resistance W_i is independent of temperature.

As mentioned previously, isotope scattering at high temperatures is slight compared with the umklapp scattering processes. We now turn to the consideration of cases where the imperfection resistance predominates. The most important of these occur in alloy systems, which have been studied extensively in connexion with their applications to thermoelectric devices. In certain of these systems, it is reasonable to suppose that the mass variation effect on the scattering of phonons predominates over the effect resulting from a change in the interatomic forces. One such system in which this should be true is that of germanium–silicon alloys. The similarity in the chemical nature of silicon and germanium and the fact that homogeneous solid solutions can be obtained over the whole range of compositions makes it reasonable to suppose that the effect of changes in the local elastic properties is small compared with the effect of local density changes, particularly since these latter are very large in this system. In view of its simplicity, we shall consider the germanium–silicon system separately here and later discuss some more complicated systems.

For an alloy of the formula $Ge_{1-x}Si_x$, the contribution from the mass variance factor to the parameter A' can be calculated just as for isotope scattering. If M_g is the mass of a germanium atom and M_s is the mass of a silicon atom, equations (5.2.40) give

$$A' = \frac{x(1-x)}{4\pi\bar{v}^3\mathcal{N}} \frac{(M_g - M_s)^2}{\bar{M}^2}, \qquad (5.2.45)$$

with

$$\bar{M} = (1-x)M_g + xM_s. \qquad (5.2.46)$$

This expression cannot be used directly in equation (5.2.39) to calculate ω_0/ω_D without making some further assumptions about the values of the parameters $\bar{v}$, κ_u, ω_D and $\mathcal{N}$. These parameters have been introduced in such a way that they refer to an alloy of a specific composition and in general are not known directly. The simplest and probably the most accurate way of determining the values is to use linear interpolation between the values at the two extremes of pure germanium and pure silicon, for which they are known fairly accurately. If this procedure is adopted, we can define $\bar{v}$, κ_u, ω_D $(= k\theta_D/\hbar)$ and $\mathcal{N}$ for an alloy of composition $Ge_{1-x}Si_x$ by the relations

$$\begin{aligned}
\bar{v} &= (1-x)\bar{v}_g + x\bar{v}_s, \\
\kappa_u &= (1-x)\kappa_{u,g} + x\kappa_{u,s}, \\
\theta_D &= (1-x)\theta_{D,g} + x\theta_{D,s}, \\
\mathcal{N} &= (1-x)\mathcal{N}_g + x\mathcal{N}_s,
\end{aligned} \qquad (5.2.47)$$

where subscripts g and s refer to the values for pure germanium and pure silicon, respectively.

With these assumptions we can evaluate expression (5.2.39) so that equation (5.2.38) enables us to predict the lattice thermal conductivity of an alloy of given composition knowing the relevant parameters at the two extreme ends. It is shown in Section 5.4 that this procedure leads to remarkably good agreement with the experimental results.

There are several alloy systems whose thermal conductivity has been investigated in connexion with their possible application to thermoelectric devices. These are all more complicated than the germanium–silicon system and it is no longer possible to assume that the mass variance parameter is the one primarily responsible for the scattering of phonons. Nevertheless it is of interest to consider what the above theory would predict for such systems. We would anticipate that a calculation of the parameter A' on the basis of the mass variance factor alone would give too low a value since we are omitting any extra effect due to changes in interatomic forces. Hence, we should find, on putting this value of A' into equation (5.2.39), a value of ω_0/ω_D which is too high. Since equation (5.2.38) is a monotonic decreasing function of ω_D/ω_0 the use of too low a value of this parameter leads to a value of κ_L/κ_u which is too high. Thus, a theory for the alloy systems which takes into account only the mass variance effect should in general predict a value of κ_L/κ_u which is higher than that observed by experiment.

Of the alloy systems considered, we first consider those which have the form $AB_{1-x}C_x$. Thus, if N is the number of molecules per unit volume, there are N atoms of type A, $(1-x)N$ of type B, and xN of type C, per unit volume. The mass per unit volume (equal to the density ρ) is thus

$$\rho = N\bar{M} = N[M_A + (1-x)M_B + xM_c], \qquad (5.2.48)$$

where $\bar{M}$ is the average mass per molecule. We use equation (5.2.23) for the cross-section which leads to a mean free path of the form

$$\frac{1}{l_i(q)} = \frac{q^4}{4\pi\rho^2} \sum_i n_i(\delta M_i)^2, \qquad (5.2.49)$$

where n_i is the number of defects per unit volume resulting in a local mass difference δM_i from that corresponding to a uniform density ρ.

In the case of the compound crystals considered here it is obviously wrong to consider the individual atoms as producing local mass variations as was assumed for the germanium–silicon system. To do so would give an expression for the mean free path l_i which is finite at the two extremes $x = 0$ and 1 and, thus, would indicate imperfection scattering in compound crystals even when these have a perfectly regular structure. To calculate the effects due to mixing we have clearly to consider the mass deviations per molecule (or for a larger unit). Thus, in the case considered, there are $(1-x)N$ centres per unit volume with mass deviations $(M_A + M_B - \bar{M})$ and xN with mass deviations $(M_A + M_C - \bar{M})$. Equation (5.2.49) then gives

$$\frac{1}{l_i(q)} = \frac{q^4}{4\pi N \bar{M}^2}\{(1-x)[M_A + M_B - \bar{M}]^2 + x[M_A + M_c - \bar{M}]^2\}.$$

This simpifies to

$$\frac{1}{l_i(q)} = \frac{q^4}{4\pi N \bar{M}^2}x(1-x)(M_B - M_c)^2. \qquad (5.2.50)$$

As previously, putting l equal to $\bar{v}\tau$, ω equal to $\bar{v}q$ and comparing with equation (5.2.32) we obtain the parameter A' which in this case is

$$A' = \frac{x(1-x)(M_B - M_c)^2}{4\pi\bar{v}^3 N \bar{M}^2}. \qquad (5.2.51)$$

This value of A' enables us, in principle, to complete the calculation as before and to predict the thermal conductivity of an alloy of intermediate composition from a knowledge of the relevant parameters at the two extremes. Unfortunately, for most of the alloy systems that have been measured, these parameters are not directly available and various approximations have to be made in their estimation.

For more complicated alloy systems with more than two atoms per molecule the above theory can readily be modified. Although the calculation of A' may be subject to considerable error, it is worth while noting that, in principle, a value can be obtained from measurements at low temperatures using the theory given in the previous section. In the absence of such measurements a value calculated from the variance of the mass differences should lead to an upper limit for the lattice thermal conductivity.

5.3 MEASUREMENTS ON ELEMENTARY AND COMPOUND SEMICONDUCTORS

5.3.1 GROUP IV ELEMENTS

It will be apparent from the preceding sections that the thermal conductivity of a solid is particularly sensitive to its detailed composition and structure. It is, therefore, of considerable importance that, in confirming the theoretical predictions with experimental measurements, as much as possible should be known about any crystalline imperfections. Further, in determining the thermal conductivity which is characteristic of the perfect solid, it is vital that these imperfections should be reduced in number as far as is possible.

It is in this context that the measurements of the thermal conductivity of *germanium* and *silicon* are considered here. Both these materials, and particularly the former, have been studied very extensively because of their application to transistors and other junction devices. In consequence, it is possible to obtain crystals of these materials which, structurally and chemically, approach more closely to the ideal crystal than those of any other materials. In addition, there is available a wealth of accurate data, on such important features as the effect of chemical and structural imperfections on the physical properties, which enable the type and concentration of such imperfections to be measured for any particular specimen with a high degree of accuracy. We may add that a very detailed knowledge of the form of the vibration spectrum of these materials is available as a result of neutron diffraction studies. With all this data available, germanium and silicon are likely to remain the proving ground for theories of thermal conductivity for a long time to come.

The first experimental results that we shall consider relate to the high temperature thermal conductivity. We wish to compare the measured values with those given by equation (5.2.6) or one of the other similar formulae. These formulae, strictly speaking, apply only above the Debye temperature. For germanium and silicon, the Debye temperatures, as determined from specific heat data, are 372°K and 645°K, respectively (1959:**12**). Equation (5.2.6), after the insertion of values for the physical constants, becomes

$$\kappa_L \eqsim \frac{5 \cdot 7 \bar{A} \delta \theta_D^3}{\gamma^2 T} \text{ W/cm °C.} \tag{5.3.1}$$

In this formula $\bar{A}$ is the mean atomic weight (72·6 for Ge and 28·0 for Si), δ is the cube root of the volume per atom (2·81 Å for Ge and 2·71 Å for Si), θ_D is the Debye temperature and γ is the Gruneisen constant. This last parameter is not known accurately for the two materials. Its value is usually taken to be 2. It is perhaps more important to note that its value should be very similar for materials of similar crystal structure.

Equation (5.3.1) leads to values of the product $\kappa_L T$ of 150 and 290 W/cm for germanium and silicon, respectively.

Turning to the experimental results we find that although a considerable number of measurements have been made at low temperatures, there are very few reliable results available above room temperature. Of the measurements that have been made, the most accurate appear to be those of Stuckes (1960:4) who obtained values for the lattice thermal conductivity of germanium and silicon in the range from 40°C to 425°C. The measured values were corrected, where necessary, for the electronic contribution. The presence of a small, but not negligible, electronic thermal conductivity in germanium at elevated temperatures was demonstrated by the experiments of Abeles (1959:13) and Kettel (1959:8).

For germanium, Stuckes found that the product of $\kappa_L T$ was not constant above the Debye temperature, although its variation was only slight. Thus, at 400°K the product had a value of 160 W/cm falling to 155 W/cm at 500°K. Above this temperature the variation was more rapid and κ_L tended to fall as $1/T^2$. This behaviour was taken as an indication that anharmonic processes involving more than three phonons were becoming important.

For silicon, the value of $\kappa_L T$ at 600°K was found to be 330 W/cm. This product varied slightly with temperatures below 600°K and more rapidly above this temperature. It is thus difficult to obtain a precise value of the product which is characteristic of three-phonon processes but the above figure should be reasonably accurate.

The values obtained experimentally are in fairly good agreement with the theoretical predictions. Taking into account the uncertainty in the value for γ in equation (5.3.1), it is more significant that the ratio of the experimental to the theoretical value is very nearly the same for the two materials. This relative agreement is improved if we take into account the fact that, strictly speaking, a small correction to the experimental results on germanium is necessary to allow for the effects of scattering due to the different isotopes present. The correction for silicon on this account is very much less.

The complications due to the presence of natural isotopes in germanium become increasingly important as the temperature is lowered. This was shown by the experiments of Geballe and Hull (1958:1) who made measurements on a specimen of normal germanium and on a specimen in which the proportion of the isotope Ge[74] had been increased to 96 per cent. The results are shown in Fig. 5.3.1.

At high temperatures, the thermal resistivity of the normal speci-men exceeds that of the enriched specimen by 0·15 cm °C/W, this quantity being independent of temperature. Ambegaokar (1959:**11**)

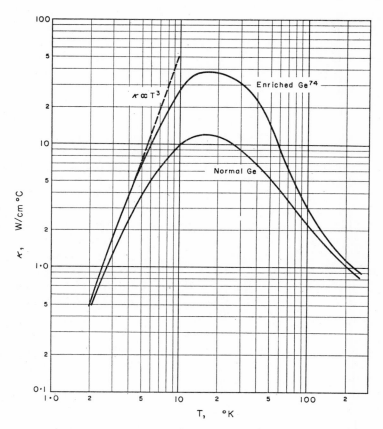

FIG. 5.3.1. Thermal conductivity of normal Ge and enriched Ge[74] [after Geballe and Hull (1958:**1**)].

showed that this is in good agreement with the theory of phonon scattering by point imperfections at high temperatures given in Section 5.2.3. The appropriate formula is equation (5.2.44) for small concentrations. The value of $\bar{A}$ is given by equation (5.2.41) with the factor $\Sigma x_i(M_i - \bar{M})^2/\bar{M}^2$ equal to $5 \cdot 85 \times 10^{-4}$. Using the values

$\theta_D = 372°K$, $\bar{v} = 3.58 \times 10^5$ cm/sec and $\mathcal{N} = 10^{24}/22.6$ cm^{-3} appropriate to germanium, we predict that W_i should be equal to 0.19 cm °C/W at high temperatures.

Turning to the results at lower temperatures, the measurements of Geballe and Hull on normal germanium show that there is no range over which the lattice thermal conductivity varies exponentially with the inverse temperature as one might have expected on the basis of equation (5.2.3). The absence of such a region at temperatures above the conductivity maximum was noted previously by Carruthers et al. (1957:**9**) who made an extensive series of measurements on germanium specimens having different impurity contents. It was assumed by them that the scattering due to the natural isotopes was responsible for the absence of this feature on the basis of the earlier work by Berman et al. (1956:**6**). However, the results of Geballe and Hull showed that even in the enriched germanium, where isotope scattering was almost completely eliminated, there was no such exponential region, although it is evident that the thermal conductivity rises more rapidly with decreasing temperature than in the normal sample (see Fig. 5.3.1).

A possible explanation of this observation was given by Geballe and Hull in terms of the particular form of the vibration spectrum of germanium. The Debye temperature of germanium, obtained on the basis of specific heat data, is 372°K, which corresponds to a value for $k\theta_D$ of 3.21×10^{-2} eV. However, it has been found from neutron diffraction experiments that the maximum energy of the transverse acoustical branches of the vibration spectrum of germanium is only about 7×10^{-3} eV. As a result, the umklapp scattering associated with phonons in this branch persists to a much lower temperature than would have been expected on the basis of the normal Debye temperature. In fact, the solid tends to behave as though it had a Debye temperature of only about 80°K; for such a solid no exponential behaviour would be observed except at very low temperatures of 10°K or less. For such temperatures, however, in real crystals, boundary scattering predominates and masks any region of exponential temperature dependence.

The difference between the thermal conductivities of normal Ge and enriched Ge^{74} at a temperature just above the conductivity maximum has been shown by Berman et al. (1959:**9**) to be in reasonable agreement with their theory of scattering by isotopes at low temperatures, an outline of which has been given in Section 5.2.2.

White and Woods (1956:**7**) and Carruthers et al. (1957:**9**) have measured the thermal conductivity of single crystals of silicon below room temperature. In neither case was an exponential dependence observed. Natural silicon consists predominantly of one isotope but, owing to the relatively small mass of the silicon atom, isotope scattering is still appreciable. No measurements on enriched silicon have yet been carried out. However, it is clear that the absence of any exponential temperature variation of the thermal conductivity in silicon is not necessarily due to the presence of isotope scattering. In fact, the experimentally observed temperature dependence may have a similar explanation to that used by Geballe and Hull to account for their results for germanium. For silicon, also, the maximum energy of the transverse acoustical branches of the vibration spectrum is much less than $k\theta_D$.

All the measurements made on germanium and silicon show that the thermal conductivity reaches a maximum at some point as the temperature decreases and falls rapidly with further decrease of temperature. The behaviour in the region below the conductivity maximum is in general agreement with the theory of boundary scattering given in Section 5.2.1. The variation with size of sample was determined by Carruthers et al. and the corresponding phonon mean free paths were obtained by combining the thermal conductivity measurements with specific heat data. They were shown to be consistent with the linear dimensions of the specimen. However, the detailed behaviour in this range possesses some complex features. Only in one case did the thermal conductivity show the expected variation; this behaviour was observed to hold accurately, for Geballe and Hull's enriched Ge^{74} sample, in the range from 2 to 5°K. For the normal sample and also for the silicon and germanium samples measured by Carruthers et al. and Rosenberg (1954:1), the thermal conductivity did not follow a T^3 law even at the lowest temperatures. It is thus clear that scattering by point imperfections affects the thermal conductivity even in the region well below the maximum where boundary scattering might have been expected to be predominant.

Callaway (1959:**14**) has considered this problem in detail and has given a theory which accounts in a satisfactory way for the difference between the thermal conductivities of the two samples measured by Geballe and Hull, at temperatures both below and above that of the conductivity maximum.

Geballe and Hull (1955:**8**) made an interesting comparison of the effects of boundary scattering on the thermal conductivity and the

Seebeck coefficient of germanium. At low temperatures, the major contribution to the Seebeck coefficient comes from the phonon-drag effect (1954:**6**) and, below 100°K, the magnitude of this effect is limited by boundary scattering of the phonons which interact with the charge carriers. Geballe and Hull found that the increase in thermal conductivity with cross-section of sample was accompanied

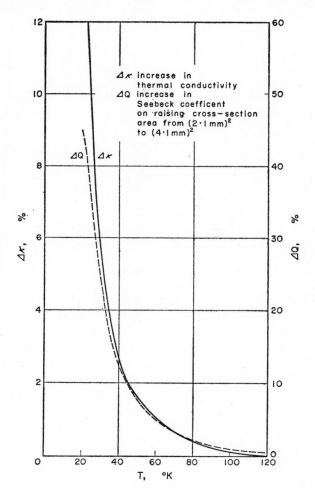

Fig. 5.3.2. The effect of boundary scattering on the thermal conductivity and Seebeck coefficient of germanium [after Geballe and Hull (1955:**8**)].

by a rise in the Seebeck coefficient. The striking similarity between the temperature variations of the increases in the two cases is shown in Fig. 5.3.2. The results show that boundary scattering of phonons has rather more marked effect on the Seebeck coefficient than on the thermal conductivity. This is because the phonon-drag effect involves only low-energy phonons which are less readily scattered by other phonons than are the high-energy heat-conduction phonons.

To sum up these observations, it will be seen that the results of measurements on pure germanium and, to a lesser extent, silicon (for which the isotope effect has not been measured directly) are in fairly good agreement with the theoretical predictions. In particular, we can be fairly confident that the appropriate physical parameters involved in the theory of the lattice thermal conductivity have been isolated, although we are less certain about the actual numerical values, particularly at high temperatures. One point of significance that emerges is the absence of any range where the thermal conductivity varies exponentially with temperature. The presence of such a region appears to have been observed only very rarely. Several authors, in particular Slack (1957:**10**) and Berman *et al.* (1956:**6**) have attributed the absence of such a region, in a large number of dielectric solids, to the presence of natural isotopes, but, in fact, this does not seem to be the case for germanium. The explanation given by Geballe and Hull may be applicable to other materials also. Clearly, much remains to be done in this field.

Before concluding this section, we may briefly consider some measurements that have been made on the lattice thermal conductivity of *diamond* which has the same crystal structure as silicon and germanium. Incidentally, semiconducting diamonds are by no means rare and the electrical properties of a number of them have been determined. However, for a number of reasons the measurements have not the same significance as those discussed above. Chemical purity probably has a profound influence on the thermal conductivity of diamond since scattering of phonons by other phonons, even at room temperature, is relatively weak. Thus, results reported for one diamond may not be characteristic of the properties of all diamonds.

Berman *et al.* (1953:**3**) have measured the thermal conductivity of a type I diamond down to low temperatures. At 300°K the thermal conductivity was found to be 5·5 W/cm °C and, in this region, to be approximately inversely proportional to the temperature. It is clear that the thermal conductivity of a good diamond exceeds that of any metal over a wide temperature range. A maximum of only about 29 W/cm °C was observed as the temperature was lowered, however, compared with a theoretically predicted value of about 1000 W/cm °C; the low experimental value was attributed to imperfection scattering. At the lowest temperatures, the calculated mean free path for phonons showed no temperature dependence and agreed well with the value predicted from Casimir's formula, equation (5.2.4), provided that the scattering of phonons at the boundaries was assumed to be only partially of a diffuse nature.

5.3.2 ELEMENTS OF GROUP V AND VI

The other elementary semiconductors have not such widespread applications as germanium and silicon so that crystals of high purity are much rarer. Nevertheless, measurements of the thermal conductivity of tellurium and selenium have assisted in broadening our knowledge of heat conduction by the lattice.

Fischer *et al.* (1957:**11**) have determined the thermal conductivity of a number of samples of *tellurium* down to temperatures of less than 2°K. The results for two of the samples are illustrated in Fig. 5.3.3. Both samples were highly pure, but, whereas Te2 was polycrystalline, Te5 was a single crystal. Above about 20°K both samples possessed approximately the same thermal conductivity but at lower temperatures the single crystal Te5 had the higher value. At about 3°K the thermal conductivity of Te5 agreed quite well with the value calculated from Casimir's formula for boundary scattering, equation (5.2.4), but it was not possible to make accurate measurements on this sample at lower temperatures.

The thermal conductivity of Te2 at the lowest temperatures was found to be proportional to T^2. Such a temperature dependence might be expected for scattering of phonons by dislocations (1956:**8**); a dislocation density of about $5 \times 10^9/cm^2$ would be needed to explain the results.

Above liquid oxygen temperature the thermal conductivity was proportional to $1/T$ but at lower temperatures a more rapid variation was observed. However, the variation was less rapid than the exponential temperature dependence which would be expected if phonon–

phonon scattering were dominant. Fischer *et al.* suggested that the maximum thermal conductivity of sample Te5 was limited to only about 9 W cm^{-1} °C^{-1} by isotope scattering; there are no less than seven isotopes present in natural tellurium.

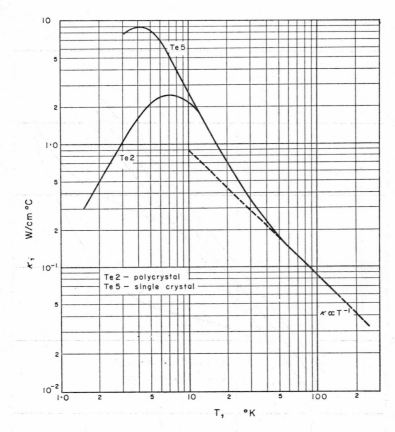

FIG. 5.3.3. Thermal conductivity of tellurium at low temperatures [after Fischer *et al.* (1957:**11**)].

The thermal conductivity of tellurium at higher temperatures has been measured by Devyatkova *et al.* (1959:**7**). All their samples were single crystals with the thermal gradient applied in the direction of the main crystal axis. Figure 5.3.4. shows the variation of thermal conductivity with temperature for three specimens. At 100°K the thermal conductivity of the purest sample agrees with Fischer's value; the other samples have lower thermal conductivities, presumably due to the scattering of phonons by impurities. At higher temperatures, only the least pure sample 3 shows the normal behaviour expected for the conduction of heat by the lattice vibrations. For this sample, the thermal resistivity can be attributed entirely to the scattering of

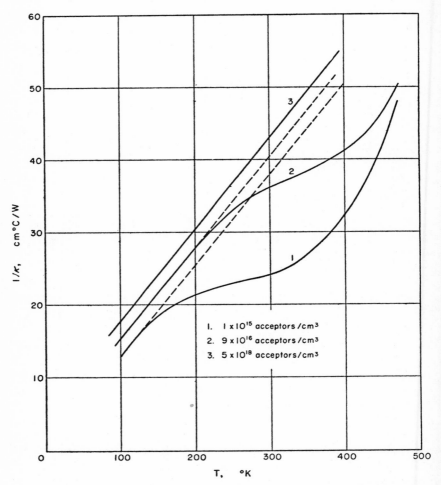

FIG. 5.3.4. Thermal resistivity of tellurium plotted against temperature [after Devyatkova *et al.* (1959:7)].

phonons by other phonons and by impurities. However, above about 130°K the thermal resistivity of the purest sample 1 starts to fall below the expected value, being little over half this value at 300°K. A similar behaviour was observed for sample 2, of intermediate purity, above about 200°K.

Devyatkova showed that the results for samples 1 and 2 could not be explained on the basis of transport of heat by charge carriers even with bipolar thermodiffusion. However, they demonstrated that the low thermal resistivity is due to the transfer of heat by radiation through the samples. Genzel (1953:**4**) has shown that the increase in thermal conductivity due to such radiation is

$$\kappa_R = \frac{16}{3} \frac{n^2 \sigma T^3}{a},\tag{5.3.2}$$

where n = refractive index, σ = Stefan's constant of radiation and a = absorption coefficient. At wavelengths shorter than that which corresponds to a quantum energy E_g, photons are strongly absorbed in a semiconductor, creating electron–hole pairs. However, at longer wavelengths the absorption coefficient becomes much smaller. It is lowest for pure materials but the presence of large concentrations of current carriers in impure materials leads to somewhat higher absorption coefficients. Thus, qualitatively, the behaviour of the three tellurium samples is easily explained. In samples 1 and 2 the low thermal resistivity must be due to radiative heat transfer; in sample 3, the high free carrier absorption of photons makes such additional heat transfer negligible. The quantitative application of Genzel's formula, averaged over all wavelengths, is complicated by the anisotropy of the tellurium crystal, but Devyatkova and her colleagues showed that there was good agreement between theory and experiment. Appreciable heat transfer by radiation must therefore be expected, at elevated temperatures, in all pure semiconductors of low lattice thermal conductivity, provided that the energy gap is large enough. In tellurium the gap width is 0·32 eV.

Amirkhanov et al. (1957:**12**) have extended the measurements on tellurium above the melting point and have determined the anisotropy of the thermal conductivity in single crystals (1959:**15**). At 100°K the thermal conductivity parallel to the cleavage planes is more than twice as great as that in the perpendicular direction.

*   *   *

White *et al.* (1958:**17**) have measured the thermal conductivity of pure *selenium* in both its crystalline and amorphous forms. Their results are shown in Fig. 5.3.5. The maximum thermal conductivity was much less than the value expected from the crystallite size even though this was no more than about 20 μ.

The thermal conductivity of amorphous selenium is about two orders of magnitude lower than for crystalline material and falls continuously as the temperature is reduced. It was shown that the value

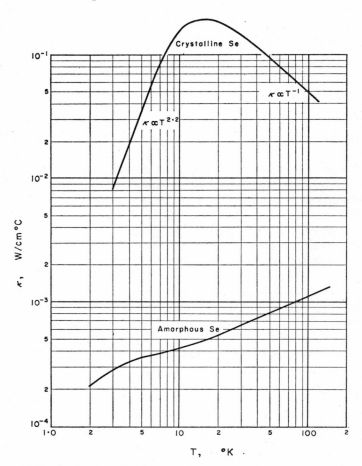

FIG. 5.3.5. Thermal conductivity of crystalline and amorphous selenium [after White *et al.* (1958:**17**)].

of the phonon free path length at the higher temperatures is close to the interatomic distance; in this range the change of thermal conductivity with temperature is due solely to the variation of the specific heat. At very low temperatures the phonon wavelength becomes much greater than the interatomic spacing; the free path length for phonons then increases and makes the variation of thermal conductivity with temperature become less steep. This behaviour was found for amorphous selenium below about 20°K.

A number of Soviet workers have studied the effects of halogen impurities on the thermal conductivity of selenium. Measurements have been made on both amorphous and crystalline material containing chlorine (1957:**13**), bromine (1957:**14**) and iodine (1957:**15**). In each case the results have shown the same character. Small additions of the impurity lead to a rapid fall in the thermal conductivity. However, beyond a certain limiting concentration, the thermal conductivity rises again without reaching the value for the undoped material. Bashshaliev (1959:**16**) has suggested that, for small concentrations, the individual atoms scatter phonons independently, but that, at higher concentrations, the density fluctuations can no longer be considered for atoms in isolation, so that the phonon scattering is less marked.

Bismuth and *antimony* are not semiconductors since in both cases the valence and conduction bands overlap. Nevertheless, both these elements display some of the characteristics of degenerate semiconductors and it is felt that they should at least be mentioned.

White and Woods (1958:**18**) have measured the thermal conductivity of both bismuth and antimony from about 2°K upwards. In bismuth, in spite of the relatively high concentration of conduction electrons, the thermal conductivity below 50°K is primarily due to the lattice waves. Above 10°K the thermal conductivity was found to be proportional to $1/T$ but a rather more rapid variation was observed below this temperature. For a pure sample of large crystal size, a thermal conductivity of about 15 W cm^{-1} °C^{-1} was attained at 4°K. The values at lower temperatures agreed with Casimir's formula for boundary scattering.

The thermal conductivity of antimony between 2 and 100°K was found to be more complex since at no temperature was the electronic component negligible. In fact, below about 7°K the electronic component is the dominant factor so that the thermal conductivity in this range is approximately proportional to the absolute temperature. The lattice component of the thermal conductivity may be determined by applying a high magnetic field, which greatly reduces the electronic component at the same time as it increases the electrical resistivity.

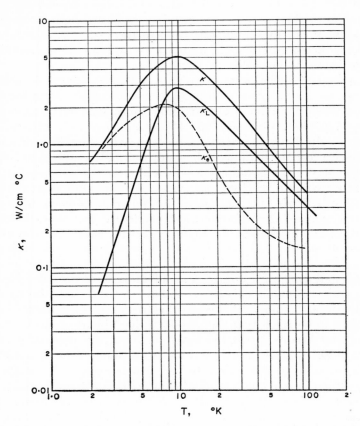

FIG. 5.3.6. Thermal conductivity of antimony plotted against temperature [after White and Woods (1958:**18**)].

Figure 5.3.6 shows how the total thermal conductivity and its two components were found to vary with temperature in White and Wood's experiments. The maximum free path length for the phonons was calculated to be only about 0·1 mm, whereas the crystals extended over 2 to 5 mm. It was suggested that scattering of phonons by electrons might have accounted for this observation.

5.3.3 COMPOUND SEMICONDUCTORS

At the present time germanium and silicon are the only semi-conductors employed in the manufacture of transistors. However, for many other applications a superior performance can be achieved by using semiconducting compounds. For example, the galvanomagnetic effects are largest for semiconductors which have a high electron mobility; thus, the increasing number of Hall effect, and other, magnetic devices are based on compounds such as indium antimonide, which has a mobility of about 80,000 cm² V⁻¹ sec⁻¹ compared with 3800 cm² V⁻¹ sec⁻¹ for germanium. Similarly, the low thermal conductivities which are needed for materials used in thermoelectric refrigeration can only be obtained with semiconducting compounds such as bismuth telluride or lead telluride. We find, therefore, a growing interest in compound semiconductors.

It is natural to consider first one of the III–V compounds which have the zinc-blende type lattice which is so closely related to the diamond-type lattice of silicon and germanium. The first measurements on the thermal conductivity of *indium antimonide*, InSb, reported by Busch and Schneider (1954:3), have already been mentioned. Although they indicated the order of magnitude of the thermal conductivity, more reliance can be placed on the work of Stuckes (1957:3) who covered the temperature range up to 400°C. She found the product $\kappa_L T$ to be 45 W/cm at room temperature. Stuckes has since measured the lattice thermal conductivity of *indium arsenide* and, from the results, the high-temperature value of $\kappa_L T$ for this material is about 80 W/cm. For *gallium arsenide* $\kappa_L T$ is about 110 W/cm (1959:17) We may compare these experimental results with the values predicted from equation (5.2.6). The Debye temperatures of InSb and GaAs have been obtained directly from measurements of the elastic constants as 200 and 346°K. Assuming a value of two for the Gruneisen parameter, equation (5.2.6) predicts values of 43 and 120 W/cm for these materials. There do not seem to be any measurements which enable the Debye temperature of InAs to be obtained directly. The best that can be done for this material is to use the Lindemann melting rule which leads to a value of 245°K. This implies that $\kappa_L T$ should be about 60 W/cm. The use of a Debye temperature some 10 per cent higher would be necessary to give $\kappa_L T$ equal to 80 W/cm on the basis of equation (5.2.6).

Stuckes found the lattice thermal conductivity of both indium antimonide and indium arsenide to vary more rapidly than $1/T$ at high temperatures. She suggested that this is due to scattering processes involving four phonons. However, the experimental evidence on indium antimonide is conflicting. Busch *et al.* (1959:**18**) and Kanai and Nii (1959:**4**) found the lattice thermal conductivity of this material to vary as $1/T$ over the temperature range 200 to 700°K.

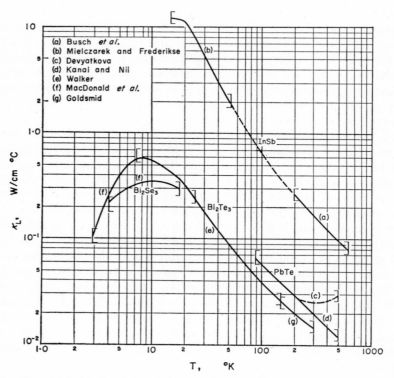

Fig. 5.3.7. Lattice thermal conductivity of semiconducting compounds.

Mielczarek and Frederikse (1959:**19**) measured the thermal conductivity of indium antimonide at low temperatures. As for other crystals, the maximum thermal conductivity is much less than that calculated for a combination of phonon–phonon and boundary scattering. This is because of the effect of isotope scattering and probably also of impurity scattering. The experimental results for indium antimonide in the high- and low-temperature ranges and the interpolated values for the intermediate region are shown in Fig. 5.3.7. The lattice thermal conductivity for some other semiconducting compounds is also shown.

The thermal conductivity of *lead telluride*, PbTe, was measured by Devyatkova (1957:**4**). She calculated the lattice component, as indicated by curve (c) in Fig. 5.3.7, by substituting the electronic component (obtained from equation 4.1.24 with $p = -\frac{1}{2}$) from the total thermal conductivity. Between 90 and 200°K the lattice component obtained in this way varied inversely with temperature. However, it is seen that Devyatkova's values above 200°K showed a considerable departure from this relationship. Devyatkova attributed this behaviour, not to an unusual temperature dependence of the real lattice thermal conductivity, nor yet to an error in estimating the electronic component, but to the transport of heat by excitons (1956:**9**). However, Kanai and Nii's results (1959:**4**) from thermal diffusivity measurements on lead telluride show no such anomalous behaviour. It is, therefore, doubtful if there is the necessity to introduce the idea of heat conduction by excitons to explain the high temperature thermal conductivity of lead telluride.

A wide range of temperature has been covered by workers on *bismuth telluride*, Bi_2Te_3. Walker (1960:**5**) has made measurements on pure single crystals from 7 to 150°K. The results of MacDonald et al. (1959:**20**) for one of their samples of bismuth telluride between 3 and 25°K agree particularly well with those of Walker in the overlapping temperature range and there is close agreement between Walker's and Goldsmid's (1958:**9**) values at 150°K. Between 50 and 150°K the lattice thermal conductivity was found to vary as $1/T$. Goldsmid's results at higher temperatures showed a rather less steep temperature dependence; it must, however, be remembered that the lattice thermal conductivity at the highest temperatures could only be obtained after subtracting an estimated electronic component which was always a substantial portion of the total heat conductivity. Nevertheless, there may be some theoretical support for a weak temperature dependence of the lattice component in certain ranges as will be mentioned at the end of this section. Below 50°K the thermal conductivity varied more rapidly with temperature, at one stage as $T^{-1.5}$, before levelling off to a maximum of about 0.6 W cm^{-1} °C^{-1} at 8°K and then falling with further decrease of temperature. The value of the maximum thermal conductivity was much lower than that expected from boundary scattering; scattering of phonons by dislocations, which are particularly dense in single crystals of bismuth telluride (1959:**21**) may be the explanation.

For the temperature range immediately above that of the maximum conductivity, Walker attempted to apply the formula for isotope scattering which Berman *et al.* found to hold for lithium fluoride and other crystals (see Section 5.2.2). In this formula the phonon free path length is proportional to $\theta_D{}^5/T^{9/2}$. Thus, when isotope scattering is dominant, and at sufficiently low temperatures for the specific heat to be proportional to T^3, it might be expected that the thermal conductivity should vary as $T^{-3/2}$. The fact that the lattice thermal conductivity of bismuth telluride does vary as $T^{-3/2}$ over a certain range of temperature may be coincidental since the specific heat varies as T^2 in this range, but different specific heats may be involved in heat conduction and thermal capacity effects. The use of a value of θ_D equal to 145°K, as obtained from low-temperature specific heat measurements, gives a phonon free path length some twenty times the observed value. However, in view of the strong dependence of the free path length on θ_D in the formula of Berman *et al.*, it is only necessary to reduce the value of θ_D to about 90°K in order to get good agreement. Probably, because of its strong anisotropy, bismuth telluride is not a good material for testing theories of heat conduction; in the temperature range from 150 to 300°K the thermal conductivity along the cleavage planes is twice as great as that in the perpendicular direction (1956:**1**).

Walker, Goldsmid, and Bowley *et al.* (1958:**11**) all observed an increase in the thermal resistivity of bismuth telluride on doping with iodine, the usual donor impurity. Figure 5.3.8 shows the lattice thermal resistivity of material doped with 0·2 per cent I, compared with that of pure bismuth telluride. It is significant that the results of each of the workers lie on the same smooth curve. The extra thermal resistivity on doping with iodine is not entirely invariant with temperature but a change of only from 3 to 7 W^{-1} cm °C was observed between 10 and 300°K. This agrees quite well with the idea of slight scattering by point imperfections at high temperatures which should lead to an extra thermal resistivity which is independent of temperature. On the other hand, at low temperatures we should expect the extra thermal resistivity to be proportional to T (cf. equations (5.2.20) and (5.2.21)); there is no evidence of such a range having been reached.

Walker has applied Ziman's formula (5.2.21) to scattering by iodine atoms, assuming that the scattering of phonons is due to changes of density, rather than of bond strength and anharmonicity, in the region of the impurity atoms. The scattering effect of a foreign atom depends

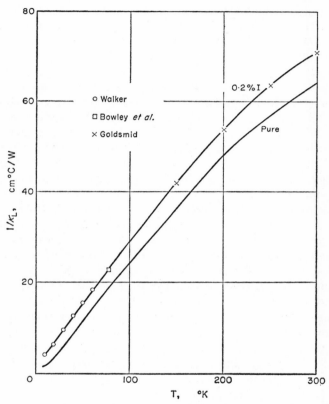

Fig. 5.3.8. Thermal resistivity of pure and iodine-doped bismuth telluride.

on the difference between its mass and that of the atom which it replaces. Clearly the effect is different when the atom is substitutional from when it is interstitial. Walker found that the results at 30°K could fit Berman's formula if part of the impurity atoms occupied each type of site. It should be noted, however, that density measurements

(1960:6) suggest that all the iodine atoms substitute for tellurium atoms.

Goldsmid analysed his observed fall in thermal conductivity on the lines of Ioffe's approach (1954:7); a scattering cross-section σ was assigned to each impurity atom. Ioffe suggested that σ/a^2, where a is the interatomic spacing, should be approximately equal to unity for a substitutional impurity but might have much larger values for interstitial impurities; he produced experimental evidence which supported his ideas. Goldsmid's results gave a value of σ/a^2 equal to 13. Such a high scattering cross-section for a substitutional impurity suggests that the introduction of iodine appreciably disturbs the elastic forces between the atoms.

MacDonald *et al.* (1959:20) found that their sample of *bismuth selenide*, Bi_2Se_3, had a maximum thermal conductivity at about 10°K of only 0·34 W cm^{-1} °C^{-1}, but at 20°K the value approached that of bismuth telluride. The work of Hashimoto (1958:8) shows that the lattice thermal conductivity of bismuth selenide in the range 100 to 250°K differs but little from that of bismuth telluride. Hashimoto also found the lattice conductivity to vary less rapidly than as $1/T$ at the higher temperatures.

Certain semiconductors have a lattice thermal conductivity lower than that of bismuth telluride, even though the phonon free path length would appear to be no more than two or three interatomic spacings for the latter material. Hockings (1959:6) has observed a value of only 0·006 W cm^{-1} °C^{-1} for *silver antimony telluride*, $AgSbTe_2$, while A. V. Ioffe found the thermal conductivity of *gallium selenide*, Ga_2Se_3, to be no more than 0·004 to 0·006 W cm^{-1} °C^{-1} over the whole temperature range from 90 to 430°K. Under these circumstances it is hardly legitimate to think in terms of heat conduction by lattice waves since the phonon free path length would be less than the interatomic spacing. A. F. Ioffe (1959:22) has suggested that, for materials with such low thermal conductivities, it is necessary to introduce the idea of a new type of heat conduction process in which each atom vibrates more or less independently, though there is always the possibility of a quantum transfer of energy from one atom to its neighbours. Energy transfer between atoms should be inhibited by anharmonicity of their vibrations, such anharmonicity, of course, being responsible for limiting heat conduction by lattice waves in the more normal situation. The thermal conductivity, corresponding to the heat transfer effect suggested by Ioffe, should be independent of temperature; it is possible that such an effect reduces the rate of variation with temperature of the thermal conductivity of both bismuth telluride and bismuth selenide above 150°K.

To conclude this section we give a table of lattice thermal conductivities of semiconductors. Some of the values in the table are more reliable than others; thus, a list of references is included so that the reader can check the methods by which the results were obtained.

Table 5.3.1 *Lattice thermal conductivity of semiconductors at room temperature*

Semiconductor	Groups	κ_L(W cm^{-1} °C^{-1})	Reference
Diamond	IV	5·5	Berman *et al* (1953:**3**)
Si		1·45	Carruthers *et al.* (1957:**9**)
Ge		0·64	Carruthers *et al.* (1957:**9**)
Se	VI	0·02	White *et al.* (1958:**17**)
Te		0·03	Fischer *et al.* (1957:**11**)
GaP	III–V	1·1	Weiss (1959:**23**)
InP		0·8	Weiss (1959:**23**)
AlSb		0·6	Weiss (1959:**23**)
GaAs		0·37	Abrahams *et al.* (1959:**17**)
InAs		0·29	Abrahams *et al.* (1959:**17**)
GaSb		0·27	Wright (1959:**24**)
InSb		0·15	Stuckes (1957:**3**)
HgTe	II–VI	0·02	Wright (1959:**24**)
Ga$_2$Se$_3$	III–VI	0·005	Ioffe (1959:**22**)
PbSe	IV–VI	0·017	Ioffe (1956:**10**)
PbTe		0·023	Ioffe (1956:**10**)
Sb$_2$Te$_3$	V–VI	0·024	Birkholz (1958:**5**)
Bi$_2$Se$_3$		0·024	Birkholz (1958:**5**)
Bi$_2$Te$_3$		0·016	Goldsmid (1958:**9**)
AgInSe$_3$	I–III–VI	0·03	Wright (1959:**24**)
AgSbTe$_2$	I–V–VI	0·006	Hockings (1959:**6**)

5.4 SEMICONDUCTOR ALLOYS

There is considerable interest in the properties of semiconductor alloys from a practical point of view owing to the fact that they can yield improved figures of merit for thermoelectric applications (1956:**11**). However, such alloys are also important in enabling us to check the validity of the simple theory of imperfection scattering given in Section 5.2.3. We shall present first the experimental results for a number of alloy systems and then compare these results with the theoretical predictions. Finally, we shall compare the effects of alloying on the carrier mobility and the thermal conductivity pointing out the implications in the choice of thermoelectric materials.

5.4.1 Measurements on Semiconductor Solid Solutions

The thermal conductivity for a number of alloys of silicon with germanium has been measured by Ioffe and Ioffe (1954:**7**) and by Steele and Rosi (1958:**19**). Their room temperature results are illustrated in Fig. 5.4.1. It will be observed that over the limited range (0–40 per cent Si) covered by the Russian workers there is a considerable discrepancy between the two sets of measurements. Steele and Rosi thought that this discrepancy might have been due to the use of sintered samples by Ioffe and Ioffe. If we accept the American results as being typical of large crystals we see that the thermal resistivity rises from a value of about 1·6 cm °C/W for germanium to a maximum value of about 9·6 cm °C/W for an intermediate alloy and falls to only about 0·9 cm °C/W for silicon. It is noticeable that the maximum thermal resistivity occurs for an alloy which is slightly richer in silicon than germanium in spite of the fact that the thermal resistivity of germanium exceeds that of silicon.

A similar type of behaviour was observed by Steele and Rosi at 80°K. At this temperature the thermal resistivities of germanium and silicon are about 0·29 and 0·13 cm °C/W, respectively. The maximum thermal resistivity in the alloy system at 80°K is about 4·3 cm °C/W. It is worth noting that, whereas the thermal conductivities of the pure elements change by a factor of about 6 times between 80°K and 300°K, the thermal conductivity of the 50 per cent Si–50 per cent Ge alloy changes by a factor of only about 2 over the same range

*   *   *

Weiss (1959:**23**) has measured the thermal conductivity of solid solutions between GaAs and GaP and between InP and InAs. While his results undoubtedly indicate the general behaviour of the systems which he studied, it is rather difficult to use them to obtain precise

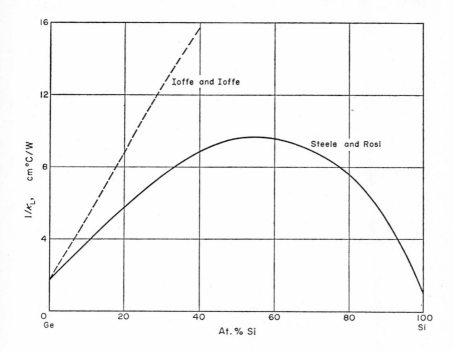

FIG. 5.4.1. Thermal resistivity of Ge–Si alloys at room temperature.

information on the variation of thermal conductivity with composition. Moreover, where a direct comparison can be made with the results of other workers it is seen that the values given by Weiss are appreciably higher. The data of Weiss as well as those of other authors are shown in Fig. 5.4.2. It will be noticed that the measurements by Abrahams *et al.* (1959:**17**) on InAs agree with those of Bowers *et al.* (1959:**1**).

Abrahams and his colleagues showed that the thermal conductivity of GaAs falls from about 0·37 W/cm °C to less than 0·05 W/cm °C on the substitution of 50 mol. per cent InAs. Bowers and his co-workers showed that the thermal conductivity of InAs falls from 0·29 W/cm °C to just over 0·1 W/cm °C on the addition of 40 per cent InP.

Bowers extended his measurements up to 800°C. At the highest temperature the thermal conductivity of InAs was found to be 0·08 W/cm °C while the value for the alloy with 40 per cent InP was

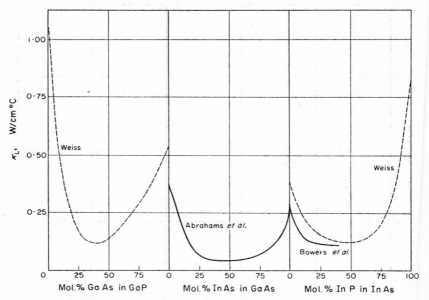

FIG. 5.4.2. Thermal conductivity of alloys of III–V compounds at room temperature.

measured as 0·05 W/cm °C. Quite clearly the variation of thermal conductivity with temperature is much greater for the pure compound than for the alloy.

The tellurides of lead and bismuth are the best compounds for use in thermoelectric refrigeration. It is, therefore, natural that the alloy systems of both compounds have received attention. In each case the thermal conductivity is reduced on alloying with a consequent increase in the thermoelectric figure of merit.

Figure 5.4.3 shows the variation of thermal resistivity with composition for solid solutions of PbSe and PbTe, as reported by Ioffe and Ioffe (1956:**12**). The lattice thermal resistivity of PbTe is 50 cm °C/W and that of PbSe only slightly higher; the lattice thermal resistivity of the 50 per cent solid solution is over 100 cm °C/W.

Figure 5.4.4 shows the lattice thermal conductivity of alloys of Bi_2Te_3 with Sb_2Te_3 and with Bi_2Se_3. Measurements were made by Birkholz (1958:5), Rosi *et al.* (1959:25) and Goldsmid (1957:16). There is

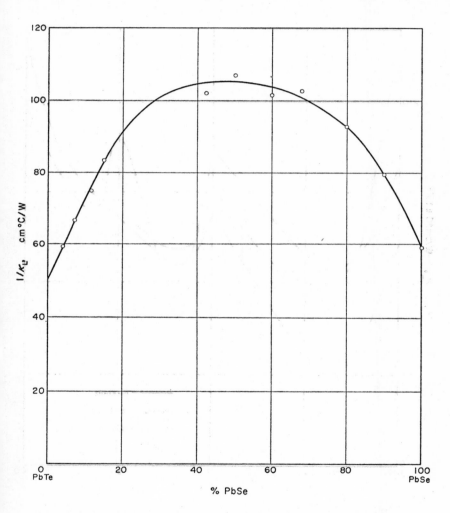

FIG. 5.4.3. Thermal resistivity of solid solutions between PbSe and PbTe at room temperatures [after Ioffe and Ioffe (1956:12)].

some disagreement as to the absolute values of the lattice thermal conductivity but, at least in the Sb_2Te_3–Bi_2Te_3 system, there is qualitative agreement between the results. The widely differing values for Sb_2Te_3 and alloys close to Sb_2Te_3 are probably due to the difficulty in separating out the electronic component of the thermal conductivity which is always exceptionally high for these compositions. There is

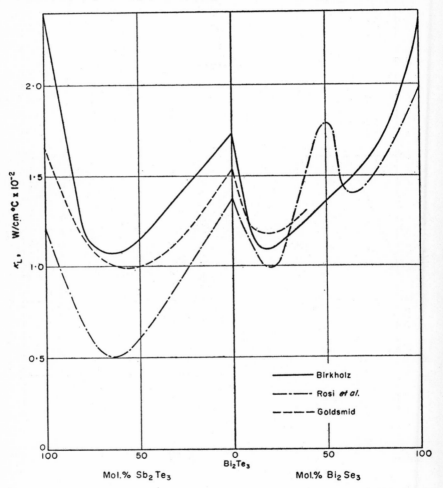

FIG. 5.4.4. Lattice thermal conductivity of alloys of Bi_2Te_3 with Sb_2Te_3 and Bi_2Se_3 at room temperature.

some suggestion that the minimum lattice thermal conductivity occurs for an alloy which lies closer to Sb_2Te_3 than to Bi_2Te_3.

The behaviour in the Bi_2Te_3–Bi_2Se_3 system is rather peculiar. The lattice thermal conductivity falls very rapidly indeed on the addition of Bi_2Se_3 to Bi_2Te_3 but a minimum value occurs at only about 20 per cent Bi_2Se_3. The measurements of Rosi and his colleagues indicate that the thermal conductivity has a maximum, near to the 50 per cent alloy, which is higher than the value for Bi_2Te_3. However, Birkholz found no such maximum. Both sets of results show that the relative fall in the thermal conductivity for dilute alloys of Bi_2Te_3 in Bi_2Se_3 is much less than that for dilute alloys of Bi_2Se_3 in Bi_2Te_3.

5.4.2 COMPARISON OF EXPERIMENT WITH THEORY OF IMPERFECTION SCATTERING

In Section 5.2.3 we showed how it is possible to calculate the reduction of thermal conductivity by imperfection scattering at high temperatures assuming that this scattering results wholly from local variations of density. In particular, we outlined the means by which this theory could be applied to germanium–silicon alloys. It was shown that the various parameters appearing in equations (5.2.39) and (5.2.45), i.e. $\bar{v}$, κ_u, θ_D and $\mathcal{N}$, could be obtained with sufficient accuracy by linear interpolation between their values at the extreme compositions. The application of the theory to alloys between compounds as well as between elements was indicated.

Before comparing the experimental results with the theory it is worth mentioning two approximate formulae which can be employed if all the requisite parameters are not known. The first of these formulae is the Debye approximation for the velocity of sound. $\bar{v}$ is given by

$$\bar{v} \doteqdot \frac{k\theta_D}{\hbar}\left(\frac{V}{6\pi^2}\right)^{1/3}, \qquad (5.4.1)$$

where V is the average volume per atom of the crystal.

It may also be the case that the Debye temperature of some material is unknown. Then θ_D may be estimated from the Lindemann melting rule

$$\theta_D \doteqdot C_L T_M^{1/2} \check{A}^{-5/6} \rho^{1/3}, \qquad (5.4.2)$$

where T_M is the melting temperature, $\bar{A}$ the mean atomic weight, and ρ the density in g/cm³. C_L is a constant (equal to about 120) for a particular crystal structure.

In the general case of an alloy consisting of any number of compounds we may write equation (5.2.39) in the form

$$\left(\frac{\omega_0}{\omega_D}\right)^2 = \frac{2\hbar\bar{v}^2 N}{\pi \kappa_u \theta_D \epsilon}, \tag{5.4.3}$$

where N is the number of *molecules* per unit volume and

$$\epsilon = \frac{\sum_i x_i(M_i - \bar{M})^2}{\bar{M}^2}. \tag{5.4.4}$$

x_i is the concentration of molecules of mass M_i and $\bar{M}$ the average mass of all molecules. It should be noted that the number of species of molecules can exceed the number of different compounds contained in the alloy if these compounds are complex. For example, if a compound AB_2 is alloyed with a compound AC_2 we must consider ABC as a separate species of molecule in equation (5.4.4).

If we combine equations (5.4.1) and (5.4.3) we obtain the useful formula

$$\left(\frac{\omega_D}{\omega_0}\right)^2 = \frac{\pi}{2}\frac{\hbar}{k^2}\left(\frac{6\pi^2}{V}\right)^{2/3}\frac{\kappa_u\epsilon}{N\theta_D}, \tag{5.4.5}$$

$$= 1\cdot32 \times 10^{13}\frac{\kappa_u\epsilon}{V^{2/3}N\theta_D},$$

if κ_u is expressed in W/cm °C, and V and $1/N$ are expressed in cm³. We may note that $1/N$ is equal to V multiplied by the number of atoms in the molecule.

We have applied equation (5.4.5), together with equation (5.4.2) where necessary, to the alloy systems mentioned in the previous subsection and obtained the appropriate values of ω_D/ω_0. Equation (5.2.38) shows that each value of $\tan^{-1}(\omega_D/\omega_0)/(\omega_D/\omega_0)$ should have been equal to the ratio κ_L/κ_u, where κ_L is the measured lattice thermal conductivity and κ_u is the thermal conductivity which would have held if only umklapp scattering had existed (κ_u being obtained by interpolation). Figure 5.4.5 shows κ_L/κ_u plotted against ω_D/ω_0 for various alloy compositions; the curve represents the values of $\tan^{-1}(\omega_D/\omega_0)/(\omega_D/\omega_0)$.

It is seen that the points corresponding to some of the alloy systems lie very close to the curve in Fig. 5.4.5. These systems include Ge–Si, InAs–InP, and Bi_2Te_3–Sb_2Te_3 for which the mean experimental values of a number of workers have been used. For other systems, PbTe–PbSe and InAs–GaAs, the measured values of κ_L/κ_u are appreciably lower than those predicted by the theory. Such exceptions to the theory are, of course, not unexpected since we have taken into account only

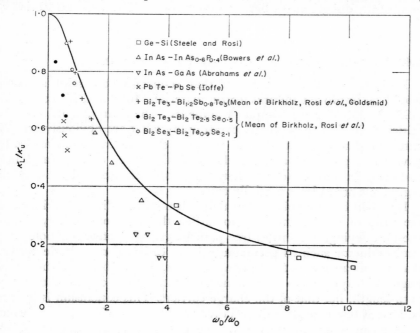

□ Ge – Si (Steele and Rosi)

△ In As – In As$_{0.6}$P$_{0.4}$ (Bowers *et al.*)

▽ In As – Ga As (Abrahams *et al.*)

× Pb Te – Pb Se (Ioffe)

+ Bi$_2$Te$_3$–Bi$_{1.2}$Sb$_{0.8}$Te$_3$ (Mean of Birkholz, Rosi *et al.*, Goldsmid)

● Bi$_2$Te$_3$–Bi$_2$Te$_{2.5}$Se$_{0.5}$ ⎫
○ Bi$_2$Se$_3$–Bi$_2$Te$_{0.9}$Se$_{2.1}$ ⎬ (Mean of Birkholz, Rosi *et al.*)
　　　　　　　　　　　　　　　⎭

FIG. 5.4.5. Experimental values of κ_L/κ_u plotted against ω_D/ω_0 for semiconductor alloys. The curve represents $\tan^{-1}(\omega_D/\omega_0)/(\omega_D/\omega_0)$.

imperfection scattering due to variations of density; it is perhaps reasonable, then, to attribute the failures of the simple theory to the presence of additional scattering due to local variations in elastic properties. However, it must be remembered that numerous assumptions and approximations have been used in the theory and it is really surprising that it holds at all well for any of the systems.

The results for the Bi_2Te_3–Bi_2Se_3 system are rather interesting. The comparatively slight reduction of thermal conductivity on the addition of Bi_2Te_3 to Bi_2Se_3 agrees quite well with the theoretical predictions; the points shown in Fig. 5.4.5 cover the range of compositions up to 30 per cent Bi_2Te_3. On the other hand, the reduction of the thermal conductivity on the addition of Bi_2Se_3 to Bi_2Te_3 is much greater than that predicted by theory; in this case the range up to 15 per cent Bi_2Se_3 is covered. The intermediate range of compositions between 15 per cent and 70 per cent Bi_2Se_3 has not been included in view of the disagreement between the results of Birkholz and Rosi *et al.*

5.4.3 SCATTERING OF ELECTRONS AND PHONONS IN ALLOYS

In justifying their prediction that semiconductor solid solutions would be improved thermoelectric materials, Ioffe and his colleagues (1956:**11**) used quite simple arguments. These arguments may be criticized in that they greatly oversimplify what are obviously complicated processes and indeed, as we shall show later, Ioffe's associates have since proposed a more elaborate theory of electron and hole scattering in alloys. Nevertheless, it has been shown that the original arguments are at least partially true.

It should first be pointed out that it is not immediately obvious that the ratio of carrier mobility to lattice thermal conductivity should rise on alloying. The mean free path length of electrons or holes in a semiconductor such as germanium is an order of magnitude greater than the mean free path of phonons. Thus, a disturbance of the lattice might be expected to have a more drastic effect on the larger free path length, i.e. that of the charge carriers. This conclusion is seen to be false if one considers the relative wavelengths which are involved.

At room temperature, the wavelengths of the phonons which are primarily responsible for the conduction of heat are only of the order of a few interatomic spacings. Now it is well known that disturbances of periodicity over the order of about a quarter wavelength are the most effective in scattering waves. Thus, the heat-conduction phonons are scattered most readily by disturbances in the short-range order of the lattice; these are the sort of disturbances that are introduced in the formation of solid solutions.

Now in *metals* the free electrons have similarly short wavelengths but in *semiconductors* the wavelengths associated with the carriers are considerably greater. It is, therefore, only disturbances in the long-range order which are effective in scattering electrons and holes in semiconductors and such disturbances are not readily produced by alloying. We conclude that the formation of solid solutions should not lower the carrier mobility; thus, the ratio of mobility to lattice thermal conductivity should rise.

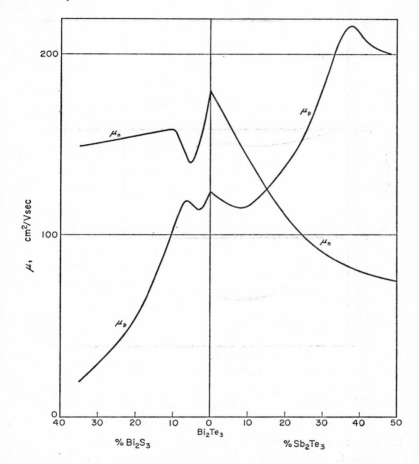

Fɪɢ. 5.4.6. Mobilities of electrons and holes in solid solutions of Sb_2Te_3 and Bi_2S_3 in Bi_2Te_3 [after Airapetyants *et al* (1957:**17**)].

More recently, Airapetyants *et al.* (1957:**17**) have carried out experiments which suggest that these ideas about alloy scattering are inadequate. In their measurements they determined the mobilities of electrons and holes in solid solutions of Sb_2Te_3 and Bi_2S_3 in Bi_2Te_3 and of SnTe and PbSe in PbTe. Their results are shown in Figs. 5.4.6 and 5.4.7. The addition of Sb_2Te_3 to Bi_2Te_3 considerably lowers the electron mobility while the addition of Bi_2S_3 has a much greater effect

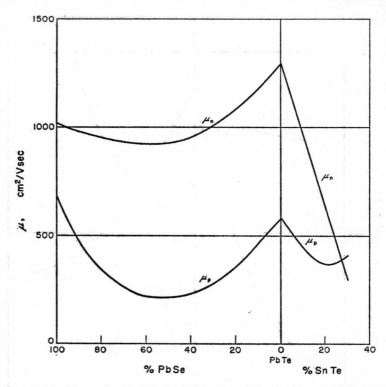

FIG. 5.4.7. Electron and hole mobilities in solid solutions of PbTe with SnTe and PbSe [after Airapetyants *et al.* (1957:**17**)].

on the hole mobility. Similarly, the addition of SnTe to PbTe reduces the electron mobility appreciably, whereas it is the mobility of holes which is most affected on adding PbSe. Airapetyants and his co-workers explained these results by associating the motion of *holes* with the *electronegative* sub-lattice and that of *electrons* with the *electropositive* sub-lattice. Thus a disturbance in the electronegative sub-lattice may be expected to reduce the hole mobility while a similar disturbance in the electropositive sub-lattice should lower the electron mobility.

There may be some truth in these ideas but they are certainly not universally applicable. For example, Airapetyants' results for the Bi_2Te_3 system were obtained using sintered materials. Measurements on large-crystal alloys of Bi_2Te_3 and Sb_2Te_3 (1960:**6**) suggest that the mobility of electrons exceeds that of holes even for the composition $BiSbTe_3$. Again, Ehrenreich (1960:**7**) has shown that there is no need to invoke alloy scattering to explain the variation of electron mobility with composition in InAs–InP alloys though, according to Airapetyants' ideas, alloy scattering of electrons (but not of holes) might be expected to occur.

Thus, at the present time it has been demonstrated experimentally that the ratio of carrier mobility to lattice thermal conductivity can be raised by alloying. However, much additional work is necessary before it will be possible to predict accurately the behaviour of the electron and hole mobilities in semiconductor solid solutions.

THE FIGURE OF MERIT FOR THERMO-ELECTRIC APPLICATIONS

IN the course of this book there has been considerable mention of semiconductors which are employed in thermoelectric applications. It is the object of this appendix to show how the figure of merit for such materials can be defined in terms of basic semiconductor parameters which include the lattice component of the thermal conductivity. The interested reader can find more extensive treatments elsewhere (1957:1, 1960:2).

The first of the thermoelectric effects was discovered by Seebeck in 1821. He showed that a potential difference can be produced by heating the junction between two dissimilar conductors. Then, in 1834, Peltier showed that there is absorption or generation of heat when an electric current flows through such a junction. This effect is, of course, quite distinct from the irreversible Joule resistance heating effect which one usually associates with the flow of current.

The Seebeck effect forms the basis of thermoelectric generation, that is the conversion of heat into electrical energy by means of thermocouples. The Peltier effect may be utilized in thermoelectric refrigeration (or for heat-pumping in general). It was first shown by Kelvin that the Seebeck and Peltier effects are simply related; as given in equation (4.1.17c)

$$\pi = QT,$$

where π is the Peltier coefficient and Q is the Seebeck coefficient.

In attempting to make practical use of thermoelectric generation, the quantity which is of greatest interest to us is the *efficiency* for a given temperature difference between the source of heat and the sink. In applying thermoelectric refrigeration, we require the highest *coefficient of performance* for a given temperature difference. In both cases the performance, under the optimum operating conditions, can be expressed in terms of a *figure of merit*. It is, perhaps, not surprising that it is the same figure of merit which applies both for thermoelectric generation and for refrigeration. This figure of merit is given in the form

$$z = \frac{(Q_1 - Q_2)^2}{\left\{ \left(\frac{\kappa_1}{\sigma_1}\right)^{1/2} + \left(\frac{\kappa_2}{\sigma_2}\right)^{1/2} \right\}^2}, \tag{A.1.1}$$

where the subscripts 1 and 2 refer to the two conductors which form the junction. It is usual, nowadays, for the junction to be composed of a p-type and an n-type semiconductor having similar thermal and electrical conductivities and approximately equal Seebeck coefficients (of opposite sign). Under these conditions, a figure of merit z for a single material may be employed, where

$$z = \frac{Q^2 \sigma}{\kappa}. \tag{A.1.2}$$

Thus, research on materials for thermoelectric applications is aimed at obtaining the highest values for z.

The ratio of electrical to thermal conductivity, σ/κ, has its highest value for metals which obey the Wiedemann–Franz law. However, in no metal can a Seebeck coefficient as high as $100 \, \mu\text{V}/°\text{C}$ be realized. Recent experience has shown that the higher Seebeck coefficients which are associated with semiconductors can lead to improved figures of merit. We shall not, therefore, consider metals any further as potential thermoelectric materials. The discussion of the properties of *intrinsic* semiconductors in Section 4.2 shows that we can also dismiss these as being inferior to *extrinsic* semiconductors.

It is, of course, obvious that the Seebeck coefficient and the electrical conductivity (and, to some extent, the thermal conductivity) of a given extrinsic semiconductor are not by any means constant; they may generally be varied over a wide range by the addition or removal of impurities. It is, therefore, desirable that we should express the figure of merit in terms of a single variable quantity together with a number of "constant" parameters. For this purpose we may employ equations (4.1.17a, b, d) and (4.1.31) to eliminate Q, σ and κ, the variable quantity then being the Fermi energy $\bar{\mu}$. We may, in principle, use the resulting expression to find the most favourable value for $\bar{\mu}$ in any particular case. This process would be extremely simple if we could use classical statistics but it is found, invariably, that the optimum conditions require that the semiconductor should be partially degenerate. We cannot, therefore, give a simple equation for the optimum value of $\bar{\mu}$; still less can we give such an equation for the corresponding

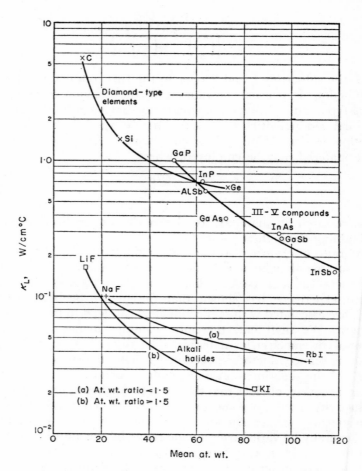

FIG. A.1.1. Lattice thermal conductivity at room temperature plotted against mean atomic weight.

figure of merit. Thus, we merely quote the conclusions which may be drawn from the detailed theory and which are well supported by the available experimental evidence.

First, it is found that the value of $\bar{\mu}$ should lie close to E_v or E_c. In other words, the Fermi level should be near the appropriate band edge (that of the valence band in a p-type semiconductor or of the conduction band in an n-type semiconductor). The Seebeck coefficient, corresponding to such a value of $\bar{\mu}$, is of the order $\pm 200 \, \mu V/°C$. The theory predicts that the rapid decrease of carrier concentration and, therefore, of electrical conductivity, as the Seebeck coefficient rises above, say, $300 \, \mu V/°C$, makes the use of compositions with lower Seebeck coefficients more desirable.

Secondly, the theory shows that, at the optimum carrier concentration, the figure of merit depends on four parameters. These are the carrier mobility μ, the lattice thermal conductivity κ_L, the effective mass m^* of the charge carriers and the scattering parameter p (see Section 4.1). It is usual to neglect any change in the value of p from one material to another; it is then found that the value of z depends on the factor

$$\frac{\mu}{\kappa_L}\left(\frac{m^*}{m}\right)^{3/2}$$

which should be as high as possible.

It has proved very difficult to make any predictions about the value of $\mu(m^*/m)^{3/2}$. However, in spite of the shortcomings of the present-day theories of heat conduction, it is still possible to make some general predictions about the behaviour of the lattice thermal conductivity which enables us to select potentially useful thermoelectric materials.

The rule which, so far, has found most widespread application, states that for a group of similar crystals the lattice thermal conductivity falls with increasing atomic weight (or, for compounds, mean atomic weight). Figure A.1.1, which is based on the observations of Ioffe, shows how this rule applies for the diamond-type elements, the III–V compounds and the alkali halides. For the last-named materials, it is necessary to distinguish between those composed of elements of similar atomic weight and those containing elements of widely different atomic weight. It seems impossible to predict which group of crystals will give the highest figures of merit. Covalent binding leads to a high carrier mobility but also to a high lattice thermal conductivity; ionic binding results in low values for both quantities. The only useful conclusion which may be drawn, then, is that the mean atomic weight

should be high; this is borne out by the fact that the two best compounds for thermoelectric refrigeration, PbTe and Bi_2Te_3, are both
composed of heavy elements.

The extension of these ideas to semiconductor alloys is given in
Section 5.4.

Appendix 2

SUMMARY OF THE THEORY OF THERMODYNAMICS OF IRREVERSIBLE PROCESSES AS APPLIED TO THE FLOWS OF CHARGE AND ENERGY

THE basic aspects of this subject have been given by Callen (1948:1) and the following is a summary of his results. Quite generally, irreversible processes result from the effect of one or more external "forces" acting on a thermodynamic system. The term "forces" as used in this context does not have its ordinary mechanical meaning and includes such quantities as temperature gradients, concentration gradients, electric fields, etc.

The effect of such forces is to give rise to certain flows, e.g. of particles and energy, in the system. In general, any force can give rise to any flow. The situation may be regarded as one in which the entropy of the system is reduced below its equilibrium value by the effect of the external forces. Any directed flow of particles or energy results in a lowering of the entropy and the tendency of the system to restrict such flows (e.g. the electrical and thermal resistances) may be interpreted in terms of internal production of entropy by the system in an attempt to get back to equilibrium.

For small departures from equilibrium, we can write a linear relation between the flows $\mathcal{J}_i$ $(i = 1, 2,..., n)$ and the forces X_i of the form

$$\mathcal{J}_i = \sum_{k=1}^{n} L_{ik} X_k, \qquad (A.2.1)$$

stating that any flow is caused by any force. The central theorem of the theory of irreversible thermodynamics is that, provided a proper choice is made for the flows $\mathcal{J}_i$ and forces X_i, the following relations hold between the phenomenological coefficients L_{ik},

$$L_{ik} = L_{ki} \; (i, k = 1, 2,..., n). \qquad (A.2.2)$$

If a magnetic field $\mathbf{B}$ acts on the system, the flows are modified and the coefficients L_{ik} are functions of $\mathbf{B}$ as well as other parameters. In this case, the above equation is modified to read

$$L_{ik}(\mathbf{B}) = L_{ki}(-\mathbf{B}) \; (i, k = 1, 2, ..., n). \tag{A.2.3}$$

These equations are called the Onsager relations.

The choice of a proper set of flows and forces is determined by writing down the expression for the rate of entropy production as a result of the irreversible process. If this is expressed in the form

$$s = \sum_{i=1}^{n} \mathcal{J}_i X_i, \tag{A.2.4}$$

where $\mathcal{J}_i$ can be interpreted as a flow and X_i as a force, then the set $(\mathcal{J}_i, X_i)$ can be related by equation (A.2.1), and equations (A.2.2) or (A.2.3) apply to the corresponding phenomenological coefficients. Usually, there are several alternative choices of flows and forces leading to the correct form of entropy production, equation (A.2.4). For all such choices, the relations (A.2.2) or (A.2.3) are valid.

As an introduction to the application of these concepts to the flows of electrons and energy in a solid, consider two bodies containing free electrons which initially are isolated from each other and from any external sources of electrons and energy. The thermodynamic states of these will be described by values of the electrochemical potential and the temperature, $\bar{\mu}_1$ and T_1 for the first body, $\bar{\mu}_2$ and T_2 for the second. At some time we let the two bodies be joined so that energy and electrons can flow from one to the other. The state of the whole system then changes with time in such a way that, until equilibrium is reached, the total entropy S is increasing, i.e. $dS/dt > 0$.

At each stage of the process we assume that the transfer of energy and electrons from one body to another is taking place sufficiently slowly so that each body is temporarily in local equilibrium, described by parameters $\bar{\mu}_1(t)$, $T_1(t)$ and $\bar{\mu}_2(t)$, $T_2(t)$ which vary (slowly) with time. In a short time interval dt, the entropy, energy and number of electrons of the bodies will change by amounts which are related through the equations

$$T_1(t)\delta S_1 = \delta E_1 - \bar{\mu}_1(t)\delta \mathcal{N}_1,$$
$$T_2(t)\delta S_2 = \delta E_2 - \bar{\mu}_2(t)\delta \mathcal{N}_2. \tag{A.2.5}$$

The further conditions of conservation of energy and electrons give

$$\delta E_1 + \delta E_2 = 0, \qquad \delta \mathcal{N}_1 + \delta \mathcal{N}_2 = 0. \tag{A.2.6}$$

The rate of change of the total entropy is

$$s = \frac{\mathrm{d}S}{\mathrm{d}t} = \frac{\mathrm{d}}{\mathrm{d}t}(S_1 + S_2)$$

and from the previous equations this is

$$s = \left(\frac{\mathrm{d}E_1}{\mathrm{d}t}\right)\left(\frac{1}{T_1} - \frac{1}{T_2}\right) - \left(\frac{\mathrm{d}\mathcal{N}_1}{\mathrm{d}t}\right)\left(\frac{\bar{\mu}_1}{T_1} - \frac{\bar{\mu}_2}{T_2}\right). \tag{A.2.7}$$

This expression must be positive and is clearly of the form (A.2.4). $(\mathrm{d}E_1/\mathrm{d}t)$ clearly represents the rate at which energy is flowing from 1 to 2 and $(\mathrm{d}\mathcal{N}_1/\mathrm{d}t)$ similarly gives the flow of electrons. Thus, we may write

$$\frac{\mathrm{d}E_1}{\mathrm{d}t} = L_{11}\left(\frac{1}{T_1} - \frac{1}{T_2}\right) + L_{12}\left(\frac{\bar{\mu}_1}{T_1} - \frac{\bar{\mu}_2}{T_2}\right), \tag{A.2.8a}$$

$$\frac{-\mathrm{d}\mathcal{N}_1}{\mathrm{d}t} = L_{21}\left(\frac{1}{T_1} - \frac{1}{T_2}\right) + L_{22}\left(\frac{\bar{\mu}_1}{T_1} - \frac{\bar{\mu}_2}{T_2}\right), \tag{A.2.8b}$$

and the relations (A.2.2) lead to the result

$$L_{12} = L_{21}. \tag{A.2.9}$$

In the above example, the flows and forces are varying with time and eventually vanish when $T_1 = T_2$, $\bar{\mu}_1 = \bar{\mu}_2$. The coefficients L_{ik}, however, will be independent of time if the forces are always small.

A more common situation than that discussed above is the steady-state condition where the differences in electrochemical potentials and temperatures between the two bodies are maintained at a constant value. In this case the system of two bodies is not an isolated one and the maintenance of a steady state requires the presence of external reservoirs of energy and electrons connected to the two bodies. Any changes in the energy and number of electrons in each body as a result of a flow of these quantities from one body to another are imme-diately compensated by flows into or out of the appropriate reservoirs, which thus maintain a constant difference of electrochemical potential and temperature between the two bodies.

In the steady state realized in this way we can write the rate of change of the energy of body 1 with time as

$$\frac{dE_1}{dt} = 0 = \left(\frac{dE_1}{dt}\right)_{int} + \left(\frac{dE_1}{dt}\right)_{ext}, \tag{A.2.10}$$

where the first term arises as the result of flow between the two bodies and the second as a result of exchange with the external reservoir.

Similar expressions can be written for the rates of change with time of N_1, E_2 and N_2. The conservation of energy and electrons gives the equations

$$\left(\frac{dE_1}{dt}\right)_{int} + \left(\frac{dE_2}{dt}\right)_{int} = 0; \qquad \left(\frac{dN_1}{dt}\right)_{int} + \left(\frac{dN_2}{dt}\right)_{int} = 0. \tag{A.2.11}$$

The division into internal and external processes leads naturally to a similar treatment as in the isolated case provided we concentrate on the internal processes, the only difference being that the forces and flows between the bodies remain constant with time. We can clearly distinguish the rate of change of the entropy of the system due to internal procesess which is given by

$$\begin{aligned} s_{int} = \frac{1}{T_1}\left(\frac{dE_1}{dt}\right)_{int} - \frac{\bar{\mu}_1}{T_1}\left(\frac{dN_1}{dt}\right)_{int} + \\ + \frac{1}{T_2}\left(\frac{dE_2}{dt}\right)_{int} - \frac{\bar{\mu}_2}{T_2}\left(\frac{dN_2}{dt}\right)_{int} \end{aligned} \tag{A.2.12}$$

and, with the use of equations (A.2.11), this reduces to the same form as equation (A.2.7).

$$\begin{aligned} s_{int} = \left(\frac{dS}{dt}\right)_{int} = \left(\frac{dE_1}{dt}\right)_{int}\left(\frac{1}{T_1} - \frac{1}{T_2}\right) - \\ - \left(\frac{dN_1}{dt}\right)_{int}\left(\frac{\bar{\mu}_1}{T_1} - \frac{\bar{\mu}_2}{T_2}\right). \end{aligned} \tag{A.2.13}$$

In the steady state this is balanced by the external source of entropy supplied to the system. Thus, from equation (A.2.10), the reservoirs connected to body 1 are supplying energy and electrons at rates $-(dE_1/dt)_{int}$ and $-(dN_1/dt)_{int}$ into a system with temperature T_1 and electrochemical potential $\bar{\mu}_1$ and are thus supplying entropy at a rate

$$\left(\frac{dS_1}{dt}\right)_{ext} = \frac{1}{T_1}\left(\frac{-dE_1}{dt}\right)_{int} - \frac{\bar{\mu}_1}{T_1}\left(\frac{-dN_1}{dt}\right)_{in}. \tag{A.2.14}$$

A similar equation holds for body 2 and we clearly have

$$s_{\text{ext}} + s_{\text{int}} = 0. \tag{A.2.15}$$

The process is thus regarded as one in which the external sources are removing entropy at a constant rate from the combined system of two bodies, this being balanced by the rate at which entropy is produced as a result of internal processes in the system.

The internal entropy production, equation (A.2.13) must be positive and this expression is the basis for writing down the linear relations between the flows and forces, which are just the same as equations (A.2.8), with the difference that the forces do not vary with time. The Onsager relations, equations (A.2.9) apply equally in this case.

The generalization of these results to the flow of electrons and energy in a continuous medium involves a more complex notation but no new principles. The combined system of two bodies is replaced by a small volume element of the medium over which the temperature and electrochemical potential, now regarded as continuous functions of position, vary by infinitesimals of the first order δT and $\delta \bar{\mu}$. The flows (dU_1/dt) and (dN_1/dt) are replaced by flow-density vectors $\mathbf{w}(\mathbf{r})$ and $\mathbf{j}(\mathbf{r})$, whose components normal to an element of unit area give the flows of energy and electrons per unit time across this element. The conservation of energy and electrons are expressed by the vector equations

$$\operatorname{div} \mathbf{w} = 0, \qquad \operatorname{div} \mathbf{j} = 0. \tag{A.2.16}$$

We can easily find the rate at which entropy is being supplied to the volume element. At the point $\mathbf{r}$, the energy flow and electron flow lead to an entropy flow $\mathbf{S}(\mathbf{r})$ into the volume element which is given by

$$\mathbf{S}(\mathbf{r}) = \frac{1}{T(\mathbf{r})}\mathbf{w}(\mathbf{r}) - \frac{\bar{\mu}(\mathbf{r})}{T(\mathbf{r})}\mathbf{j}(\mathbf{r}). \tag{A.2.17}$$

The assumption of local equilibrium is clearly involved in this expression. The rate at which entropy is being supplied per unit volume to the volume element, as a result of the flows of energy and electrons in and out, is the negative divergence $(-\operatorname{div} \mathbf{S})$ of this entropy flow. In the steady state, this must be balanced by the rate of internal entropy production in the volume element. Denoting this source strength by s_{int} per unit volume, we have

$$s_{\text{int}} - \operatorname{div} \mathbf{S} = 0. \tag{A.2.18}$$

The last three equations, with the use of straightforward vector algebra give

$$s_{int} = \mathbf{w} \cdot \mathbf{grad}\left(\frac{1}{T}\right) - \mathbf{j} \cdot \mathbf{grad}\left(\frac{\bar{\mu}}{T}\right) \tag{A.2.19}$$

which is the generalization of equation (A.2.13).

Equation (A.2.19) is the basic expression for the rate of internal entropy production and for the application of the central theorem of irreversible thermodynamics. Making the choice of flows as the components of $-\mathbf{j}$ and $\mathbf{w}$, the corresponding forces are the components of $\mathbf{grad}(\bar{\mu}/T)$ and $\mathbf{grad}(1/T)$. The general linear relations existing between these can be written as

$$-j_i = \sum_{k=1}^{3} L_{ik}{}^{(1)} \frac{\partial}{\partial x_k}\left(\frac{\bar{\mu}}{T}\right) + \sum_{k=1}^{3} L_{ik}{}^{(2)} \frac{\partial}{\partial x_k}\left(\frac{1}{T}\right),$$

$$w_i = \sum_{k=1}^{3} L_{ik}{}^{(3)} \frac{\partial}{\partial x_k}\left(\frac{\bar{\mu}}{T}\right) + \sum_{k=1}^{3} L_{ik}{}^{(4)} \frac{\partial}{\partial x_k}\left(\frac{1}{T}\right). \tag{A.2.20}$$

For obvious reasons the coefficients have been grouped into sets characterizing the relationships between a particular physical type of flow and a particular physical type of force, independently of direction. The Onsager relations take the form

$$L_{ik}{}^{(1)}(\mathbf{B}) = L_{ki}{}^{(1)}(-\mathbf{B}); \qquad L_{ik}{}^{(4)}(\mathbf{B}) = L_{ki}{}^{(4)}(-\mathbf{B});$$
$$L_{ik}{}^{(2)}(\mathbf{B}) = L_{ki}{}^{(3)}(-\mathbf{B}). \tag{A.2.21}$$

Equations (A.2.20) are the basis of the phenomenological discussion of Section 3.5.

In the derivation of the above results, the flows $-\mathbf{j}$ and $\mathbf{w}$ refer to the total flows through the volume element considered. The local equilibrium thermodynamic state of this element is assumed to be specified by just two parameters, viz. the electrochemical potential $\bar{\mu}$ which is common to all electrons and the temperature T which is common to all electrons and phonons.

In many cases in dealing with solids it is convenient to consider the total flows as being made up from contributions of different subsystems of the solid. For example, in considering the thermal conductivity, we may wish to consider the total energy flow as the sum of contributions from the electron system and from the phonon system, since these involve essentially different processes from each other. The characteristic feature of a sub-system in this context is that the internal interactions within the sub-system are very much stronger than the external interactions with other sub-systems. Thus, although the various sub-systems are themselves always locally in equilibrium, it is possible, as a result of external processes, for them to be maintained out of equilibrium with other sub-systems within the same volume element. It is, in fact, this possibility which is the foundation of many of the important application of solids, including the transistor, the maser and so-called hot-electron phenomena.

We shall not attempt to give a general treatment here but will discuss the simple division into an electron sub-system and a phonon sub-system. Thus, we shall assume that the state of a volume element of the solid can be specified by giving the local values of the electro-chemical potential $\bar{\mu}$ and temperature T_e of the electron system and the temperature T_p of the phonon system. Correspondingly, we distinguish three flows, viz. a flow of electrons $\mathbf{j}$, a flow of energy in the electron system $\mathbf{w}_e$ and a flow of energy in the phonon system $\mathbf{w}_p$. Reference back to equation (A.2.17) then shows that we have a total entropy flow which is made up of two parts, viz.

$$\mathbf{S} = \mathbf{S}_e + \mathbf{S}_p, \tag{A.2.22}$$

where

$$\mathbf{S}_e = \frac{1}{T_e}\mathbf{w}_e - \frac{\bar{\mu}}{T_e}\mathbf{j}$$

and

$$\mathbf{S}_p = \frac{1}{T_p}\mathbf{w}_p.$$

The rate of internal entropy production per unit volume is given by the divergence of $\mathbf{S}$ and, in full, this is

$$s = \frac{1}{T_p}\text{div}\,\mathbf{w}_p + \mathbf{w}_p \cdot \mathbf{grad}\left(\frac{1}{T_p}\right) + \frac{1}{T_e}\text{div}\,\mathbf{w}_e + \mathbf{w}_e \cdot \mathbf{grad}\,\frac{1}{T_e} -$$
$$- \frac{\bar{\mu}}{T_e}\text{div}\,\mathbf{j} - \mathbf{j} \cdot \mathbf{grad}\left(\frac{\bar{\mu}}{T_e}\right). \tag{A.2.23}$$

In the previous case we had $\text{div}\,\mathbf{j} = 0$ and $\text{div}\,\mathbf{w} = 0$. The first of these expressing the conservation of electrons is still valid but we cannot now assume that div $\mathbf{w}_p$ and div $\mathbf{w}_e$ are zero since energy may be exchanged between the two systems.

If we denote by (dE_e^p/dt) the rate at which energy is being transferred per unit volume from the electron system to the phonon system $(\equiv -dE_p^e/dt)$, then

$$\text{div } \mathbf{w}_e = -\left(\frac{dE_e^p}{dt}\right) \tag{A.2.24}$$

and expression (A.2.23) for the rate of entropy production becomes

$$s = \mathbf{w}_p \cdot \mathbf{grad}\left(\frac{1}{T_p}\right) + \mathbf{w}_e \cdot \mathbf{grad}\left(\frac{1}{T_e}\right) - \mathbf{j} \cdot \mathbf{grad}\left(\frac{\bar{\mu}}{T_e}\right) +$$
$$+ \left(\frac{dE_e^p}{dt}\right)\left[\frac{1}{T_p} - \frac{1}{T_e}\right]. \tag{A.2.25}$$

This expression contains three contributions, the first term referring to entropy production within the phonon system, the next two terms being associated with entropy production in the electron system and the last being associated with interactions between the two. In accordance with the general principles of irreversible thermodynamics, we can write linear relations between the flows and forces involved in this expression. In doing so, however, we have to take into account the fact that scalar forces such as occur in the last term clearly cannot give rise to a vector flow such as those occurring in the other terms. The phenomenological relations are therefore of the form

$$-\mathbf{j} = L^{(1)} \cdot \mathbf{grad}\left(\frac{\bar{\mu}}{T_e}\right) + L^{(2)} \cdot \mathbf{grad}\left(\frac{1}{T_e}\right) + L^{(3)} \cdot \mathbf{grad}\left(\frac{1}{T_p}\right), \tag{A.2.26a}$$

$$\mathbf{w}_e = L^{(4)} \cdot \mathbf{grad}\left(\frac{\bar{\mu}}{T_e}\right) + L^{(5)} \cdot \mathbf{grad}\left(\frac{1}{T_e}\right) + L^{(6)} \cdot \mathbf{grad}\left(\frac{1}{T_p}\right), \tag{A.2.26b}$$

$$\mathbf{w}_p = L^{(7)} \cdot \mathbf{grad}\left(\frac{\bar{\mu}}{T_e}\right) + L^{(8)} \cdot \mathbf{grad}\left(\frac{1}{T_e}\right) + L^{(9)} \cdot \mathbf{grad}\left(\frac{1}{T_p}\right), \tag{A.2.26c}$$

$$\left(\frac{dE_e^p}{dt}\right) = L\left[\frac{1}{T_p} - \frac{1}{T_e}\right]. \tag{A.2.26d}$$

In the first three equations the $L^{(n)}$ are all tensors of the second order whereas the coefficient L in the last equation is a scalar. The

Onsager relations lead to $L^{(1)}$, $L^{(5)}$ and $L^{(9)}$ as being symmetrical and to other relations such as

$$L_{ik}{}^{(2)} = L_{ki}{}^{(4)}, \text{ etc.}$$

Equation (A.2.26d) clearly has the physical significance of tending to adjust the respective energies of the electron and phonon systems until they are in equilibrium. An alternative way of writing this is to introduce the specific heat per unit volume of the electron system C_e, take $\delta E_e{}^p = -C_e \delta T_e$ and, hence, express the equation in the form

$$\left(\frac{dT_e}{dt}\right) = \left(\frac{T_p - T_e}{\tau_{ep}}\right), \tag{A.2.27}$$

where τ_{ep} is called the electron–phonon relaxation time. We have assumed that the differences of T_p and T_e from the common thermal equilibrium value T are both small. The relaxation time τ_{ep} is clearly a measure of the time required to restore equality of temperatures between the two systems when the processes maintaining a difference in temperatures are removed.

In the treatment throughout this book, we have assumed that τ_{ep} is very large compared with the internal relaxation times τ_e and τ_p of the separate electron and phonon systems. This corresponds to the case of weak interaction, the two systems being regarded as independent of each other. We can thus write separate expressions for the rates of entropy production in the two systems

$$s_e = \mathbf{w}_e \cdot \mathbf{grad}\left(\frac{1}{T_e}\right) - \mathbf{j} \cdot \mathbf{grad}\left(\frac{\bar{\mu}}{T_e}\right), \tag{A.2.28a}$$

$$s_p = \mathbf{w}_p \cdot \mathbf{grad}\left(\frac{1}{T_p}\right). \tag{A.2.28b}$$

The corresponding phenomenological relations are clearly of the form (A.2.26 a, b and c) with $L^{(3)}$, $L^{(6)}$, $L^{(7)}$ and $L^{(8)}$ all equal to zero. Since, in most cases of interest, the departures of T_e and T_p from the common equilibrium temperature are small, both T_e and T_p can be replaced with sufficient accuracy by the temperature T as ordinarily defined.

The more general case when τ_{ep} is comparable with one or other of the internal relaxation times τ_e or τ_p will be discussed only briefly. Invariably this tends to arise as a result of the very rapid increase of

τ_p as the temperature is lowered, because of the corresponding disappearance of umklapp processes. The situation where τ_p becomes comparable with τ_{ep} tends to set in at higher temperatures for semiconductors than for metals because in the latter case the extra phonon scattering due to the presence of a large number of electrons tends to keep τ_p down. When this situation arises, it is no longer valid to regard the two systems as being independent. This is the condition under which the so-called phonon-drag effects become important, where entropy production in one system is influenced by entropy production in the other. Correspondingly, forces acting primarily on one system can induce flows in the other. For such situations, equations (A.2.26) have to be used in full.

Appendix 3

DISCUSSION OF THE VARIATIONAL
THEOREMS FOR ELECTRONS AND PHONONS

WE shall first discuss the simplest case, that of electrons. From equation (3.6.17) we have an expression for the rate of entropy production which we shall denote by $s_{e,f}$, the subscript f denoting that the field term of the Boltzmann equation (in the absence of a magnetic field) is used in the expression

$$s_{e,f} = -\frac{1}{4\pi^3} \sum_n \int \frac{\partial f_0}{\partial E} \mathbf{v} \cdot \left[E \, \mathbf{grad}\left(\frac{1}{T}\right) - \mathbf{grad}\left(\frac{\mu}{T}\right) \right] f_1 \, d\mathbf{k}. \quad (A.3.1)$$

We shall write

$$X = -\frac{1}{4\pi^3} \frac{\partial f_0}{\partial E} \mathbf{v} \cdot \left[E \, \mathbf{grad}\left(\frac{1}{T}\right) - \mathbf{grad}\left(\frac{\mu}{T}\right) \right] \quad (A.3.2)$$

and use the general expression

$$s_{e,f}(F) = \sum_n \int XF \, d\mathbf{k} \quad (A.3.3)$$

where F is any function of n and $\mathbf{k}$. Thus, expression (A.3.1) will be written as $s_{e,f}(f_1)$ where f_1 is the true solution of the Boltzmann equation.

Using the expression (3.6.14), we see that the Boltzmann equation is written, with use of (A.3.2), as

$$X = -\frac{1}{4\pi^3 T} \left(\frac{\partial f}{\partial t} \right)_{\text{scatter}} \quad (A.3.4)$$

in the absence of a magnetic field. The form of $(\partial f/\partial t)_{\text{scatter}}$ is given by equation (3.7.6) as

213

$$\left(\frac{\partial f}{\partial t}\right)_{\text{scatter}} = \frac{1}{4\pi^3 kT} \sum_{n'} \int (f_1' - f_1) V(n, \mathbf{k}; n', \mathbf{k}') \, d\mathbf{k}'. \quad \text{(A.3.5)}$$

Combining the last three equations, we obtain

$$s_{e,f}(F) = -\frac{1}{(4\pi^3)^2 kT^2} \sum_{n} \sum_{n'} \iint F(f_1' - f_1) V \, d\mathbf{k}' d\mathbf{k}.$$

Since the summations and integrals are taken over all variables we may interchange primed and unprimed symbols. The basic property of $V(n, \mathbf{k}; n', \mathbf{k}')$ is that it is unchanged by this process. Thus, we get a second expression for $s_{e,f}(F)$ which when combined with the above gives

$$s_{e,f}(F) = \frac{1}{(4\pi^3)^2 2kT^2} \sum_{n} \sum_{n'} \iint (F' - F)(f_1' - f_1) V \, d\mathbf{k}' d\mathbf{k}. \quad \text{(A.3.6)}$$

Equation (3.7.10) is a special case of this, when $F = f_1$, and we are led to define a function

$$s_{e,s}(F) = \frac{1}{(4\pi^3)^2 2kT^2} \sum_{n} \sum_{n'} \iint (F' - F)^2 V \, d\mathbf{k}' d\mathbf{k}, \quad \text{(A.3.7)}$$

which, when $F = f_1$, is the entropy production calculated from the scattering term in the Boltzmann equation, as indicated by the subscript s.

The variational principle in its general form asserts that

$$\frac{s_{e,s}(F)}{s_{e,f}^2(F)} \geqslant \frac{s_{e,s}(f_1)}{s_{e,f}^2(f_1)} \left(\equiv \frac{1}{s_e(f_1)} \right), \quad \text{(A.3.8)}$$

where F is any trial function and f_1 is the true solution of the Boltzmann equation. This result follows directly from consideration of the inequality

$$\frac{1}{(4\pi^3)^2 2kT^2} \sum_{n} \sum_{n'} \iint [a(f_1' - f_1) + b(F' - F)]^2 V \, d\mathbf{k}' d\mathbf{k} \geqslant 0, \quad \text{(A.3.9)}$$

which is true for all values of a and b because of the positive definite character of V. On expansion, and using equations (A.3.6) and (A.3.7), we obtain

$$a^2 s_{e,s}(f_1) + 2ab s_{e,f}(F) + b^2 s_{e,s}(F) \geqslant 0, \tag{A.3.10}$$

for all values of a and b. This can only be the case if

$$s_{e,f}^2(F) \leqslant s_{e,s}(F) s_{e,s}(f_1). \tag{A.3.11}$$

Since $s_{e,f}(f_1) = s_{e,s}(f_1)$ we can write this as

$$\frac{s_{e,s}(F)}{s_{e,f}^2(F)} \geqslant \frac{s_{e,s}(f_1)}{s_{e,f}^2(f_1)} = \frac{1}{s_e(f_1)}.$$

Thus, any trial function F used in the left-hand side of this expression gives an expression for the reciprocal of the entropy production which is greater than the true value. Alternatively, we may say that the true solution minimizes the expression $s_{e,s}/s_{e,f}^2$.

In some cases, it is convenient to require that the trial function F satisfies the auxiliary condition

$$s_{e,s}(F) = s_{e,f}(F). \tag{A.3.12}$$

In this case, equation (A.3.8) reduces to

$$s_e(F) \leqslant s_e(f_1) \tag{A.3.13}$$

showing that the true solution corresponds to maximum entropy production by the system, and any other function, satisfying the auxiliary condition (A.3.12) leads to a smaller rate of entropy production

The proof of the variational principle for the phonon entropy production follows along very similar lines and uses the same basic properties of the scattering function. For the three-phonon processes considered in Section 3.8, we have

$$s_{p,f}(F) = \sum_j \int X_p F \, d\mathbf{q}$$

with

$$X_p = -\frac{1}{8\pi^3} \frac{\partial N_0}{\partial(\hbar\omega)} \hbar\omega \mathbf{v} \cdot \mathbf{grad}\frac{1}{T}.$$

The Boltzmann equation is

$$X_p = -\frac{1}{8\pi^3 T} \left(\frac{\partial N}{\partial t}\right)_{\text{scatter}}$$

and $(\partial N/\partial t)_{\text{scatter}}$ is given by equation (3.8.10).

15

These results lead to

$$s_{p,f}(F) = \frac{1}{(8\pi^3)^3 2kT^2} \int\!\!\int\!\!\int (\mathcal{N}_1'' - \mathcal{N}_1' - \mathcal{N})(F'' - F' - F) \times$$

$$\times\, U(\mathbf{q}, \mathbf{q}'; \mathbf{q}'')\, d\mathbf{q}d\mathbf{q}'d\mathbf{q}''$$

using the same principles (symmetry of U in $\mathbf{q}$ and $\mathbf{q}'$) as were used in deriving the analogous equation for the electron case, equation (A.3.6). The definition of the function

$$s_{p,s}(F) = \frac{1}{(8\pi^3)^3 2kT^2} \int\!\!\int\!\!\int (F'' - F' - F)^2 U\, d\mathbf{q}d\mathbf{q}'d\mathbf{q}''$$

leads to the variational principle, obtained by considering the analogue of equation (A.3.9) for the phonon case, in the form

$$s_{p,f}{}^2(F) \leqslant s_{p,s}(F)s_{p,s}(\mathcal{N}_1).$$

This is the form in which the principle appears in equation (3.8.15).

Appendix 4

FERMI–DIRAC INTEGRALS

THE definition of the Fermi–Dirac integral of order r and argument η is

$$F_r(\eta) = \int_0^\infty \frac{x^r}{1 + \exp(x - \eta)} \, dx. \qquad (A.4.1)$$

Since the denominator of the integral remains finite as $x \to 0$, the integrals diverge if $r < -1$ and are defined only for $r \geqslant -1$. For the special case $r = 0$, the function can be expressed analytically,

$$F_0(\eta) = \int_0^\infty \frac{dx}{1 + \exp(x - \eta)} = \int_0^\infty \frac{\exp(\eta - x)}{[\exp(\eta - x) + 1]} \, dx,$$

$$= [-\ln(\exp(\eta - x) + 1)]_0^\infty = \ln[1 + \exp(\eta)]. \qquad (A.4.2)$$

For all other values of r, the functions have to be evaluated numerically, or expressed in the form of series. The expressions which are used depend on the value of the argument η.

When η is negative, we write

$$F_r(\eta) = \int_0^\infty x^r \exp(\eta - x)\{1 + \exp(\eta - x)\}^{-1} \, dx,$$

and, since for this case $\exp(\eta - x)$ is less than unity over the whole range of integration, the factor in parentheses can be expanded in a uniformly convergent series to give

$$F_r(\eta) = \int_0^\infty \{x^r \exp(\eta - x) \sum_{n=0}^\infty (-1)^n \exp[n(\eta - x)]\} \, dx,$$

$$= \sum_{n=0}^\infty (-1)^n \exp[(n+1)\eta] \int_0^\infty x^r \exp[(n+1)(-x)] \, dx.$$

217

In the integral, we put $(n+1)x = u$ and obtain

$$F_r(\eta) = \sum_{n=0} (-1)^n \frac{\exp[(n+1)\eta]}{(n+1)^{r+1}} \int_0^\infty u^r \exp(-u)\, du$$

$$= \sum_{n=0} (-1)^n \frac{\exp[(n+1)\eta]}{(n+1)^{r+1}} \Gamma(r+1). \tag{A.4.3}$$

This series converges for negative values of η, the convergence being very rapid when $-\eta$ is large. The leading term of the series is

$$\exp(\eta)\Gamma(r+1) \tag{A.4.4}$$

which is the non-degenerate approximation to $F_r(\eta)$ used in Chapter 4.

When η is positive, the above procedure is no longer valid. The most comprehensive treatment for this case has been given by Dingle (1957:**18**), who arrived at the general formula

$$F_r(\eta) = \cos(r\pi) F_r(-\eta) + 2\Gamma(r+1)\eta^{r+1} \times$$

$$\times \left\{ \sum_{n=0}^{[(r+1)/2]} \frac{t_{2n}\eta^{-2n}}{\Gamma(r+2-2n)} + \frac{\sin(r\pi)}{\pi} \sum_{n=[(r+1)/2]}^{\infty} \Gamma(2n-r-1) t_{2n}\eta^{-2n} \right\}. \tag{A.4.5}$$

In the summations, the notation $[\frac{1}{2}(r+1)]$, for example, is used to denote the largest integer contained in $\frac{1}{2}(r+1)$ (i.e. 1 for $r = 2$, 2 for $r = 3$, etc.). The functions t_{2n} are defined by

$$t_0 = \tfrac{1}{2}, \qquad t_{2n} = \tfrac{1}{2}(2\pi)^{2n}[1-2^{(1-2n)}]B_n/(2n)!$$

where the numbers B_n are the so-called Bernoulli numbers. The first few of these are

$$B_1 = \frac{1}{6}, \qquad B_2 = \frac{1}{30}, \qquad B_3 = \frac{1}{42}, \qquad B_4 = \frac{1}{30}, \qquad B_5 = \frac{5}{66}.$$

Thus, we find that

$$t_2 = \frac{\pi^2}{12}, \qquad t_4 = \frac{7\pi^4}{720}, \text{ etc.} \tag{A.4.6}$$

In the expression (A.4.5), the second summation in parentheses is an asymptotic series, whose terms in general start to diverge beyond a certain stage in the series. When η is large, the terms up to this stage are the only ones that need be retained. In a subsequent paper (1958:20) Dingle has shown how to transform this term into a rapidly convergent series. For sufficiently large η, the term makes a contribution to $F_r(\eta)$ which is negligible in comparison with that of the first summation and, since in this case $F_r(-\eta)$ is also small and negligible, the expression (A.4.5) becomes, for sufficiently large η

$$F_r(\eta) = 2\Gamma(r+1)\eta^{r+1} \sum_{n=0}^{[(r+1)/2]} \frac{t_{2n}\eta^{-2n}}{\Gamma(r+2-2n)}.$$

The first two terms of this $(r \geqslant 1)$ are

$$\frac{1}{(r+1)}\eta^{r+1} + \frac{r\pi^2}{6}\eta^{r-1} \tag{A.4.7}$$

which are the leading terms in the series given in equation (4.1.26).

One case which can be discussed generally is that when r is an integer. The second term in parentheses in equation (A.4.5) is then identically zero and the first summation terminates. Since $\cos(r\pi) = (-1)^r$ we obtain

$$F_r(\eta) = (-1)^r F_r(-\eta) + 2r!\eta^{r+1} \sum_{n=0}^{[(r+1)/2]} \frac{t_{2n}\eta^{-2n}}{(r+1-2n)!} \tag{A.4.8}$$

when r is an integer. Thus, for example,

$$F_1(\eta) = -F_1(-\eta) + \frac{\eta^2}{2} + \frac{\pi^2}{6},$$

$$F_2(\eta) = F_2(-\eta) + \frac{\eta^3}{3} + \frac{\pi^2}{3}\eta.$$

These expressions are valid for all η.

Tables of the Fermi–Dirac integrals have been given by the following authors:

(a) Dingle (1957:18). Tabulation of $F_r(\eta)$ for $r = -1, 0, 1, 2, 3, 4,$ $0 \leqslant \eta \leqslant 10$, and $0 \cdot 1$ intervals of η. The actual tables are for the function $(1/r!)F_r(\eta)$.

(b) Beer et al. (1955:9). Tabulation of $F_r(\eta)$ for $r = -\frac{1}{2}, \frac{1}{2}, \frac{3}{2}, \frac{5}{2}, \frac{7}{2},$ $\frac{9}{2}, \frac{11}{2}$ and $-4 \leqslant \eta \leqslant 20$, at intervals $0 \cdot 1$ of η.

(c) McDougall and Stoner (1938:2). Tabulation of $F_{1/2}(\eta)$ and $F_{3/2}(\eta)$ for $-4 \leqslant \eta \leqslant 20$ at intervals $0 \cdot 1$ of η.

(d) Rhodes (1950:4). Tabulation of $F_r(\eta)$ for $r = 1, 2, 3, 4$ and $-4 \leqslant \eta \leqslant 0$ at intervals $0 \cdot 1$ of η.

LIST OF SYMBOLS

A cross-section area, atomic weight, parameter in imperfection–scattering theory (5.2.2).

A' parameter in imperfection–scattering theory (5.2.3).

a absorption coefficient, interatomic spacing.

$\mathbf{a}$ unit cell vector.

an   (subscript) anharmonic.

B parameter in thermal conductivity expression (5.2.1), parameter in imperfection scattering theory (5.2.3).

$\mathbf{B}$ magnetic induction.

b amplitude of vibration, parameter in thermal conductivity expression (5.2.1). (subscript) boundary.

C thermal capacity, specific heat.

C_L constant in melting rule (5.4.2).

c linear dimension, concentration.

c (subscript) conduction band, electron.

D dimension.

$\mathscr{E}$ electric field intensity.

E energy.

E_G energy gap.

e electronic charge.

e (subscript) electronic.

$\mathbf{F}$ force.

F_r Fermi–Dirac integral (4.1).

f distribution function (3.3.5), thermal conductivity function (5.2.1).

f (subscript) field.

G number of states (3.3.5).

g density of states distribution function (3.3.5).

$\mathscr{H}$ Hamiltonian operator (3.2).

h Planck's constant.

$\hbar$ $h/2\pi$.

$\mathbf{I}$ electric current.

i	electric current density.
i	(subscript) imperfection.
imp	(subscript) imperfection.
$\mathcal{J}$	flow (A.2).
j	charge flow vector.
j	(subscript) branch or group index.
K_s	transport integral (4.1).
k	Boltzmann's constant.
k	electron wave vector (3.3.2).
k_d	thermal diffusivity (2.4.2).
L	Lorenz number (1.2), transport coefficient (3.5.1).
l	length, mean free path of phonons.
M	rate function (3.8.1), mass per atom.
m	mass.
m^*	effective mass tensor (3.3.3).
m_c	effective mass of electron.
m_v	effective mass of hole.
$\mathcal{N}$	number of particles, phonon distribution function (3.4.2).
n	refractive index, band index (3.3.2).
p	exponent of energy in scattering law for electrons (3.7.3).
p	momentum.
p'	exponent of energy in scattering law for holes (4.1).
p	(subscript) phonon.
Q	Seebeck coefficient.
q	charge per particle, modulus of **9**.
q	phonon wave vector (3.4.1).
R	trial function (3.8.2), radius, gas constant.
$\mathbf{R}_L$	lattice translation vector.
R	(subscript) radiation.
r	parameter depending on scattering law (4.2).
r	position vector.
r_0	distance between nearest-neighbour atoms.
S	entropy, phonon scattering parameter (5.2.2).
s	rate of entropy production.
s	(subscript) scatter.
T	absolute temperature.
T_m	melting temperature.
ΔT	temperature difference.
t	time.
U	rate function for phonons (3.8.2).

U	displacement vector (3.4.2).
u	periodic function (3.3.2).
u	(subscript) umklapp.
V	potential function (3.3.1), potential difference, volume.
v	velocity.
$\bar{v}$	mean sound velocity.
v	(subscript) valence band.
W	transition probability (3.3.4), thermal resistivity.
w	energy flow vector.
X	force (A.2).
x	parameter in imperfection scattering theory (5.2.2), Cartesian co-ordinate, concentration.
z	thermoelectric figure of merit (2.5.2).
α	amplitude ratio.
β	phase difference.
γ	Gruneisen parameter (5.2).
Δ_1	deformation potential parameter (3.7.3).
δ	cube root of atomic volume.
ϵ	energy relative to band edge, mass variance parameter (5.4.2).
$\boldsymbol{\epsilon}$	unit displacement vector (3.4.1).
η	reduced Fermi potential for electrons (4.1).
θ	angle, reduced Fermi potential for holes (4.1).
θ_D	Debye temperature.
π	Peltier coefficient.
κ	thermal conductivity.
κ_e	electronic thermal conductivity (1.2).
κ_L	lattice thermal conductivity (1.1).
μ	carrier mobility, chemical potential (3.3.5).
$\bar{\mu}$	electrochemical potential or Fermi level (3.3.5).
ρ	electrical resistivity, density.
σ	electrical conductivity, Stefan's constant of radiation, scattering cross-section (5.2.2).
τ	relaxation time (3.7.3).
$\boldsymbol{\tau}$	reciprocal lattice vector.
τ'	relaxation time for holes.
τ_0	energy independent factor in relaxatio time (3.7.3).
ϕ	electrostatic potential.
χ	compressibility.
ψ	wave function (3.2).
ω	angular frequency.

ω_D Debye characteristic frequency (3.4.1).

ω_0 frequency used in scattering theory (5.2.3).

Note: Figures in brackets refer to sections or sub-sections where complete definitions may be found.

REFERENCES

1861:1 ÅNGSTRÖM A. J., *Ann. Physik.* **114,** 513.
1865:1 FORBES J. D., *Trans. Roy. Soc. Edinburgh* **23,** 133; **24,** 73.
1896:1 RAYLEIGH Lord, *Theory of Sound*, Vol. 2. Macmillan, New York.
1898:1 LEES, C. H., *Phil. Trans. Roy. Soc. London* **191,** 399.
1900:1 KOHLRAUSCH, F., *Ann. Physik* **1,** 132.
1900:2 JAEGER W. and DIESSELHORST H., *Wiss. Abhandl. physik-.tech. Reichsanstalt* **3,** 269.
1908:1 LEES C. H., *Phil. Trans. Roy. Soc. London* **208,** 381.
1910:1 LINDEMANN F. A., *Phys. Z.* **11,** 609.
1911:1 EUCKEN A., *Ann. Physik* **34,** 185.
1914:1 DEBYE P., *Vorträge über die kinetische Theorie*, p. 43. Teubner.
1928:1 EUCKEN A. and KUHN E., *Z. Physik Chem. Frankfurt* **134,** 193.
1929:1 PEIERLS R. E., *Ann. Physik* **3,** 1055.
1935:1 DE HAAS W. J. and BIERMASZ T., *Physica* **2,** 673.
1935:2 BLACKMAN, M., *Phil. Mag.* **19,** 989.
1938:1 CASIMIR H. B. G., *Physica* **5,** 495.
1938:2 MCDOUGALL J. and STONER E. C., *Phil. Trans. Roy. Soc. London* A**237,** 67
1941:1 POMERANCHUK I., *Phys. Rev.* **60,** 820.
1941:2 KOHLER M., *Ann. Physik* **40,** 601.
1948:1 CALLEN, H. B., *Phys. Rev.* **73,** 1349.
1949:1 KITTEL C., *Phys. Rev.* **75,** 972.
1949:2 HERRING C. and NICHOLS M. H., *Revs. Modern Phys.* **21,** 185.
1950:1 CONWELL E. and WEISSKOPF V. F., *Phys. Rev.* **77,** 388.
1950:2 SHOCKLEY W., *Electrons and Holes in Semiconductors*. D. Van Nostrand, New York.
1950:3 BARDEEN J. and SHOCKLEY W., *Phys. Rev.* **80,** 72.
1950:4 RHODES P., *Proc. Roy. Soc. London* A**204,** 396.
1951:1 KLEMENS P. G., *Proc. Roy. Soc. London* A**208,** 108.
1952:1 IOFFE A. V. and IOFFE A. F., *Zh. Tekh. Fiz.* **22,** 2005.
1953:1 OLSEN N. L. and ROSENBERG H. M., *Advances in Phys.* **2,** 28.
1953:2 WILSON A. H., *The Theory of Metals*, 2nd ed. Cambridge University Press.
1953:3 BERMAN R., SIMON F. E. and ZIMAN J. M., *Proc. Roy. Soc. London* A**220,** 171.
1953:4 GENZEL L., *Z. Phys.* **135,** 177.
1954:1 ROSENBERG H. M., *Proc. Phys. Soc. London* A**67,** 837.
1954:2 FRANCL J. and KINGERY W. D., *J. Am. Ceram. Soc.* **37,** 80.
1954:3 BUSCH G. and SCHNEIDER M., *Physica* **20,** 1084.
1954:4 MORIN F. J. and MAITA J. P., *Phys. Rev.* **94,** 1325.
1954:5 LEIBFRIED G. and SCHLÖMANN E., *Nachr. Akad. Wiss. Göttingen Math-physik Kl.* **2a,** 71.

1954:6 HERRING C., *Phys. Rev.* **96,** 1163.
1954:7 IOFFE A. V. and IOFFE A. F., *Doklady Akad. Nauk. S.S.S.R.* **98,** 757.
1955:1 ROSENBERG H. M., *Phil. Trans. Roy. Soc. London* A**247,** 441.
1955:2 FRIEDBERG S. A., *Temperature*, vol. 2, p. 359. Reinhold, New York.
1955:3 PEIERLS R. E., *Quantum Theory of Solids*. Clarendon Press, Oxford.
1955:4 SCHIFF L. I., *Quantum Mechanics*. McGraw-Hill, New York.
1955:5 REITZ J. R., *Solid State Physics*, vol. 1. Academic Press, New York.
1955:6 PRICE P. J., *Phil. Mag.* **46,** 1252.
1955:7 DUGDALE J. S. and MacDONALD D. K. C., *Phys. Rev.* **98,** 1751.
1955:8 GEBALLE T. H. and HULL G. W., *Report Conf. Phys. d. Basses Temp. Paris*, p. 460.
1955:9 BEER A. C., CHASE M. N. and CHOQUARD P. F., *Helv. Phys. Acta* **28,** 529.
1956:1 GOLDSMID H. J., *Proc. Phys. Soc. London* B**69,** 203.
1956:2 STUCKES A. D. and CHASMAR R. P., *Semiconductor Conference Report*, p. 119, Physical Society, London.
1956:3 ZIMAN J. M., *Can. J. Phys.* **34,** 1256.
1956:4 SONDHEIMER E. H., *Proc. Roy. Soc. London* A**234,** 391.
1956:5 HERRING C. and VOGT E., *Phys. Rev.* **101,** 944.
1956:6 BERMAN R., FOSTER E. L. and ZIMAN J. M., *Proc. Roy. Soc. London* A**237,** 344.
1956:7 WHITE G. K. and WOODS S. B., *Phys. Rev.* **103,** 569.
1956:8 KLEMENS P. G., *Handbuch der Physik*, vol. 14, p. 198. Springer Verlag, Berlin.
1956:9 PIKUS, G. E., *Zh. Tekh. Fiz.* **26,** 49.
1956:10 IOFFE A. F., *Can. J. Phys.* **34,** 1342.
1956:11 IOFFE A. F., AIRAPETYANTS S. V., IOFFE A. V., KOLOMOETS N. V. and STIL'BANS L. S., *Doklady Akad. Nauk. S.S.S.R.* **106,** 981.
1956:12 IOFFE A. V. and IOFFE A. F., *Izvest. Akad. Nauk S.S.S.R.* **20,** 65.
1957:1 IOFFE A. F., *Semiconductor Thermoelements and Thermoelectric Cooling*. Infosearch, London.
1957:2 BLATT E. J., *Solid State Physics*, vol. 4. Academic Press, New York.
1957:3 STUCKES A. D., *Phys. Rev.* **107,** 427.
1957:4 DEVYATKOVA E. D., *Zh. Tekh. Fiz.* **27,** 461; *Soviet Phys. Tech. Phys.* **2,** 414.
1957:5 GERSHTEIN E. Z., STAVITSKAYA T. S. and STIL'BANS L. S., *Zh. Tekh. Fiz.* **27,** 2472; *Soviet Phys., Tech. Phys.* **2,** 2302.
1957:6 STEELE M. C., *Phys. Rev.* **107,** 81.
1957:7 DRABBLE J. R. and WOLFE R., *J. Electronics & Cont.* **3,** 259.
1957:8 LAWSON A. W., *J. Phys. Chem. Solids* **3,** 154.
1957:9 CARRUTHERS J. A., GEBALLE T. H., ROSENBERG H. M. and ZIMAN J. M., *Proc. Roy. Soc. London* A**238,** 502.
1957:10 SLACK G. A., *Phys. Rev.* **105,** 829.
1957:11 FISCHER G., WHITE G. K. and WOODS S. B., *Phys. Rev.* **106,** 480.
1957:12 AMIRKHANOV K. I., BAGDUEV G. B. and KAZLAEV M. A., *Doklady Akad. Nauk S.S.S.R.* **117,** 953.
1957:13 ALIEV G. M. and ABDULLAEV G. B., *Doklady Akad. Nauk S.S.S.R.* **116,** 598.
1957:14 ABDULLAEV G. B. and BASHSHALIEV A. A., *Zh. Tekh. Fiz.* **27,** 1971.
1957:15 ABDULLAEV G. B. and ALIEV M. I., *Doklady Akad. Nauk S.S.S.R.* **114,** 995.
1957:16 GOLDSMID H. J., Ph.D. Thesis, University of London.

1957:17 AIRAPETYANTS S. V., EFIMOVA B. A., STAVITSKAYA T. S., STIL'BANS L. S. and SYSOEVA L. M., *Zh. Tekh. Fiz.* **27,** 2167; *Soviet Phys., Tech. Phys.* **2,** 2009.

1957:18 DINGLE R. B., *Appl. Sci. Research* B**6,** 225.

1958:1 GEBALLE T. H. and HULL G. W., *Phys. Rev.* **110,** 773.

1958:2 IOFFE A. V. and IOFFE A. F., *Zh. Tekh. Fiz.* **28,** 2357; *Soviet Phys., Tech. Phys.* **3,** 2163.

1958:3 KAGANOV M. A., *Zh. Tekh. Fiz.* **28,** 2364; *Soviet Phys., Tech. Phys.* **3,** 2169.

1958:4 NII R., *J. Phys. Soc. Japan* **13,** 769.

1958:5 BIRKHOLZ U., *Z. Naturforsch.* **13a,** 780.

1958:6 HARMAN T. C., *J. Appl. Phys.* **29,** 1373.

1958:7 SLATER J. C., *Revs. Modern Phys.* **30,** 197.

1958:8 HASHIMOTO K., *Mem. Fac. Sci. Kyusyu Univ.* B**2,** 187.

1958:9 GOLDSMID H. J., *Proc. Phys. Soc. London* **72,** 17.

1958:10 GOLDSMID H. J., *Proc. Phys. Soc. London* **71,** 633.

1958:11 BOWLEY A. E., DELVES R. and GOLDSMID H. J., *Proc. Phys. Soc. London* **72,** 401.

1958:12 AUSTIN I. G., *Proc. Phys. Soc. London* **72,** 545.

1958:13 WHITE G. K. and WOODS S. B., *Phil. Mag.* **3,** 785.

1958:14 TOXEN A. M., *Phys. Rev.* **110,** 585.

1958:15 BROCKHOUSE B. N. and IYENGAR P. K., *Phys. Rev.* **111,** 747.

1958:16 KLEMENS P. G., *Solid State Physics*, vol. 7, p. 1. Academic Press, New York.

1958:17 WHITE G. K., WOODS S. B. and ELFORD M. T., *Phys. Rev.* **112,** 111.

1958:18 WHITE G. K. and WOODS S. B., *Phil. Mag.* **3,** 342.

1958:19 STEELE M. C. and ROSI F. D., *J. Appl. Phys.* **29,** 1517.

1958:20 DINGLE R. B., *Proc. Roy. Soc. London* A**244,** 484.

1959:1 BOWERS R., URE R. W., BAUERLE J. E. and CORNISH A. J., *J. Appl. Phys.* **30,** 930.

1959:2 SWANN W. F. G., *J. Franklin Inst.* **267,** 363.

1959:3 CARSLAW H. S. and JAEGER J. C., *Conduction of Heat in Solids*, 2nd ed., p. 136. Oxford University Press.

1959:4 KANAI Y. and NII R., *J. Phys. Chem. Solids* **8,** 338.

1959:5 HARMAN T. C., CAHN J. H. and LOGAN M. J., *J. Appl. Phys.* **30,** 1351.

1959:6 HOCKINGS E. F., *J. Phys. Chem. Solids* **10,** 341.

1959:7 DEVYATKOVA E. D., MOIZHES B. YA. and SMIRNOV I. A., *Fiz. Tverdogo Tela* **1,** 613; *Soviet Phys., Solid State* **1,** 555.

1959:8 KETTEL F., *J. Phys. Chem. Solids* **10,** 59.

1959:9 BERMAN R., NETTLEY P. T., SHEARD F. W., SPENCER A. N., STEVENSON R. W. H. and ZIMAN J. M., *Proc. Roy. Soc. London* A**253,** 403.

1959:10 KEYES R. W., *Phys. Rev.* **115,** 564.

1959:11 AMBEGAOKAR V., *Phys. Rev.* **114,** 488.

1959:12 PHILLIPS J. C., *Phys. Rev.* **113,** 147.

1959:13 ABELES B., *J. Phys. Chem. Solids* **8,** 340.

1959:14 CALLAWAY J., *Phys. Rev.* **113,** 1046.

1959:15 AMIRKHANOV K. I., BAGDUEV G. B. and KAZLAEV M. A., *Doklady Akad. Nauk S.S.S.R.* **124,** 554.

1959:16 BASHSHALIEV A. A., *Fiz. Tverdogo Tela* **1,** 348; *Soviet Phys., Solid State* **1,** 311.

1959:17 ABRAHAMS M. S., BRAUNSTEIN R. and ROSI F. D., *J. Phys. Chem. Solids* **10,** 204.

1959:18 BUSCH G., STEIGMEIER E. and WETTSTEIN E., *Helv. Phys. Acta* **32,** 463.

1959:19 MIELCZAREK E. V. and FREDERIKSE H. P. R., *Phys. Rev.* **115,** 888.

1959:20 MACDONALD D. K. C., MOOSER E., PEARSON W. B., TEMPLETON I. M. and WOODS S. B., *Phil. Mag.* **4,** 433.

1959:21 WRIGHT D. A., *Research* **12,** 300.

1959:22 IOFFE A. F., *Fiz. Tverdogo Tela* **1,** 160; *Soviet Phys., Solid State* **1,** 141.

1959:23 WEISS H., *Ann. Physik* **4,** 121.

1959:24 WRIGHT D. A., *Electronic Eng.* **31,** 659.

1959:25 ROSI F. D., ABELES B. and JENSEN R. V., *J. Phys. Chem. Solids* **10,** 191.

1960:1 GREEN A. and COWLES L. E. J., *J. Sci. Instr.* **37,** 349.

1960:2 GOLDSMID H. J., *Applications of Thermoelectricity.* Methuen, London.

1960:3 KLEMENS P. G., *Phys. Rev.* **119,** 507.

1960:4 STUCKES A. D., *Phil. Mag.* **5,** 84 (1960).

1960:5 WALKER P. A., *Proc. Phys. Soc. London* **76,** 113.

1960:6 GOLDSMID H. J., *Report of Int. Conf. on Semiconductor Physics, Prague.*

1960:7 EHRENREICH H., *J. Phys. Chem. Solids* **12,** 97.

AUTHOR INDEX

SUBJECT INDEX